TIME, CELLS, AND AGING

BERNARD L. STREHLER
GERONTOLOGY BRANCH, BALTIMORE CITY HOSPITALS, BALTIMORE, MARYLAND

ACADEMIC PRESS • NEW YORK AND LONDON

ACADEMIC PRESS, INC.
111 Fifth Avenue, New York, New York 10003

United Kingdom Edition published by
ACADEMIC PRESS, INC. (LONDON) LTD.
Berkeley Square House, London W1X 6BA

LIBRARY OF CONGRESS CATALOG CARD NUMBER: 62-13111

Fourth Printing, 1970

PRINTED IN THE UNITED STATES OF AMERICA

To all the following,
for their contributions along the way:

B.S., P.A.S., A.S., D.A.S., T.P.S., B.L.S., J.A.S.,
C.T.S., P.A.S., D.S., L.M.S., L.C.S., L.T.S.,
D.R.H., R.L., M.O., W.D.M., W.E.C., J.F.,
H.G., L.Z., E.K., N.W.S., & J.H.C.

Preface

In the course of development of biological disciplines, there are certain obvious stages. These include the development of an awareness of a group of related phenomena, exploratory research which may suggest a series of relationships, a formal statement of various views or hypotheses of interrelations among the contributory phenomena, and finally, a testing and revision of the basic and detailed concepts making up the discipline.

The biology of the aging process is not yet in the category of a completely developed discipline, for although it deals fundamentally with the causes and mechanisms underlying the gradual deterioration of structure and function characteristic of aging, there has not yet been a sufficiently detailed description and testing of the process to permit more than a tentative theoretical formulation. Thus the field has been beset with a plethora of partial theories in various stages of undress and even the basic definitions of the phenomenon were not generally agreed upon. Fortunately in recent years the more gross theoretical statements of the nature of aging are not encountered so frequently, as various lines of general testing have taken place both here and abroad.

The discipline of gerontology, is, then, currently between its second and third stage of development. There has not been, and still is not available, a sufficient body of detailed basic information to support a general theoretical formulation such as genetics or biochemistry enjoy, but there are sufficient landmarks to warrant an attempt in this direction. The stage was set for such an effort by Comfort's excellent monograph, "The Biology of Senescence," and by various other symposium volumes, such as those supported by the AIBS and NSF in 1957 and by the AAAS in 1959. The present monograph is an attempt to summarize the major lines of information on aging and to indicate thereby some of the major areas for theoretical and experimental exploration. This book should hardly be considered as a statement of a theory of aging, unless the concept of adverse change in a variety of different chemical loci as a result of evolutionary inadvertencies can be considered a "theory."

Many friends, colleagues, and institutions, some of whom are listed in the acknowledgments, have helped make this book possible. They include, particularly, my graduate school mentor, Dr. W. D. McElroy, some of whose boundless curiosity and energy have taken root in my own outlook, Dr. James Franck, whose kindly and penetrating critical capacity have inspired so many, and Dr. N. W. Shock, whose unswerving dedication to the understanding of the aging problem has so influenced its course and whose monumental bibliographic volumes on the subject were of central usefulness in the extensive literature search. Thanks are due to the Marine Biological Laboratory, Woods Hole, Massachusetts for the use of their excellent library facilities and reprint collection, to Matthew Pollack for able help in reference work, to my sister, Mrs. Alice Clymer, for typing the manuscript and, most of all, to my wife, Theodora, for her kindly and unfaltering encouragement when frequent doubt assailed.

It is the author's hope that some who read this book will also find one or another aspect of the problem of sufficient challenge to engage their attention, and that they will also enjoy the pleasure of contributing to the unfolding of a phenomenon and field.

B. L. STREHLER

Baltimore, Maryland
June 1962

Contents

CHAPTER I

Introduction

Among the evolved characters which frequently occur in the self-replicating systems we call living organisms is the termination of the individual. This "natural death" of the living units which carry for a time the unbroken line of descent from the first primordial origin of life is of little consequence to the vast majority of living things, for the places of those that die are soon occupied by other individuals.

In higher forms of life the evolution of physical features which permits survival in inhospitable environments is paralleled by the development of adaptive behavior, that is, of devices which make use of some of the energy available in food or light either to modify or move about in the environment. Those organisms which are generally most successful have evolved both an appropriate behavior pattern and a supporting physical structure of sufficient size and durability to withstand the assaults of inanimate and living nature, at least up to the time of reproduction.

Two aspects of behavior have received particular emphasis in the line of evolution leading to present-day man. The first of these is a greater and greater dependence upon reaction patterns predicated upon the successful responses of the past. These may be formalized in the genome as instincts or automatic responses of various grades of complexity or may be recorded in less indelible form as memory, history, or custom.

A second aspect of behavior which has undergone enormous development in man is what might be called reasoned conscious behavior. Its essence might be described as the choice of response to a given set of current environmental circumstances, not by fixed reflex, but through a search for an appropriate response through a review of recorded experience and instinct. The system which performs this monitoring and integrating function is the conscious mind.

A biologist's view is elegantly described in Homer Smith's "From Fish to Philosopher" (*1*), which reads in part:

"The bold facts are that, for matter to know itself in ME, ten billion neurons in my brain, and many, many times that number of functional connections, are required to give me the past, the present and the all too inaccurately derived future that contrive this moment. Five hundred million years of vertebrate evolution have been required to produce that brain, composed of a dozen-odd sorts of atoms; and, given an adequate internal environment, it can know itself in awareness for at most some three- or four-score years."

It is this development of conscious behavior and self-awareness that makes the death of the individual an apparently more consequential matter than the cessation of an unfeeling piece of protoplasm.

Man's interest in the phenomenon is a reflection of the contradiction between the evolutionary processes which have resulted in a fierce desire for continued individual survival, a fear of and curiosity about death on the one hand, and on the other, in an imperfect capacity to maintain and repair the ravages of time or injury.

Man is curious about aging and death for two reasons at least. He is automatically curious about all aspects of nature, a curiosity which has clear survival value to those possessing it. Second, he is aware of death as a generality—as the end of his associations with loved ones, parents, and friends through their demise; and by abstract extension, of the forseeable end of his own physical being and personality.

It is no wonder, then, that mankind is engaged in a continuing struggle with death; that he devotes considerable resources to disease prevention, that his religions, more often than not, either promise a personal escape from the fear of nonexistence through immortality, promote a mystical extension of the personality concept beyond the individual into greater or lesser expanses of nature, and foster the illusion of at least partial identity between the outside and inside world; or in revulsion at the seeming hopelessness of the battle, deny altogether the importance of the center of man's self-preservative instinct, the regard for and defense of self.

During the past decade there has been a great resurgence of interest in the biology and cell physiology of the aging process. This renewed interest stems from at least two sources. First, it is now generally agreed that the understanding in basic terms of the aging process walks hand-in-hand with needed programs of medical and social care and rehabilitation. Second, cellular function in biochemical and biophysical terms has been elucidated to such an extent that testable, sensible hypotheses of mechanism can now be posed.

As de Ropp (*2*) points out in his recent book, "Man Against Aging," "For the present . . . the understanding of the nature of the process in man and his relatives is the challenge facing us. Only by understanding is it likely that we can control; only by imaginative, energetic and dispassionate study can we understand."

This book reviews the present status of our understanding of the cell biology of aging. It is an attempt to summarize, synthesize, and categorize the cellular basis of aging, its origins in the instability of molecular systems, and its expression in the physiological, behavioral, and actuarial aspects of man and other animals.

CHAPTER II

Definitions, criteria, categories, and origins of age changes

A. DEFINITIONS

1. *Time*

AGING, AS WE shall see shortly, is defined as a certain kind of change in living systems due to the passage of time. But before proceeding to a discussion of the peculiarities of the aging process, we shall first consider certain subjective and objective properties of time.

It is curious that such a familiar concept and dimension as time is so difficult to define. Generally, we measure time without defining it, and it is dubious whether an adequate definition of the word "time" can be given because the words used to define it themselves involve the concepts of change, acceleration, velocity, etc., which possess an implicit time function.

There are, in general, three kinds of questions we ask about time (*3*). These are: (*a*) how is it measured, (*b*) how do we establish the order of events in a time sequence, and (*c*) how do we establish the direction of time change?

a. Time Measurement

The first of these three questions is the easiest to answer. We measure time essentially by comparing ratios—by counting the number of natural periods or oscillations which a reference time standard undergoes during an unknown time interval. For example, our primary time standard is the rate of rotation of the earth, which, although not absolutely constant, is decreasing at such a slow rate that, for all practical purposes, it may be treated as a constant standard. Secondary standards of time, such as pendulums, clocks, fixed frequency oscillators, etc., are calibrated against this primary standard. Calibration in this case involves the determination of the ratio of the numbers of periods or oscillations of one standard as compared to another. It is probably the phenomenally constant ratios which various reliable time standards have in their periodicities that convinces us of the uniformity of the flow of time.[1]

b. Time Order

The second property of time outlined above relates to the order of events. The concept of time order can perhaps best be illustrated by appeal to an idealized model. Consider a portion of the universe consisting of material objects (spheres) moving about with reference to each other. It is possible to erect a three-dimensional coordinate system and thus to assign to each object a definite point in that coordinate system at each time. Now, suppose that a large number of such coordinate points were taken at different instants for all of the spheres in the ensemble. Without further reference to the system, it would be possible for a machine or intelligence to arrange the instantaneous coordinates derived

[1] Perhaps even more convincing, although somewhat less of a commonplace in human experience, is the precise internal consistency of the natural laws which contain time as a variable. Let us consider briefly two of these relationships as exemplified by simple laws. They are that distance is equal to the velocity times time, i.e., $d = vt$, and that $f = ma$, or that acceleration is equal to force divided by mass.

If time proceeded at a nonuniform rate, we might expect contradictions between the physical laws that make use of time as a variable. For example, the distance traveled per unit time by an object would stand in a different relationship to the change in velocity or acceleration of the object during a given time interval except for the unlikely condition that time and mass were to vary in a reciprocal manner. Thus, we conclude with considerable certainty either (*a*) that time flows at a constant rate, a rate so uniform, in fact, that we cannot detect inconsistencies in the natural laws making use of time as a variable, or (*b*) that the various functions which, together with time, enter into the formulation of quantitative physical laws undergo simultaneous and completely consistent variation, so as to compensate for any hypothetical temporal inhomogeneity.

at different random instants in an unequivocal order on the basis of the greatest similarity (i.e., the smallest difference) between two sets of coordinates representing different instants. Disregarding possible interactive forces between the spheres or collisions between them, a very curious observation could be made, namely, that the relative distances along the coordinate axes for the various spheres stand in a constant ratio to each other. That is, if the distance between the coordinates for ball I at two instants is five times the distance at the same two instants for ball II, then the ratio of the differences between their positions at any two other instants will also be five to one. This is equivalent to saying that an object in free space, not subject to any disturbing force, will travel a constant distance per unit time if time is measured with a clock based upon the uniform motion of another object in the same frame of reference.

From such a model, of course, and from the kinds of measurement that we have described we could not determine whether time flows smoothly or, for that matter, in which direction it was flowing, but only that it moved at the same rate for all the objects in the ensemble and that, given enough instantaneous measurements without regard to the exact time interval between them, it is possible to establish an order of events based upon the smallest difference in coordinates between successive measurements.[2]

[2] The discussion may also be extended to those situations where the spheres interact because of gravitational, electrostatic, or other forces. Such interactions between objects generally are not linear functions of the distances between them, but rather become more powerful as the objects approach each other. For example, both Newton's law of gravitational attraction and Coulomb's law of electrostatic attraction or repulsion use the inverse square of the distance function, as well as the product of masses, or charges, respectively.

Let us now look more closely at the consequences of the fact that equations $D = vt$ and $f = ma$ both have an implicit or explicit time function within them. The second expression modifies the model which we have just discussed in the sense that the velocities of the objects are affected by their interaction with other material objects either through collision or through the operation of force through a distance. The extent to which the velocities of objects change with time are, of course, given by the departures from the constant ratios of distances discussed above. It was perhaps the proudest achievement of classical physics to *c. Time Direction*

By a rigorous application of the above and other laws of classical physics, it should be possible to arrange events in a time order provided that sufficient numbers of separate instantaneous measurements of positions were made just as it would be possible to arrange the frames of a moving picture in an order approximating the natural one. However, we should not be able to tell in which direction the objects were moving, i.e., we could not tell which was earlier or which was later purely from the sequential arrangement of instantaneous measurement of coordinates. The laws of classical mechanics, operating as they do with frictionless, perfectly elastic objects, cannot tell us what the direction of events is. The assignment of a direction to the passage of time is only possible within the framework of the statistical behavior of large ensembles of elastic bodies or of inelastic, frictional, larger bodies.

The first law of thermodynamics states that the total energy of an isolated system remains constant; the second law, however, states that there will be a gradual tendency of energy to be distributed uniformly among the pieces of matter in the closed system because there are many ways in which thermal kinetic energy can be redistributed between a hot object and a cold one so as to decrease their temperature difference, but a lesser number of ways in which the energy in a cold object can be concentrated so as to transfer heat to a warm object. To be sure, there will

determine the relationships of forces, velocities, distances, etc., and to show that the time used in the equation $D = vt$ is the same time that enters into the equation for acceleration. It was quite conceivable that time might vary in its rate from instant to instant. Departures from the uniform movement of time would not be detectable through the use of the $D = vt$ law unless time moved at different rates in different parts of the coordinate system. Similarly, we could not detect inhomogeneities in the time scale if both acceleration and velocity were similarly affected. Since the physical laws employing velocity and acceleration are obeyed to a remarkable degree of internal consistency, we can conclude either that time proceeds at a constant rate in various portions of a given frame of reference (Lorentz contraction excluded), or that some instantaneous signal coordinated the time references in various parts of the coordinate system. The former seems like a more parsimonious assumption.

be occasional instances, even in systems containing many interacting molecules and atoms, where *cold* objects will heat *warm* ones. But because there is no *a priori* preference for the location of heat energy in a polymolecular system, the total heat energy will tend to be distributed at random. This condition results in a gradual transfer of heat from hot to cold objects in the vast majority of cases.

It is the fact that it is less likely for energy to become concentrated as a result of interactions between atoms and molecules than it is for it to become less concentrated that determines the past and the future. In general, the universe, at least that portion of it which we can observe, is moving toward a condition of greater probability, equilibrium, or randomness of energy distribution. Whenever two systems interact, in other words, the chances are that there will be an equalization of their thermal energies as well as other forms of energy. The direction of time is therefore seen to be determined by the direction in which energy distribution tends to go spontaneously. In other words, we can tell whether a given photograph of the universe is earlier or later than another on the basis of the degree of approach to final equilibrium that the two stages represent, that closer to equilibrium being the later view. The smaller the compartment of the universe is with which one deals the more likely it is that it will be found to be moving away from equilibrium, i.e., operating in essentially negative time. By and large at any given time, however, the vast majority of systems will be moving toward equilibrium.[3]

[3] The above arguments are based on classical concepts of mechanics. However, it seems to me that there are even some processes involving only single atoms which are, to all intents and purposes, irreversible. One such example is the occurrence of radioactive decay. This process involves such a great release of energy by a single atom that it would be virtually impossible for thermal accidents to yield local energy sufficient to reverse the process during any conceivable period of time. Moreover, the preceding sentence ignores the problem of recapture of the radiant energy simultaneously with the occurrence of an appropriate thermal fluctuation. The improbability of even a single event such as this occurring to a single atom or the even more unlikely fusions of two products of nuclear fission make it appear that the nearly simultaneous decay of millions of such atomic nuclei in atomic explo-

In summary, then, we have shown that time is measured either through a comparison of ratios of periodicities of periodic oscillators or of relative positions of freely moving objects. It was shown that it is possible to assign an order to a number of instantaneously measured coordinates of a system of whatever complexity one may wish to examine but that it is not possible with such simple systems obeying classical laws of mechanics to assign unequivocally a direction to time. The assignment of a direction to time is made on the basis of the probability of energy distributions among ensembles of atoms and molecules, or upon the fact that certain essentially irreversible processes such as radioactive decay or coordinated capture of light energy by stars could not, in fact, take place with any finite probability.

Aside from the usefulness of a physical orientation toward the objective properties of time in treating a subject such as aging, there is an even more cogent reason for discussing the march of the universe toward a more probable condition. This is the fact that living systems are themselves subject to the movement toward an increased probability of arrangement of their atoms and of heat. The processes of heat equalization and structural disorganization we have described are spoken of as the increase of entropy within

sions or in the center of billions of distant stars could not take place even transitorially in anything less than an infinite period of time.

Consider also the absurdity from the standpoint of general laws of physics of producing a reversal of such a cataclysmic event as a supernova. The remains of the supernova represented by the ring nebula in Lyra, for example, would demand that light quanta originating from no observable source on the periphery of the universe must move deliberately and in a coordinated fashion toward that star which, if time is proceeding in reverse, must be viewed as a huge blotter for light which will ultimately convert all of the radiant energy arriving simultaneously from outer space into a new and highly organized mass of the star. How much more reasonable (probable) is the conventional view! Remember also that the same arguments must be applied to each and every star in the universe. In reverse time these suns must be continual sinks for radiant energy originating, so it would seem, spontaneously in space. Given enough time perhaps such a universe could develop, but how much more likely it seems that time really moves in a direction of radioactive decay, dissipation of potential energy through frictional loss, etc., etc.

the universe. Entropy will increase spontaneously in any macrosystem which is not already in its most stable condition and which possesses sufficient ambient thermal energy to permit reactions to occur. Aging and most other disorganizing changes, of course, would not take place at absolute zero because change involves the motion at least of molecules and their parts (*4*).

2. *Aging*

In order to define aging adequately, it is necessary to define a living system. It is generally accepted among biologists that living organisms are mutable chemical systems making use of the energy and matter in their environment to produce more of themselves. Because life is capable of variation through mutation, a given supply of energy and matter is capable of being utilized by a number of different kinds of living systems. Among all the possible forms of life, only those have survived which are capable in the long run of utilizing successfully the food and energy and of competing successfully with other forms of life that could use the available stores of these commodities. The living species of today are the successful progeny of lines of life that have descended from the first primordial piece of protoplasm through billions of years of vicissitudes, challenge, and death.

Early in evolution the development of the individual took place, for generally that life survived best which did not consist of a continuous unbounded mass of protoplasm. The individual organism has the advantage that it can be more readily distributed to great distances than could be a massive syncytium. It can carry on its vital functions efficiently in favorable ecological niches without the undue burden of sustaining that portion of itself lying on unfavorable ground.

With the exception of clonal aging, which we will discuss at length later, the aging process does not appear to be a characteristic of a species or line of animals but, rather, of the individual representatives of a species.

Obviously those variations in the physical structure of organisms which have survival value for a species are those which act to increase the probability that the line will survive over long periods of time. Some specialized adaptations subserving this general quasi-objective have taken the form of an increased rate of reproduction or adaptation to new kinds of food.

On the other hand, other groups of plants and animals have persisted evolutionarily by increasing the durability of the individual carriers of the genetic material rather than by merely increasing their number. In the latter case, the adaptations are frequently the production of more resistant physical structures, e.g., the thick bark on long-lived sequoias, the heavy shells on tortoises; means of surviving periods of low food or water supply (e.g., seeds, hibernation, fat storage, etc.); or third, of reactions to environmental changes which are called adaptive behavior and which in turn increase the probability of survival at least to the reproductive age.

Clearly there is a very great selective disadvantage to those lines of animals or plants which fail to reach reproductive age. They will be removed from the contest within one generation. Decreases in adaptation beyond the reproductive period cannot be evaluated categorically for their effects on the evolutionary selection process. In certain groups of animals or plants, postreproductive physiological decline might actually increase the probability of the successful propagation of the race over a long period of time. In other cases, there may be some detrimental effects of aging which, however, are not sufficiently strong to result in the elimination of the genetic line. In a vast majority of cases it may well be that adverse changes in the postreproductive period have little or no effect upon the survival of the race.

Whatever the evolutionary origin of senescence may be, we shall *define it here,* as we have earlier, *as the changes which occur generally in the postreproductive period and which result in a decreased survival capacity on the part of the individual organism.* It must be clear from the above definition that different evolutionary lines might very well decline in their survival capacities for entirely different reasons. It may also be, however, that there are one or more

common mechanisms of aging, possibly because of similarities in the developmental or evolutionary history of many kinds of animals and plants.

Comfort, whose view is operationally similar to the above, has stated his definition in the following terms (*5*): "Senescence is a deteriorative process. What is being measured, when we measure it, is a decrease in viability and an increase in vulnerability. Other definitions are possible but they tend to ignore the raison d'être of human and scientific concern with age processes. Senescence shows itself as an increasing probability of death with increasing chronological age. The study of senescence is the study of the group of processes, different in different organisms, which lead to this increase in vulnerability."

Medawar (*6*) defines it as follows: "Senescence, then, may be defined as that change of the bodily faculties and sensibilities and energies which accompanies aging, and which renders the individual progressively more likely to die from accidental causes of random incidence. Strictly speaking, the word "accidental" is redundant, for all deaths are in some degree accidental. No death is wholly 'natural'; no one dies merely of the burden of the years."

B. CRITERIA OF AGE CHANGES

We shall later enumerate in detail the kinds of events which could possibly lead to age changes. It should first be emphasized that aging, as here defined, is a property of the organism and not of its environment. Age changes due to the basic aging process should occur even in the most propitious environments in order to be considered as true age changes.

Age changes, moreover, should be the characteristics of a group of animals, not just of individuals within that group for, in the latter case, the age-associated change might be a reflection of a deleterious genetic mutation.

One of the chief objectives of aging research is the description of the nature of the basic underlying changes in structure and function which lead to the gradual dysfunction and, finally, to the death of the individual organism.

Much of the confusion which has surrounded the biological concept of aging in the past is due both to a failure to establish a useable definition of aging and objective criteria by which the results of specific research on animals at several different ages can be evaluated.

We have recently suggested four criteria (*7*), criteria which are in essence general, arbitrary definitions of what constitutes or is meant by biological aging, as tentative guideposts in the search for basic mechanisms of the aging process. The criteria which, it appears to us, any age-associated change should meet before being considered a part of any basic aging process are four in number and include the following concepts: (1) universality, (2) progressiveness, (3) intrinsicality, and (4) deleteriousness.

The basic postulate underlying these criteria is that there exist gradual changes in the structure of organisms which are not due to preventable diseases or other gross accidents and which eventually lead to the increased probability of death of the individual *as he grows older* with the passage of time. Such changes are consistent with the implied criteria stated by Medawar (*6*) in 1951 and Comfort (*5*) in 1956, and discussed in detail in the recently published Gatlinburg Symposium volume on aging. These specific criteria were chosen for the following reasons:

1. *Universality*

If a given observed phenomenon is truly a part of the aging process, it should occur in all older members of the species. This criterion eliminates many specific, hereditary aberrations and diseases which are dependent upon a given environment. Certain kinds of changes, occurring with greater frequency in older populations but which are not universal, such as the incidence of cancer, are not necessarily excluded from the basic aging process. Aging might well be characterized by decreased resistance to the development of tumors. The fact that some old individuals do not develop tumors is not evidence that an underlying change involving resistance to tumors is unassociated with the aging processes. Some individuals might never develop tumors simply because they have not been exposed to the tumor-inducing agent (e.g., carcinogens, viruses, radiation, somatic mutations, etc.). Similarly, exceptional human beings of great age possessing few or no arteriosclerotic lesions would eliminate arteriosclerosis as a basic cause of aging. On the other hand, however, there may very well be common universal, age-dependent changes in both affected and unaffected individuals which would produce damage to blood vessels if certain environmental factors (e.g., nutrition) were appropriately altered. By contrast, any basic cause of age changes will be found to occur in all older individuals of a species whether it expresses itself as a recognizable disease lesion or not.

2. *Intrinsicality*

Like universality, this criterion is designed to eliminate age-correlated changes which are due to the operation of factors outside of the organism. It is included as an additional criterion because certain age changes may be universal but still be a consequence of environmental effects on the living system. For example, genetic damage due to the absorption of cosmic radiation will certainly occur in all animals possessing reasonably long lives. Such damage would thus be universal but it would not be intrinsic to the system because it is the result of a modifiable, environmental variable.

3. *Progressiveness*

Aging is usually considered to be a process rather than a sudden event. It follows, therefore, that its onset should be a gradual and cumulative occurrence. Many age-correlated changes occur suddenly. Among these are the changes which follow the occurrence of a coronary artery occlusion, a cerebrovascular accident, or the initiation of a tumor. These three events, which incidentally account for the majority of deaths in the older age group in Western countries, are not themselves considered to be as part of the aging process even though they might occur universally. The predisposing factors, on the other hand, may very well be part of the aging process.

Generally, processes are gradual in their occurrence because they are due to changes in small subunits of structure, e.g., in cells or even in subcellular organelles or molecules. The individual events at the molecular level leading to dysfunction at the cellular level and ultimately reaching up to the behavior of the organism, of course, do occur in a very short time, but the large number of events necessary to produce gross change tends to smooth out the statistical fluctuations occurring at the micro level and to give the processes an appearance of smooth-flowing uniformity.

4. *Deleteriousness*

This final criterion is based upon the fact that the most characteristic change occurring during the aging process is the decline in functional capacity which is reflected in an increased mortality rate. Universal, intrinsic, and gradual changes must also contribute to the increased probability of death if they are to be considered as part of the basic biological aging process. Some age-correlated changes which meet the first three criteria may thus be eliminated because they may simply be the final stages in adaptive processes and actually result in an improvement in the organism's survival capacity. As such, they would be classed as part of the developmental process rather than of aging. Not all developmental processes, however, are necessarily eliminated, for certain of them may become de-adaptive in their final or extreme expression. Thus, while certain aspects of development may indeed have great relevance to the basic biology of aging, it is equally apparent that this is only true of those developmental changes whose ultimate expressions in time decrease the organism's capacity to survive or which constitute a mixture of adaptive and deadaptive effects.

The above criteria appear reasonable from a biological standpoint. However, their application to specific observations is not usually a simple matter. Some of the difficulties in applying them are outlined below.

Concerning *universality:* it is apparent that no series of measurements could possibly embrace all of the individuals of a species. Therefore, in practice one can only estimate the probability that a phenomenon is universal on the basis of the size of the measured sample, the distribution of the individual measured values, and the average change in the total population of individuals measured. Even in the absence of measurements, however, universality may be expected for certain types of changes. For example, any changes which are a consequence of the laws of thermodynamics, particularly the second law of thermodynamics, must be expected to express themselves to some extent in all organisms. Time breeds disorder in both animate and inanimate chemical systems. Living systems can, at best, only postpone or replace or repair the effects of time and temperature.

Intrinsicality is probably the most difficult of the four criteria to evaluate because its applicability cannot be assessed in the absence of some understanding of the mechanism of an age-associated change. In the absence of an understanding of a mechanism, one of the better tests of this criterion is inability to modify (ameliorate) the age-dependent change through the agency of controlled environmental variables within the range of extremes usually experienced by the organism. Ability to accelerate an age-dependent process is, of course, not evidence of its lack of intrinsicality.

Progressiveness of an age change can be established by measuring the same function repeatedly in the same animal throughout its lifetime. Alternatively, structural examination of animals of various ages kept as nearly uniform genetically as possible has been used in most age studies. However, the usual cross-sectional age studies are generally not sufficient to meet this criterion.

The harmfulness of a given anatomical or physiological change clearly depends, at least in part, on the environment in which the change occurs. For example, a loss in visual acuity or of teeth is less of a problem to civilized man than these same effects would be to an individual living in a primitive culture without the advantages of ocular or dental prostheses. Civilization can effectively counteract some of the age-induced defects to a point where they are no longer important in determining survival capacity. Similarly, a number of changes which were highly detrimental or even fatal a few decades ago, e.g., decreased resistance to infectious diseases among older animals, are less of a problem in civilized countries because of the advance of public health measures and the development of effective antibiotic treatment.

Because of the considerable variability from individual to individual in the expression of various age correlated changes, it is difficult to assess the extent to which any given observed change contributes to the decreased survival capacity. Clearly, in the first place, any age-correlated change will also be correlated with the increased probability of death characteristic of older organisms. Such correlations or their lack may be misleading, for, if a given age change is correlated with some other process which is itself the real deleterious agent, one might reach a false conclusion of causality between the deleterious effect and the other variable. Conversely, the lack of demonstrable correlation between an age change and the mortality rate does not rule out the change as a deleterious one, for the change might be harmful but still be overshadowed by other age-dependent or correlated processes.

C. CATEGORIES OF AGE CHANGES

It is possible to classify the kinds of changes leading to the decreased functional capacity of old animals in many ways. They are, however, divisible into two general categories: those which are the result of the normal aging process and those which are the result of environmental factors. This division into the two kinds of causes was discussed by Medawar (*6*) in the following terms: "Senescence, as it is measured by increase of vulnerability, or the likelihood of an individual's dying, is therefore of at least twofold origin. There is (*a*) the innate or ingrained senescence, which is, in a general sense, developmental or the effect of nature; and (*b*) the senescence comprised of the accumulated sum of the effects of recurrent stress or injury or infection. The latter is environmental in origin and thus, in a paradoxically technical sense, the effect of 'nurture.' "

We shall here use somewhat different terminology. We shall call those processes which are an intrinsic portion of the life history of a species *determinate processes;* those which are the results of unpredictable environmental influences we shall term *ancillary processes*. Parenthetically, it should be pointed out here that disease processes, inasmuch as they are a departure from the normal behavior of organisms, must be classified in the ancillary category. The logical antithesis of this view has been taken on occasion by those pathologists who view senescence as the sum total of all of the disease processes to which the organism has been subjected during his lifetime. This viewpoint fails to take account of the fact that even in the most hospitable environment there is an evident aging process which expresses itself both in changes in structure and in function as well as in resistance to the inroads of various disease processes.

Determinate processes are those which occur with certainty in all animals of a given species regardless of their environment and experience. This definition, of course, includes the definition of normal aging and such processes can be considered to be a consequence of any one or a combination of the following general features of the physical world: (*a*) the finite stability of any machine (*8*), (*b*) the fact that any machine will make errors at a certain rate in carrying out its normal functions, (*c*) the fact that evolutionary selection may largely ignore the debilities of old age, or (*d*) even as has been suggested by Williams (*9*), of built-in factors which lead to an increased survival capacity at an early age but which produce a decreased survival capacity later.

Ancillary processes which lead to the decreased vitality of old organisms may, on the other hand, be considered as consequences of gross accidental events which are not a result of the structural organization of an organism per se. In other words, ancillary processes are a consequence of deleterious agents in the environment and are generally subject to modification, whereas determinate processes by their very nature are an inherent part of the machine. In certain cases, ancillary processes may mimic features of determinate processes. Cell death, for example, is a normal feature of the developmental history of many kinds of animals. Cell death also may occur in response to various harmful, environmental factors, such as irradiation, disease, freezing, malnutrition, stress, etc. We cannot, as of now, reach firm conclusions about the extent to which "normal aging and ancillary processes, such as disease and accidents, contribute to the debilities of old age." Certainly both are important factors.

We shall return at a later point in this discussion to a more detailed consideration of the evolutionary aspects of age changes. In order to discuss these factors in a more critical framework, however, we shall first attempt to sketch the origins and relationships of the various categories of age changes (*10*). Table I outlines some of these relationships. Note that the change of most general interest—the decreased survival capacity of individual animals with age—is based upon a hierarchy of events proceeding from elementary interactions of molecules at the cellular and subcellular level to the very complex interactions of whole organisms' societies and their environments. Obviously, each of the higher levels of function or organization is dependent on less complex phenomena, structures, or processes.

D. ORIGINS OF AGE CHANGES

Subsequent chapters in this discussion will deal in more detail with varied expressions of aging at the different structural levels of organization. For example, mortality rates and theories bearing upon them will be discussed; the results of general performance capacity and physiological tests will be surveyed; some detailed studies of histological and cytological findings, as well as the biochemical changes in cells and subcellular components will be reviewed. Although the more complex phenomena will first be explored, where possible they will be related to more elementary levels of understanding. At the base of all these changes, however, lie the four sources of adverse change at the molecular or cellular level shown in Table I. Evolutionary selection operates ultimately at the level of the individual chemical catalyst (*11*). Thus, genes affect function and through it survival capacity, by virtue of their direct or indirect effects on the kinds and rates of various chemical reactions occurring at the cellular level. In this context, genes may be

TABLE I

ORIGIN AND CATEGORIES OF AGE CHANGES

Level of organization	Manifestation	Measure
Population	Increased probability of death (aging)	Mortality rates
	↑	
Individual	Decreased adaptation	General performance, morbidity
	↑	
Integrated function (organ system)	Decreased ability to perform special functions	Physiological tests
	↑	
Tissue	Changes in tissues	Histological changes, biochemical tests
	↑	
Cell	Changes in cells	Histology, etc., cell physiology
	↑	
Subcellular elements and molecules	Changes in subcellular elements or extracellular environments, such as nuclei, membranes, particulates and other organelles, solutes, stroma	Histochemistry, biochemistry
	Arising from changes in synthetic rate, utilization rate, transport rate, storage rate (e.g., formation of precipitate, exhaustion of store)	
	↑	
	Result from failure of design (deficiencies in genetic properties) to take into account deleterious effects of	

Accidents (stochastic processes)		Genetics and development (genetic processes)	
Inadequacy of design (inability to repair and/or avoid gross damage)	Omission of design (inability to repair effects of microaccidents)	Errors in design (presence of slow, but harmful side-reactions, catalyzed and uncatalyzed)	Contradictions in design (opposing effects of same design feature at different times, in different cells, in different environments)

viewed as the producers of systems of collaborating catalysts which make use of environmental matter and energy in such a way as to result in their own perpetuation. The processes outlined in Table I and which give rise to the elemental changes in structure and ultimately in function arise from two contrasting types of processes. The first of these is the so-called *stochastic processes,* i.e., those which result from an improbable event that has no structural counterpart in the genetic make-up of the organism. The second group is the *genetic processes.*

The distinctions between the genetic and stochastic processes contributing to change in organisms are illustrated in the following terms (see Tables II and III): In any given physical system there is a certain probability that any possible reaction will occur. Living systems make use of catalysts which increase the probability that certain events will occur. This is effected by lowering the energetic barriers to the favored reactions. In other words, catalysts influence the rates but not the kinds of reactions that can occur. From among all of the possible reactions, the genetic apparatus of a given organism selects those possible transformations which, through evolutionary selection, have yielded continuing lines of functioning cooperative protoplasm. To the extent that the occurrence of a given catalyzed reaction changes the concentrations of reactants and products, it may also affect the rates of other uncatalyzed reactions and thus have an influence on purely stochastic events. However, even in the absence of catalysts, random syntheses and disruptions of molecules will occur in any system. *We refer to those reactions for which no catalysts are present as molecular stochastic processes.*

Just as there are events occurring at the molecular level for which no genetic counterpart exists, there are events occurring at the macromolecular level whose occurrence is not taken into account in the genetic program. Such processes or events are referred to generally as accidents.

Since accidents, in both the colloquial and specialized sense of the word, influence the probability that an individual will survive to reproductive age, it is not surprising that evolution has favored the development of forms whose

TABLE II

STOCHASTIC CAUSES OF AGING

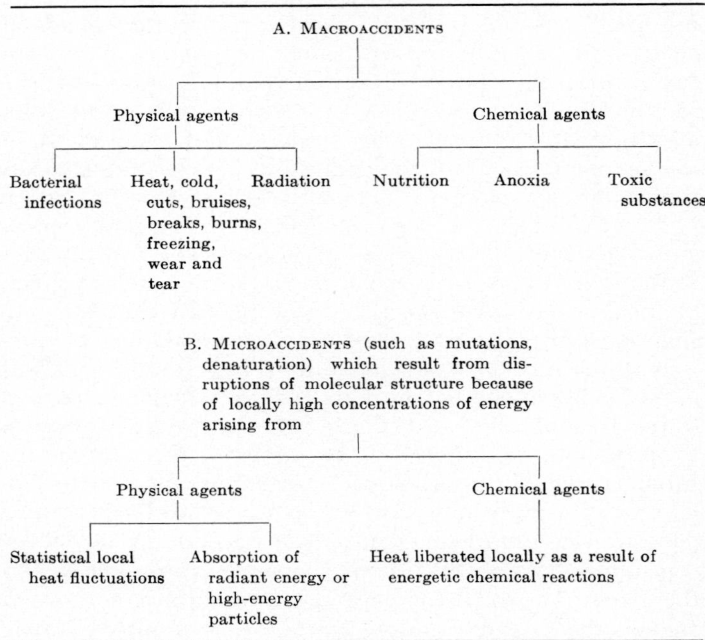

structure and behavior tend to minimize the probabilities of accidental demise. The genome tends to compensate for and adapt itself to the regularly recurring events in the environment. *Extremely rare or unique events would only possess an antagonizing counterpart in the genome by chance, since natural selection would have had no prior opportunity to select for the compensated variant.*

Of the factors producing change at the molecular or cellular level, only one, that of macroscopic accidents, can be expected to be altered appreciably by foreseeable modification of the environment. The other two basic groups of causes of age change (aging proper) are probably only susceptible to evolutionary selection or to specific prostheses in certain cases (reading glasses, false teeth, etc.). Let us now

TABLE III

Genetic Causes of Aging

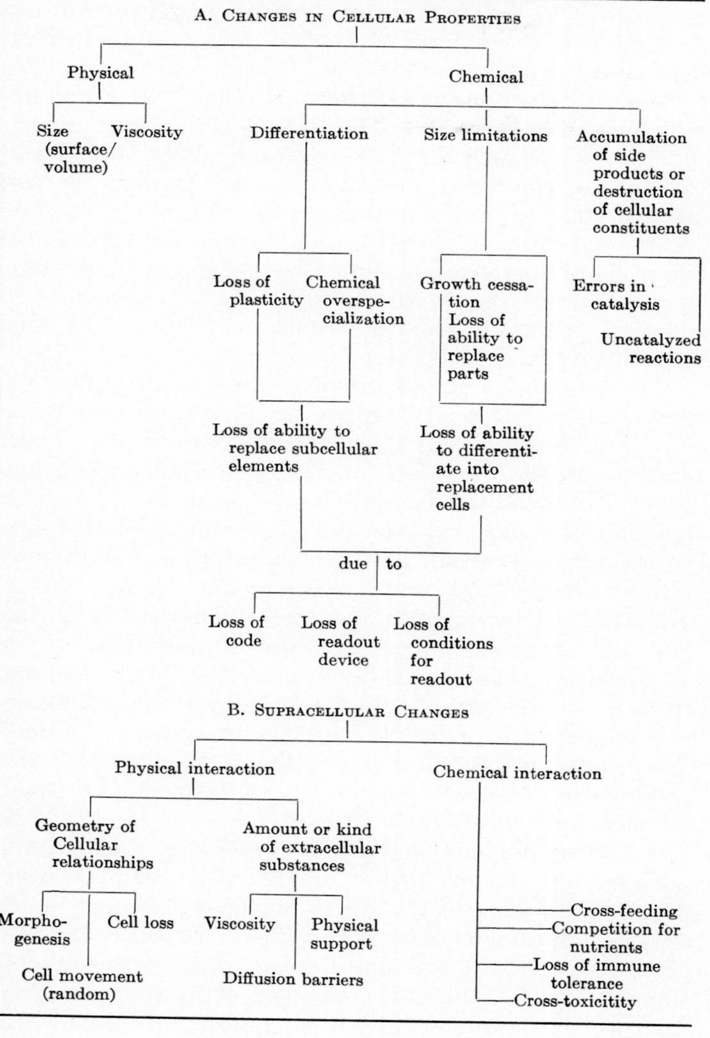

proceed to consider in greater detail the nature of the stochastic and genetic causes of aging or age-dependent structural alterations.

Each of the major kinds of alterations of structure can be subdivided into two categories: physical or chemical agents which produce disruptive changes.

Macroaccidents or events may be defined as events involving simultaneous disruptive effects on a large number of molecules or even the whole organism. They have several features in common. The first of these is that they are usually due to environmental causes. Certain macroaccidents apparently arise from instabilities in the behavior of the parts of organisms, but selection pressure, by and large, has tended to favor the development of a homogeneous and relatively serene internal environment in which the components of the organism can function.

The second feature of macroaccidents is that they are, in principle, frequently capable of prediction and therefore are usually subject to modification or control. There are, of course, limitations in the degrees of control and genetic anticipation that can be expected. It is precisely by the development of devices which can predict future events and thus permit anticipatory behavior that the evolution in higher organisms is characterized. In man, the development of intelligence and the organization of society and civilization has permitted the minimization of environmental inhomogeneities. This has been achieved through group effort, objective measurement, recording, and prediction of natural forces and future events. *Intelligence, in a real sense, is analogous to the most primitive catalytic capacity in its predictable interactions with specific spatial or temporal sequences.*

A listing of macroaccidents, whether they be bacterial antigens, on the one hand, or recurring complex social pressures, on the other, to which organisms have responded adaptively through natural selection or learned behavior is given in Table II. Note that for each of these agents some compensatory reactions or responses exist; thus, bacterial infections elicit antibody production; heat and cold, a redistribution of circulation, cuts, bruises, breaks, burns, and freezing frequently elicit replacement of damaged parts by newly regenerated replacement tissues, such as scars, or, in the case of some animals, even of complete organs or limbs. Ordinary wear and tear finds its compensatory antagonists in the regular cycle of replacement and renewal which characterizes those tissues subject to the most vigorous assault. Continuing high levels of solar radiation result in adaptive coloration changes or in the selection of pigmented races. Fluctuations in food supply or in the quality of nutrition is compensated in part, at least, by the storage of food reserves in adipose tissue or in behavioral patterns resulting in the storage of grain by humans and of acorns by squirrels. Fluctuations in the oxygen and CO_2 content result in the short run in changes in the rate of breathing and, in the long run, in changes in hemoglobin content or in the development of new capillary beds. A capacity to detoxify certain noxious substances, to develop immunity to some or a tolerance of others is another adaptation to gross macroaccidents. Other living beings are among the most prominent of the causes of accidents and many behavioral aspects of organisms reflect real or anticipated dangers from other living creatures.

Stochastic processes at the micro level, that is, those involving the reaction of small molecules or aggregates of molecules, may also result in deleterious changes with the passage of time. Since all possible reactions will occur at some rate, what determines the rate of given disruptive reactions? There are in fact only two fundamental factors which enter into the determination of the probability of the reaction. The first of these is the probability that the reactant will get into the proper position to undergo the transition in question. The second involves the probability that energy will be distributed in such a manner as to facilitate the occurrence of the transformation. In order for a reaction to occur, in other words, the atoms making up the reactive molecules must get into the proper position and the environment must furnish sufficient energy to overcome the activation barrier to the reaction.

We have discussed the fact that thermal energy tends to be distributed with essentially equal probability among the various modes that it can occupy. In order for a chemical bond to be broken, however, the molecules of the system must collide in such a manner that there is a highly improbable distribution of thermal energy. This results in the stretching of a particular bond in the reactive molecule, a necessary preliminary to reaction. In this manner, the thermal energy of molecular movement prior to collision is converted into an improbable potential energy distribution.

What are the sources of energy for molecular systems, granted that any structure will have a certain inherent instability if it is subject to local energy fluctuations which exceed the bond energies maintaining the structure? Such local energy fluctuations can, in principle, arise only from three types of events. These are the redistribution of heat energy, the absorption of radiant energy, or the occurrence of chemical or nuclear reactions which result in local concentrations of heat.

Heat. Random local fluctuations in energy about some average value, as a result of the operation of the Maxwell-Boltzmann distribution law, will occasionally result in local energy concentrations sufficiently high to permit the alteration of structures in the vicinity.

Radiation. A second path by which molecules or polymolecular structures may become unstable is through the localization of energy as a result of the absorption of radiant energy such as light. For a short time, after the absorption of a quantum of light, an absorbing system will be in an excited state (*12*). The energy stored in this temporary form will be dissipated shortly in one of four ways: (*a*) through the reemission of light in the form of fluorescence or phosphorescence; (*b*) through a chemical reaction between the unstable (excited state) and some other molecule in the environment; (*c*) by the breaking of a bond in the excited molecule before its excitation energy can be dissipated; and (*d*) by transfer of the energy to some other molecule, resulting either in reaction or in further redistribution of the excitation energy as heat energy. The last three possibilities are capable of promoting disruptive chemical reactions.

The reactions catalyzed by light differ in no qualitative

respect from the reactions arising by thermal fluctuations in local energy. However, they do differ in the relative rate of different kinds of reactions. In the first place, the energy available in a quantum of light in the visible region of the spectrum is considerably greater than the average energy of a thermal fluctuation. Consequently, while the rate of thermally activated reactions will decrease rapidly as the activation barrier increases, the only requirement for a photo-catalyzed reaction is that the energy in the reactive state be somewhat less than the energy available in the quantum and that a mechanism be available for translating the excitation energy into free energy of activation. In summary, then, photo-catalyzed reactions will frequently yield different products than thermally activated reactions because they afford a means to achieve higher activation energies than are usually attainable through collisional intermolecular heat transfer at ambient temperatures.

Ionizing radiation (*13*) also promotes chemical reactions but, in this case, the catalysis involves the direct production of unstable and reactive species through the transfer of momentum from the ionizing particle to the receiving molecule or through the removal of electrons from a stable molecular configuration by collision or near collision between it and a high velocity charged particle or quantum.

Chemical Reaction. The third major source of energy capable of producing molecular disruption is the liberation of a locally high concentration of thermal energy as a result of the occurrence of chemical reactions. The potential differences between oxidants and reductants in biological systems are such that at maximum about 60 kcal./mole is liberated. The average energy liberated per chemical reaction in so-called coupled oxidations is considerably less than the above value. One surprising fact should be emphasized, however. This is the fact that *the energy available locally at the end of a reaction may be considerably greater than the free energy liberated by a reaction.* This is a consequence of the fact that a molecule must absorb thermal energy before it can react. When products are formed, however, a portion or all of the activation energy plus the free energy of reaction is liberated locally. Stated otherwise, the energy available at the termination of a chemical reaction is equal to the activation energy of the reverse process.

In view of the foregoing, what is the effect of enzyme catalysis upon the local heat liberated at the time of a chemical reaction? Although a catalyst will increase the total rate of reaction, it will, curiously, decrease the amount of the total energy liberated at the instant of reaction by the amount that it decreases the activation energy. Thus, even though an intermediate in a reaction sequence might be transformed noncatalytically into its product, there may well be an advantage, as far as the long-term survival of the catalytic system is concerned, to inserting a catalyst which would decrease the energy liberated locally at the end of the reaction. Stated in other words, since catalyzed reactions are characterized by lowered activation energies, it likewise follows that the energy possessed by the product at the moment of its formation will be less for catalyzed reactions than for uncatalyzed ones. *Enzymes thus function to decrease the probability of damage per reaction as well as to speed up the rate of reaction (10).*

We cannot, at the present time, evaluate the extent to which uncatalyzed chemical reactions promoted by one or another of the three sources of activation energy contribute to the over-all decline in function characteristic of senescence. We do know, however, that certain kinds of age change can be accelerated either by raising the temperature or by exposing tissues to visible, ultraviolet or ionizing radiation. The importance of these factors in normal mammalian senescence has not yet been determined.

Gene-Controlled Aging. In addition to the destructive effects of macroaccidents and the slow degradation of living systems by the occurrence of chemical reactions beyond the province of genetically controlled catalysts, there is a third broad category of age changes that is a part of the aging process. This consists of the changes in cells and of multicellular structures, tissues, and organs, which occur as a result of the operation of genetically determined factors. That is, these changes are either the direct or indirect result of the presence of catalysts. We shall, first, consider briefly changes occurring at the cellular level and then proceed to discuss in general outline the changes which occur at the supracellular level.

In the most general sense, the chemical constitution of cells will change if the rate at which each substance appears (either through a process of synthesis or of transport from the outside of the cell) is not equal to the rate of its disappearance due to transport out of the cell or through its utilization. In this context, *aging may be viewed as change in constitution due to the inequality of the rates of appearance and disappearance of specific chemical structures, changes which are not directed toward the production of a more effectively adapted organism.* This process differs from the chemical differentiation process which occurs in development in that the latter results in a controlled change in constitution directed toward the production of functionally specialized cells or multicellular structures having a higher survival value than their undifferentiated precursors possessed. Developmental alterations, by and large, appear to be under direct genetic control even though it is, of course, possible to alter the intensity or rate of certain developmental processes by manipulating the external environment.

At the cellular level, those changes which are genetic in origin are detailed in Table III. These changes are produced, in turn, by changes in one or more of the following factors so as to yield a steady state which is incompatible with continued survival: (*a*) rate of synthesis, (*b*) rate of utilization, (*c*) rate of transport, (*d*) rate of storage or depletion of stores, and (*e*) rate of entropy change, rearrangement, disorganization, or organization.

The various possible published and unpublished theories of the mechanism of aging are simply expressions of the above hypothesis in various degrees or refinement and sophistication.

Of particular importance in determining the steady state are such factors as cell surface-to-volume ratio, cytoplasmic viscosity, and the geometric arrangement of cells. These factors would appear to be extremely important in determining the ingress and egress of diffusible constituents. Intracellular chemical changes also include by-products of catalyzed or uncatalyzed reactions, as well as continuations or extensions of the normal differentiation process.

The hypothesis of differentiation as a prime causative factor in cellular aging has, from time to time, received support from biologists. The possibility that senescence may actually be a consequence of cellular overdifferentiation has been explored recently (*11*). The teleological concept that senescence is the price which organisms pay for the luxury of differentiation was particularly favored by Pearl (*14*).

The fact that many organisms attain a finite adult size, and the consequences of this observation, as regards repair processes and the maintenance of chemical constancy, have been discussed in detail by Comfort (*5*) and by Bidder (*15*).

During recent years a number of theories (*16–19*) have been suggested which are based upon the idea of a deterioration of the genetic code or information content during the aging of organisms. Such losses (of code or of metabolic machinery for following the synthetic directions contained in the code) would be extremely difficult to repair once they occurred within a cell. However, presumably, they might be circumvented by simply discarding damaged cells as they occur.

Another category of chemical changes in cellular properties which are directly attributable to the presence of genetically controlled catalysts is the occurrence of slow rates of chemical reactions between components. Since catalysts may change the steady-state concentration of intermediates, they may indirectly promote the occurrence of uncatalyzed reactions purely by mass action. Such reactions might either involve the destruction or alteration of cytoplasmic components or they might produce insoluble or toxic products which could not be removed from the cells. Such reactions might also occur because of errors in catalysis, that is, because of an incomplete specificity in catalytic activity, or because of the occurrence of noncatalyzed reactions between highly reactive intermediates in metabolic sequences.

The foregoing changes might be expected in practically any organism whether single-celled or composed of many cells. However, multicellular organisms, despite the fact that they possess certain advantages as a consequence of their multicellular specialized organization, also face certain disadvantages as a result of this multicellular character. These sensitivities arise from the fact that the same collaborative organization which permits the multicellular animal to survive more effectively in the face of a hostile environment also demands a series of limitations on the capacities of the individual cells and, moreover, imposes a series of obligatory interdependences and interactions which introduce new sources of instability.

Such instabilities result either from chemical or physical relationships or from interactions between cells. Physical and chemical interactions between cells are moderated by the nature of the nonliving matter between cells, as well as by their geometrical relationships. The geometrical factor which results in coherent cell function will be altered by changes in cell size, by the elimination of certain cells through death, by the random movement of cells with relation to each other (in a process which might be called "cellular diffusion"), or through a continuation of various morphogenetic processes.

Of great potential importance in regulating the interactions between cells are the gels, membranes, fibers, and particles which make up the intercellular substances. Because of their location between the living cells, such structures may have striking influences on the rate of diffusion of metabolites and waste products into and out of cells and between the cells making up a tissue.

Chemical interactions between the cells of a multicellular organism largely depend upon the kind and concentration of diffusible substances passing from one cell to another. These interactions involve inhibition or stimulation of cellular function by cross-feeding. They involve competition for nutrients. They involve reaction to toxic or regulatory substances produced by one cell and utilized or detoxified by another. They may involve interaction between cells of the same organism by autoimmunological responses.

We shall discuss many of these possibilities in greater detail in the sections devoted to the detailed consideration of mechanisms operating at the cellular and tissue levels. Obviously, much of the material discussed above has been suggested or considered earlier and more eloquently by others, although some of the possibilities here discussed may possess some uniqueness. Unfortunately, we cannot, on the whole, yet decide which of these many alternatives are the major contributing factors to the normal aging process. Moreover, it is clear even now that practically all of these possibilities must take place at some rate during aging. *The major general scientific objective of aging research is,* therefore, *the assessment of the relative contributions of each of these processes and the detailed specific mechanisms of their occurrence.* It is hoped that this brief categorization and discussion of the major general and specific possibilities will furnish a critical framework for the future testing and evaluation of the relative contribution of various factors in biological senescence.

CHAPTER III

The distribution of cellular aging

In his excellent monograph, "The Biology of Senescence," Comfort (*5*) discussed in a highly competent and entertaining manner much of the available literature and knowledge on the occurrence of senescence in various animal and plant species. The reader is referred to Comfort's book for a more exhaustive discussion of the distribution of senescence than will be undertaken here. The present discussion will be devoted to a consideration of the special features and relationships among three main types of biological systems: (*a*) those that clearly do not age, (*b*) those that possibly do not show the process, and (*c*) those that clearly go through an aging process leading eventually to the death of the individual organism.

A. NONAGING SYSTEMS

1. *The Germ Line*

August Weismann held strong views on the so-called immortality of the germ line. By the germ line, he meant the unbroken chain of genetic succession extending back to the very first self-producing cell. He visualized the soma as an appendix derived from, attached to, and caring for the needs of the all-important germ line. He states his thesis in the following words (*20*):

"I hope that I have thrown new light upon some important points and I now propose to conclude with the following short abstract of the results of my enquiry.

"I. Natural death occurs only among multicellular beings; it is not found among unicellular organisms. The process of encystment in the latter is in no way comparable with death.

"II. Natural death first appears among the lowest Heteroplastid Metazoa, in the limitation of all the cells collectively to one generation, and of the somatic or body-cells proper to a restricted period: the somatic cells afterwards in the higher Metazoa came to last several and even many generations, and life was lengthened to a corresponding degree.

"III. This limitation went hand in hand with a differentiation of the cells of the organism into reproductive and somatic cells, in accordance with the principle of division of labour. This differentiation took place by the operation of natural selection.

"IV. The fundamental biogenetic law applies only to multicellular beings; it does not apply to unicellular forms of life. This depends on the one hand upon the mode of reproduction by fission which obtains among the Monoplastides (unicellular organisms), and on the other upon the necessity, induced by sexual reproduction, for the maintenance of a unicellular stage in the development of the Polyplastides (multicellular organisms).

"V. Death itself, and the longer or shorter duration of life, both depend entirely on adaptation. Death is not an essential attribute of living matter; it is neither necessarily associated with reproduction, nor a necessary consequence of it.

"In conclusion, I should wish to call attention to an idea which is rather implied than expressed in this essay:—it is, that reproduction did not first make its appearance coincidentally with death. Reproduction is in truth an essential attribute of living matter, just as is the growth which gives rise to it. It is as impossible to imagine life enduring without reproduction as it would be to conceive life lasting without the capacity for absorption of food and without the power of metabolism. Life is continuous and not periodically interrupted: ever since its first appearance upon the earth, in the lowest organisms, it has continued without break: the forms in which it is manifested have alone undergone change. Every individual alive today—even the very highest—is to be derived in an unbroken line from the first and lowest forms.

"Let us now consider how it happened that the multicellular animals and plants, which arose from unicellular forms of life, came to lose this power of living forever.

"The answer to this question is closely bound up with the principle of the division of labour which appeared among multicellular organisms at a very early stage, and which has gradually led to the production of greater and greater complexity in their structure.

"The first multicellular organism was probably a cluster of similar cells, but these units soon lost their original homogeneity. As the result of mere relative position, some of the cells were especially fitted to provide for the nutrition of the colony, while others undertook the work of reproduction. Hence the single group would come to be divided into two groups of cells, which may be called somatic and reproductive—the cells of the body as opposed to those which are concerned with reproduction. This differentiation was not at first absolute, and indeed it is not always so today. Among the lower Metazoa, such as the polypes, the capacity for reproduction still exists to such a degree in the somatic cells, that a small number of them are able to give rise to a new organism,—in fact new individuals are normally produced by means of so-called buds. Furthermore, it is well known that many of the higher animals have retained considerable powers of regeneration; the salamander can replace its lost tail or foot, and the snail can reproduce its horns, eyes, etc.

"As the complexity of the Metazoan body increased, the two groups of cells became more sharply separated from each other. Very soon the somatic cells surpassed the reproductive in number, and during this increase they became more and more broken up by the principle of the division of labour into sharply separated systems of tissues. As these changes took place, the power of reproducing large parts of the organism was lost, while the power of reproducing the whole individual became concentrated in the reproductive cells alone.

"But it does not therefore follow that the somatic cells were compelled to lose the power of unlimited cell-production, although in accordance with the law of heredity, they could only give rise to cells which resembled themselves, and belonged to the same differentiated histological system. But as the fact of normal death seems to teach us that they have lost even this power, the causes of the loss must be sought outside the organism, that is to say, in the external conditions of life; and we have already seen that death can be very well explained as a secondarily acquired adaptation. The reproductive cells cannot lose the capacity for unlimited reproduction, or the species to which they belong would suffer extinction. But the somatic cells have lost this power to a gradually increasing extent, so that at length they became restricted to a fixed, though perhaps very large number of cell-generations. This restriction, which implies the continual influx of new individuals, has been explained above as a result of the impossibility of entirely protecting the individual from accidents, and from the deterioration which follows them. Normal death could not take place among unicellular organisms, because the individual and the reproductive cell are one and the same: on the other hand, normal death is possible, and as we see, has made its appearance, among multicellular organisms in which the somatic and reproductive cells are distinct."

Weismann's arguments are still generally tenable whether his detailed extension of the Haeckelian view of the evolution of metazoa is correct or not. The essential absence of deteriorative processes in the germ line may be accepted without serious reservation.

2. *Protozoa*

However, despite the persuasiveness of Weismann's words and his prediction that there should be no aging in unicellular organisms in which there is no dichotomy between the germ line and the soma, fifty years or so of research on the aging of protozoa left the issue much in doubt. For contrary to expectation it did appear that a number of isolated lines or clones of commonly investigated protozoan species undergo senescence unless periodic sexual crossing occurs. These observations did much to confuse the issues. In Comfort's words, in "The Biology of Senescence," "A large part of the literature included in the bibliographies of senescence deals with the presence or absence of aging in protozoan clones. Maupas (*21*) appears to have been the first to draw an analogy between somatic aging in metazoa and the behavior of protozoan populations. He predicted that such populations would display a life cycle including a phase analogous to metazoan senescence, and ending in the death of the population, unless nuclear re-organization by conjugation, or some similar mechanism, brought about the 'rejuvenation' of the stock. For many years, a vigorous competition was conducted between protozoologists in seeing how many asexual generations of *Paramecium, Eudorina,* and similar creatures they could rear. In the course of this process, much nonsense was written about potential immortality but a great deal was learned about protozoan reproduction and culture methods. It became evident that some clones deteriorate and others, including somatic cells such as fibroblasts and tissue cultures, do not."

Despite much violent controversy and many confusing interludes, the situation now seems to be resolved by the work of Sonneborn, who has shown that there are indeed certain strains of *Paramecium* which are capable of going on indefinitely without conjugation and without endomixis, a substitute for cross-fertilization. On the other hand, the survival in culture of many species of ciliates and other protozoa requires periodic cross-fertilization or endomixis. There seems to be less doubt that bacteria, yeast, and clones of many kinds of plants, propagated vegetatively, do not exhibit senescence, although other clonally perpetuated species, such as strawberries, seem to undergo a gradual senescence associated with susceptibility to a virus infection.

B. ON SPECIES WHICH MAY NOT AGE

According to Weismann, senescence of the soma may be considered as a selectively advantageous adaptation. If this is a tenable position immortal species of metazoa would not be expected to exist. In order to discuss this question sensibly it is first necessary to discuss what one means by aging of an individual. There certainly is no question in our minds when we state that an individual human being or an individual mammal, such as a pet dog or race horse, ages. As a matter of fact, in organisms reproducing exclusively by sexual means there appears to be no difficulty in defining individuals, i.e., an individual is a collection of cells or organelles functioning in an integrated manner in response to environmental stimuli.

Individuals may cease to exist in one of four ways: (*a*) first, they may be eliminated as functioning entities as a result of environmental assaults or a gradual deterioration consequent to the business of living (aging): (*b*) individuals may cease to exist by giving rise through a process of fission into two or more individuals, or, (*c*) conversely, as in the case of slime molds or in ***Hydractinia*** where stolonic fusion occurs, individuals may cease to exist by the coalescence of the protoplasm originally belonging to several individuals or potential individuals; (*d*) the fourth means by which an individual may cease to exist is through a process of gradual change in his constituent parts, either through the replacement of subcellular constituents or through the gradual replacement of cells as they wear out. Organisms which retain this capacity for continued replacement will not necessarily undergo senescence; indeed, provided that the rate of replacement is sufficient to offset the deleterious effects of the passage of time, they would be expected to be immortal, or at least to have indeterminate lifetimes, even though the "individuals" would gradually be transformed into other individuals as their constituents are replaced.

There are thus three categories of organisms: those which clearly never have an opportunity to age because they divide and yield to new growing organisms before age changes can become determinative; those which clearly do age, primarily because they do not replace worn or lost parts at a rate sufficient to compensate for the assaults of time and environment; and a third class of organisms which fails to show aging as a whole because of a continual replacement regimen, even though there is an attrition of their constituent parts, either, for example, molecules or subcellular organelles in the case of single-celled organisms or even large groups of cells in multicellular organisms. There seems to be no *a priori* reason why this third type of animal should not be successful and survive, provided that there is no severe selective disadvantage inherent in a regular replacement of cells or their parts. It appears likely that certain coelenterates of the class Anthozoa may fit into this last category. Ashworth and Annandale (*22*) in 1904 in a paper entitled "Observations on Some Aged Specimens of Sagartia Troglodytes and on the Duration of Life in Coelenterates" delightfully describe certain aspects of the natural and unnatural history of anemones. This species, which incidentally is viviparous, was kept in captivity in at least one recorded case by an English spinster for a period of about 50 years. The animals were kept in small jars. Their water was changed every 20 days and the animals were fed regularly although not luxuriously. There was no evidence of any decline in physiological capacity or reproductive function during this entire period. Even longer instances of culture of anemones in captivity have been reported. The following is a quotation from Ashworth and Annandale.

"These specimens of *Sagartia troglodytes* were collected by Miss Anne Nelson (Mrs. George Brown) on the coast of Arran, some few years previous to 1862 (the exact date has not been recorded), and were placed in bell-jars containing sea-water. In 1862 they were transferred to the care of Miss Jessie Nelson, in whose possession they still remain, and to whom we are indebted for the opportunities of observing these interesting anemones. Sixteen of the original specimens are still living, so that they have lived in captivity for about fifty years. They are kept in a bell-jar about 13 inches in diameter and 9 in depth. The original specimens are all together on a piece of stone, which bears a number of deep depressions in which the anemones have ensconced themselves. These conditions closely resemble those in which *S. troglodytes* is usually found, the specific name of this anemone being derived from its favourite habit of dwelling in holes and crevices of the rock. These specimens have been under constant observation since 1862, and there can be no doubt that they are the original ones." Ashworth and Annandale also stated that certain corals live for at least 22 to 28 years, as estimated from the size of the colony, and growth rate.

We concur generally with Comfort who says, "Evidence that the life-span of sea anemones is 'indeterminate' is probably stronger than for any other metazoan group." Comfort continues, "Dalyell's celebrated specimens of *Actinia* lived for 70 years in captivity without any sign of deterioration. An even more famous batch of sea anemones were collected 'some years prior to 1862' and were first identified as *Sagartia troglodytes* by Ashworth and Annandale; later as *Cereus pedunculatus* by Stephenson (*23*). They remained in the aquarium of Edinburgh University, Department of Zoology, until 1940 or 1942, when they were all simultaneously found dead. Budding continued freely throughout life, and the animals underwent no obvious change during 80 to 90 years of continuous observation."

From these and similar studies, one central fact emerges, namely, that *there is no inherent factor which automatically produces senescence in all lines of animals and plants.* There are indeed reasons for believing that senescence does not occur in all metazoans, thus placing them on a par with the long-lived plants, or with clones such as bananas derived from seeds centuries ago. The extent to which bacteria, clones, and other single-celled organisms will deteriorate with time, if they are prevented from dividing, is another question. Unfortunately, the very conditions that are used to inhibit cellular division may themselves induce degenerative changes in the inhibited individuals.

C. SYSTEMS SHOWING AGING

1. *General Considerations*

A vast variety of living organisms in practically every plant and animal phylum show changes which can be classified as a true aging process. Is the capacity for indefinite existence limited only to such lowly but elegant forms as the sea anemone? *A priori,* there seems to be no reason why a complex metazoan, even a vertebrate, should last only for a finite time as an individual. Again Weismann (*20*) has some germane comments on the subject, which because of their perceptiveness and elegance are quoted *in extenso* as follows:

"The immortality of unicellular organisms and of germ-cells is, as I said years ago, not absolute, but potential; for they are not, like the gods of ancient Greece, compelled to live forever. Thus we are told that Ares received a wound which would have proved fatal to any mortal, but although he roared as loud as ten thousand bulls, he could not die. The organisms in question can, and the majority of them do die, but a part of each lives on. But is it one and the same substance which continues to live? Does not life, here and everywhere else, depend on assimilation, that is on a constant change of material? What then is immortal? Apparently not a substance at all, but a certain form of motion. The protoplasm of unicellular beings possesses such an arrangement in its chemical and molecular structure, that the cycle of material which makes up life is ever repeating itself, and can always begin afresh so long as the external conditions remain favourable. In this respect it may be compared to the circulation of water on the earth. Water evaporates, is condensed into cloud, falls to the earth as rain, only once more to evaporate, and thus the cycle repeats itself. And just as there exists no inherent cause in the physical and chemical nature of water, which interrupts this circulation, so in the physical nature of the protoplasm of unicellular beings there is nothing which puts an end to the cycle of existence,—that is fission, growth by assimilation, and then fission again. It is this property which I have called immortality, and in organic nature it is the only real immortality to be met with. It is a purely biological conception, and must be distinguished from the immortality of non-living, that is of inorganic matter.

"If then this real immortality is simply a cyclical movement conditional on certain physical properties of protoplasm, why should it be inconceivable that this property, under certain circumstances, should alter to some extent, so that the phases of metabolic activity should not exactly repeat themselves, but after a certain number of cycles should come to an end, resulting in death? All living matter varies, and why is it inconceivable that variations of protoplasm should arise which, while fulfilling better certain functions advantageous to the individual, should be associated with a metabolism that does not exactly repeat itself, a metabolism that sooner or later comes to a stand-still? To my mind the descent of the immortal to the condition of mortality, is less to be marvelled at than the fact that monoplastids and germ-cells have remained immortal. The slightest change in the properties of living matter might involve such a descent, and certain essential peculiarities in the composition of this substance must be most rigidly maintained, in order that the metabolic cycle may sweep on with perfect smoothness, and raise no obstacle against its own persistence. Even if we know nothing further of these essential peculiarities of structure, we may at least maintain that the rigorous and unceasing operation of natural selection is necessary to maintain them. Any deviation from this standard ends in death. I believe that I have shown that organs which have ceased to be useful become rudimentary, and ultimately disappear owing to the principle of panmixia alone,—not because of the direct effect of disuse, but because natural selection no longer maintains them at their former level. What is true of organs is also true of their functions; for function is but the expression of certain peculiarities of structure, whether we can directly perceive the connection or not. If then the immortality of unicellular beings rests on the fact that the structural arrangement of their substance is so accurately adjusted that the metabolic cycle always comes back to the same point,—why should, or rather, how could this property of the protoplasm, which is the cause of immortality, be retained when it ceased to be necessary? And clearly it is no longer of use in the somatic cells of heteroplastids. From the moment that natural selection relaxed its hold upon this property of the protoplasm, the power of panmixia began to be felt, and ultimately led to its disappearance. Prof. Vines will probably ask how this process can be conceived. I answer, quite simply. Let us suppose that certain individuals appeared among the monoplastids with such variation of the chemical or molecular characters, that the continuous recurrence of their metabolic cycle came to an end, so that natural death became a necessity. These individuals could never give rise to a persistent variety.

"But if individuals with a similar variation in their somatic cells arose among the heteroplastids, no detriment would be felt by the species: the body-cells would indeed die, but the undying germ-cells would secure the continuance of the species. By means of the distinction between somatic and germ-cells, natural selection was enabled to direct its attention, to speak metaphorically, to the immortality of the germ-cells, and to an entirely different range of properties among the somatic cells, such as the capacity for movement, irritability, increased powers of assimilation, etc., etc. We do not yet know whether an increase in these properties is directly connected with a change of constitution involving the loss of immortality, but it is not impossible that this may be the case; and, if so, the somatic cells would have ceased to be immortal more quickly than if panmixia were the only agency at work."

Another general hypothesis of the origin of senescence is given in the following stimulating commentary by Bidder (*15*):

"Giant trees, cultures of chick cells and of paramecium, measurements of plaice and of sponges all indicate that indefinite growth is natural. Galileo proved it fatal to swiftly moving land animals; therefore, swiftly moving mammals and birds were impossible until their ancestors had evolved the mechanism for maintaining specific size within an error not impairing adequate efficiency. Even without evidence of evergrowing organisms, we could not suppose that the close correspondence to specific size, which we see in all swiftly moving creatures of earth or air, results from mere 'senescent' fading out of the Zygotic impulse to cell division and cell increase. Specific size is probably most important to birds, with their airoplane mechanics strictly enjoining conformity of scale to plan; but to men it is most noticeable in man. Only familiarity prevents marvel at the rarity of meeting a man more than 20% taller or shorter than 5½ feet, or of discovering his remains in any place, or any race, or any epoch. Probably our erect posture enforces accurate proportions of length to weight, for running.

"Adequate efficiency could only be obtained by the evolution of some mechanism to stop natural growth as soon as specific size is reached. This mechanism may be called the regulator, avoiding the word 'inhibitor' so we do not connote a physiological assumption. However ignorant we are of its nature, its action is traced in anthropometric statistics: a steady diminution in growth rate from a maximum at puberty to the vanishing point in the twenties. That the regulator works through change in the constitution of the blood is shown by the perpetual division of Carrell's chick cells in embryonic plasma, whereas cell division is ended in the heart of a hen.

"I have suggested that senescence is the result of the continued action of the regulator after growth is stopped. The regulator does efficiently all that concerns the welfare of the species. Man is within two centimeters of the same height between 18 and 60; he gently rises two centimeters between 20 and 27 and still more gently loses one centimeter by forty or thereabouts.

"If primitive man at 18 begat a son, the species had no more need of him by 37, when his son could hunt for the food for the grandchildren. Therefore, the dwindling of cartilage, muscle, and nerve cells, which we call senescence, did not affect the survival of the species; the checking of growth had secured that by insuring a perfect physique between 20 and 40. Effects of continued negative growth after 37 were of indifference to the race; probably no man ever reached 60 years old until language attained such importance in the equipment of the species that long experience became valuable in the man who could neither fight nor hunt. This negative growth is not the manifestation of a weakness inherent in protoplasm or characteristic of nucleated cells; it is the unimportant by-product of a regulating mechanism necessary to the survival of swiftly moving land animals, a mechanism evolved by selection and survival as have been evolved the jointing of mammalian limbs, and with similar perfection."

Now what is the evidence relevant to Bidder's statement that systems which cease growing will, of necessity, senesce and, conversely, that systems which exhibit continued growth will not be subject to senescent change?

Bidder based his argument almost entirely upon studies of a salt-water fish, the plaice. The male of this species apparently does stop growing after a number of years and also shows an increased mortality thereafter. The female of the species, however, does not appear to achieve a specific size and moreover, no increase in mortality was observable. Unfortunately, the inroads made upon wild populations of fish by natural predators and by man make it almost impossible to judge the validity of their mortality statistics. It appears likely that many species, including the plaice, are killed before they have an opportunity to develop senescence. The same appears to be true of birds, which in the wild rarely show any increased mortality as a function of age. Certain of them, such as parrots, may live to extremely great ages, compared to mammals of comparable size. Among fish, the sturgeon, *Acipenser stellatus,* also appears to grow at an approximately constant rate for upward of 30 years, according to a report by Schmalhausen (see ref. *5*).

On the other hand, there appears to be little doubt that certain, and probably most, species of fish undergo a real senescence, reminiscent in many ways of mammalian senescence, provided they are sheltered from predators or disease for sufficiently long periods of time. Most aquariists are familiar with the appearance of aging in tropical fish. "Mollies" appear to be particularly conspicuous in this respect.

Perhaps even more interesting than the possible absence

of senescence in fish, such as the sturgeon or female plaice which grow continuously, is the question of whether a fish of finite size need necessarily senesce. Again the answer appears to be in the negative, although the evolutionary pathways that have led to burgeoning Metazoa may only occasionally have produced the appropriate genotype.

Among reptiles, also, are to be found cases of very great individual age. For example, individual box turtles, of greater than 120 years of age, have been reported. The evidence in one of these cases, consisted of an engraved marking on the shell of an individual turtle. Oliver (*24*), in 1935, in an article entitled, "Young Billy Johnson's Old Box Turtle," describes the circumstances surrounding the capture of this marked individual. Evidence for the great longevity of turtles does not alone hang upon such single isolated instances. The maximum recorded longevities (in years) obtained mainly from the critical studies of Flower (*25*) and summarized in Comfort's book, are: 150+, 100+, 102, 100+, 90+, 85+, 123+, 118+, 129, etc. Chelonians thus appear, by all odds, to be among the very longest lived of animals.

Birds, also, as mentioned above, exhibit very great longevities. The oldest authentic record given by Flower (*25*) is that of the eagle owl *Bubo bubo,* which lived to the great age of 68 years.

While a detailed recounting of the maximum ages achieved by individuals of a number of different species in the various phyla will not be undertaken here, it may well be that certain of the highly evolved species as, for example, the common clam, *Venus mercenaria* (which is, on the basis of growth rings, believed to live for more than 40 years), may also be examples of animals with indeterminate life spans. In Table IV we list only the maximum longevities recorded for individual animals in each of the major phyla. A more detailed treatment may be found either in Flower's (*25*) "Monographs" or Comfort's book (*5*).

In summary, there appears to be no good and substantiated reason for assuming that all metazoan species undergo senescence. However, the absence of symptoms of senescence may in some species be covered by a high standing death

TABLE IV

MAXIMUM AGES OF INDIVIDUALS IN VARIOUS PHYLA

Phylum	Species	Max. age attained (years)	References (see ref. 5)	Evidence of age
Porifera	*Suberites carnosus*	15	Arndt	Captive individuals
Coelenterata	*Cereus pedunculatus*	85–90	Ashworth and Annandale	Captive individuals
Flatworm	*Taeniorrhynchus saginatus*	35+	Penfold, Penfold and Phillips	Individual case history
Nematoda	*Wuchereria bancrofti*	17	Knabe	Case history
Annelida	*Sabella pavonia*	10+	Wilson	Captive individual
Arthropoda				
Arachnida	*Tarantula*	11–20	Baerg	Kept in captivity
Crustacea	*Homarus americana* (lobster)	50	Herrick, 1911	Size of captured specimens
Insecta	Termites	25–60	Snyder	Characteristics of wild specimens
	Stenamma westwoodi (hymenoptera)	16–18		Captive individual
Echinodermata	*Marthasterias glacialis*	7+	Wilson	Captive individual
Mollusca	*Venus mercenaria*	40+	Hopkins	Growth rings
	Megalonaias gigantea	54	Chamberlain	Growth rings
Rotifera	*Rotaria macrura*	0.16	Spemann	Captive individual
Vertebrates				
Fish	*Silurus glanis*	60+	Flower	
Amphibia	*Megalobratrachus*	52+	Flower	
Reptiles	*Testudo sumeiri*	152+	Flower	
Birds	*Bubo bubo*	68+	Flower	
Mammals	*Homo sapiens*	118+	Authenticated human birth and death records	

rate due either to fluctuations in an otherwise hospitable environment, or to the decimation of individuals on a regular basis by predators.

On the other hand, there seems to be no doubt that the vast majority of animal species which have been investigated do undergo senescence. For example, this is true in certain Protozoa where clonal aging takes place. In the protozoan, *Tokophrya,* a type of aging occurs which is reminiscent of metazoan aging.

2. *Protozoa*

Mast (*26*), in 1931, who studied the effects of starvation on the length of life of amoebae, found that the individual amoeba could exist for 16 days without food in the presence of a less than optimal salt medium, but that they would last from 18 to 22 days in the presence of properly balanced salt. Jennings (*27*) discussion of death and senescence in Protozoa and invertebrates gives a reasonably cogent summary of their senescence. Following the pioneering studies of Maupas alluded to earlier, by far the most extensive investigations reported were those of Calkins (*28, 29*), who studied the organism, *Uroleptus mogulus* Engelm and many other species of Protozoa. He clearly showed that it was necessary for periodic sexual crossing to occur in order to keep a *Uroleptus* strain going and that there was a relationship between the vitality of the strain and the time which had elapsed since sexual crossing. With respect to *Paramecium bursaria* and other ciliates, Jennings makes the following points: first, that some clones, such as *Eudorina,* may be immortal; second, that even though sexual crossing or its counterpart, endomixis, will produce a revitalized strain of animals, it also yields large numbers of short-lived clones, as well as a few long-lived ones; third, he contends that the rejuvenatory function is distinct from genetic segregation.

The situation in paramecia was clouded by Woodruff (*30, 31*) who kept single isolation lines of *Paramecium* going without sexual crossing for more than 13,000 generations. However, although sexual crossing did not occur, he noted a "new phenomenon" which he called "endomixis" (autogamy). The discussion had proceeded in a complete circle when in 1957, Sonneborn and Rofolko (*32*) reported, "Variety 15 of *Paramecium multimicronucleatum* differs both from *Paramecium aurelia* and from other varieties of *Paramecium* in having failed to manifest a capacity to undergo autogamy. Long continued isolation lines of several strains of this variety have also failed to manifest any signs of aging." Similarly Beers (*33*), in 1929 reported that the ciliate, *Didinium,* will reproduce at least for 1384 generations without sexual reproduction or endomixis, and without any sign of loss of vigor as measured by the average number of generations per day.

Austin's studies (*34*) on *Uroleptus mobilis* showed that starvation prolonged the life cycle of this protozoan, which exhibits clonal aging, for more than 50 days. This was only about a 10% increase in average longevity. The clones normally live for about one and a half years and then die out. Sonneborn, in certain selected lines of *Paramecium aurelia,* showed that endomixis did not occur. However, these lines eventually died out in contrast to *Paramecium multimicronucleatum.*

All of these studies on Protozoa lead to the conclusion that certain species require sexual crossing or its equivalent, autogamy, in order to maintain the vigor of the line, while others do not. There does not seem to be any universal and necessary relationship between a sexual mechanism or a need for sexual crossing in order for vigor to be maintained. Perhaps, as Sonneborn has suggested more recently (*35*), clonal aging occurs in species that have their potential conjugants close to hand, whereas species which generally are quite sparse in their distribution and which must wait for long periods of time in order for conjugation to take place, have devised means of avoiding clonal aging.

A few of the comments made by Sonneborn at a recent symposium may be used to summarize the above (*36*).

"Different species of *Paramecium* differ enormously in length of clonal life. Under conditions of excess available food and exclusion of all other organisms, one species lives about two months. Another species lives for about eighteen months. Another may live for years. The short-lived species are inbreeders, yielding fertile, vigorous progeny, even after self-fertilization. The long-lived species normally cannot or do not mate with close relatives; to provide the time necessary for finding suitable unrelated mates, natural selection has preserved genic combinations that result in long clonal life. In still other ciliates, such as *Tetrahymena pyriformis,* clonal cultures have been followed by other workers for decades; these clones have, however, lost their micronucleae and may be considered genetically dead."

Regarding the kinds of age changes that occur in *Paramecium,* Sonneborn and Dippel (*37*) state, "The earliest visible signs of aging in *Paramecium aurelia,* variety 4, are deviations from the normal number of nuclei. At a clonal age of 40 to 50 days since the clone arose at fertilization, animals with one to four instead of the normal two micronuclei are found, and this is traceable to abnormalities in the orientation and elongation of the nuclear spindles at fission. About ten days later, the micronuclear division figures show both clumping of chromosomes at metaphase and also anaphase bridges. There are evidences of other abnormalities in the process of fission. The macro nuclei and oral apparatus lie near the end of the body instead of near the middle, apparently a consequence of failure of the middle of the body to grow normally during fission. This abnormality in growth is further evidenced by failure of the fission to be completed, the two daughter cells remaining united as a chain of two. In very old clones (eighty or more days) all of the preceding appearances are more common and more extreme. In general, the abnormalities are those resulting from disturbances of the time relations in the duplication and separation of the dividing parts; the nuclei and oral apparatus, and the fission zone. The micro nuclei and the oral apparatus begin to divide after the fission plane appears and after the macro nucleus divides. The latter, in fact, divide precociously. This asynchrony in the division of normally correlated parts leads to the formation of amicronucleate and gulletless animals. Altogether, the most conspicuous visible feature of aging in this organism is the breakdown of the normal correlation in the timing of the division and duplication of the component parts of the cell."

Elsewhere, Sonneborn and Schneller (*38*) comment, "Of particular significance as an index of aging is the progeny test, the proportion of normal, viable offspring produced by self-fertilization. This declines gradually, from virtually 100% to zero. The basis of this effect lies in the progressive deterioration of cytoplasm with the age of the clone. The processes involved in sexual reproduction are most sensitive to the action and age of cytoplasm. This leads to increasing proportions of death during sexual reproduction. There is also increasing frequency of death among those that complete sexual reproduction; this death occurs when the new genetic equipment comes into action, that is, after several fissions. Finally, even the vegetative nuclei are damaged. Normal nuclei from vigorous young individuals, introduced by mating into enucleate old animals become damaged within a few days.

"Crosses of cells from a young clone to an old clone show that the nuclei of the old clone carry some dominant lethals but, if the old clone is not too old, the first generation appears normal or nearly so. The second generation, obtained when the first generation is still young, is highly nonviable. The old-by-young hybrids thus carry in recessive condition lethal chromosomal combinations. The amount of damage carried is proportional to the age of the old parent. Most of the analyzed damage is in the form of chromosomal aberrations, though some gene mutations also seem to be present."

Gelber (*39*), in 1938, made a careful study of the effect of the interendomitic intervals on the mortality after the occurrence of endomixus in *Paramecium aurelia.* He showed that the shorter the time between successive endomixes, the lower the mortality in the progeny, anticipating some of the results reported by Sonneborn. If the number of days between endomixus was 10, only 5.9% of the progeny died; if the interval was 18 days, then 21.3% died; and if the interendomictic interval was 28 days, then as high as 41.8% of the progeny died.

All in all, it does not seem likely that a great deal can be deduced about aging of Metazoa from a study of the process of clonal aging in Protozoa. Perhaps the closest resemblance between protozoan and metazoan senescence is that shown by the suctorian, *Tokophrya infusionum,* which has been examined extensively by Rudzinska (*40*). In *Tokophrya,* which reproduces by a sort of budding process, there is a clear morphological difference between the parent and offspring, a distinction which is generally lacking in other types of Protozoa.

Tokophrya pierces the cell walls of other Protozoa, upon which it feeds, with muliple spearlike tubes that stand out all over its surface. It then siphons the contents of the victim (e.g., *Tetrahymena*) into its own body. In *Tokophrya,* reproduction occurs in an unusual manner; the young are formed in the upper part of the old individual. After they are released they swim away and find their own points of attachment. These animals are most voracious eaters and the amount they consume influences their longevity. With very heavy feeding, the mean life expectancy is only a few days; with heavy feeding interspersed with starvation, the life expectancy is about 10 days on the average; if the animals are fed a very meager diet and intermittently starved, the average longevity may be 14 to 17 days, although some individuals may live as long as 21 to 22 days. In contrast to the ciliates where clonal aging appears to be a consequence of genetic changes appearing in a deteriorating cytoplasm, in *Tokophrya* there occurs a much more obvious cytoplasmic deterioration and an accumulation of pigment or waste products. These are shown in the accompanying electron photomicrograph (Fig. 1), which illustrates both young and old individuals.

3. *Coelenterates*

Aging comparable to that occurring in man and other metazoans probably makes its first appearance in the coelenterates. There appears to be some controversy regarding the presence or absence of aging processes in Hydrozoa, particularly in *Hydra.* Boecker (*41*), Berninger (*42*), and

---

FIG. 1. *Light and electron photomicrographs of young and old* Tokophrya. *A and B: Note particularly the shortening of tentacles with aging. Magnification: × 800. C: Feulgen-stained* Tokophrya. *The macronucleus of the young individual is spherical; that of the older one irregular and much larger. Magnification: × 1800. D and E: Electron micrographs of young and old* Tokophrya *cytoplasm. Magnification: × 31,000. Note relatively greater numbers of cristae in the mitochondria of young individuals and the lipidlike pigment bodies in old cytoplasm. (Photographs kindly supplied by Dr. M. Rudzinska)*

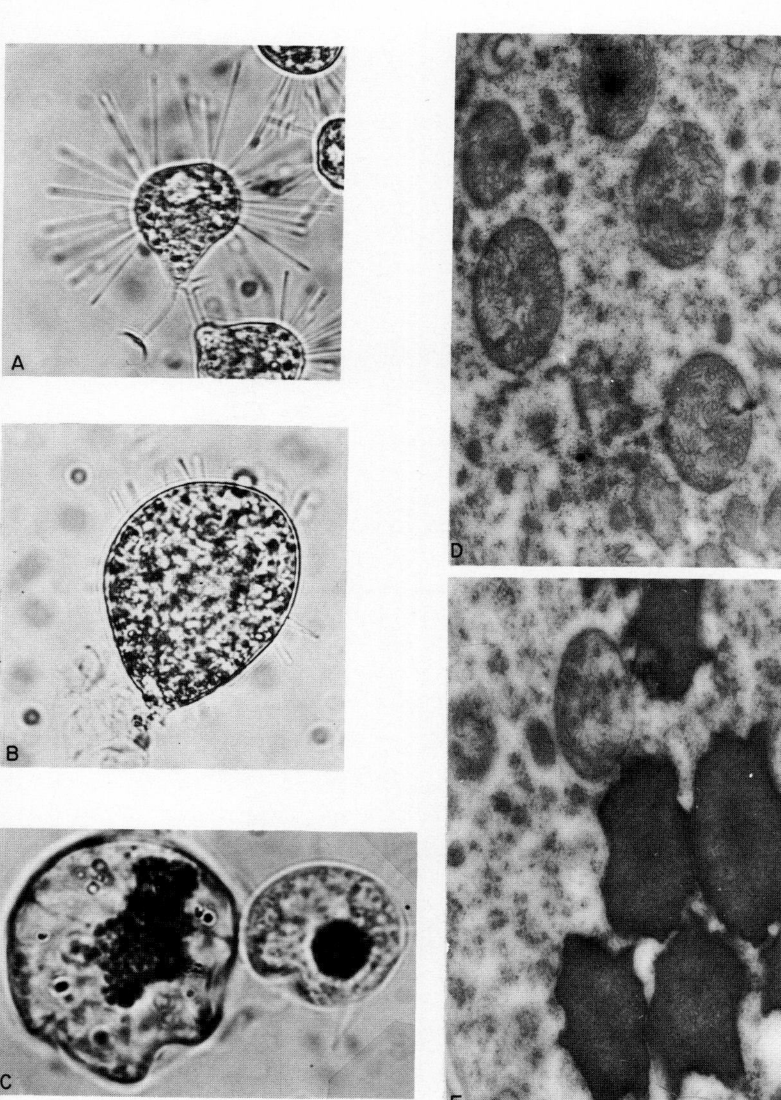

FIG. 1

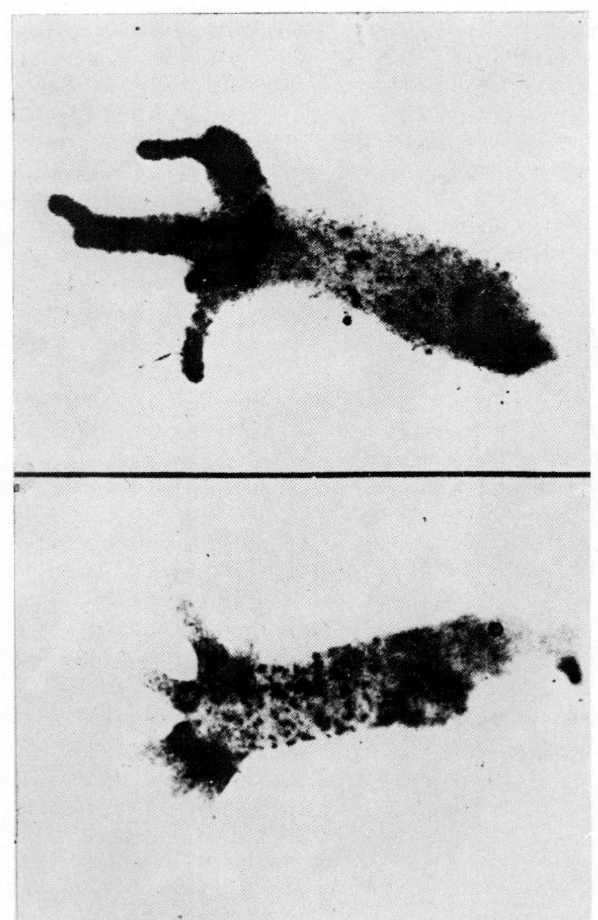

FIG. 2. *Movement of* C_{14} *label in* Hydra. *On left, location of label after 16 hours exposure to* C_{14} O_2. *On right, distribution of label 48 hours later after transfer to nonradioactive medium (from Lenhoff, ref.* 125).

Hertwig (*43*) found that their cultures of *Hydra* underwent a sort of depression with accompanying cytological changes. However, Goetsch (*44*) improved culture conditions and kept individuals of *Pelmatohydra oligactis* and another species alive for 27 months. He believed that, like the actinians, *Hydra* were capable of maintaining themselves in *status quo* indefinitely. Gross, on the other hand, failed to keep any individual of *Pelmatohydra oligactis* alive for more than about a year and noted changes which he called "senile" beginning at about the fourth month of life. Pearl and Miner (*45*) used Hase's (*46*) data to construct a life table for *Hydra*. David (*47*) kept records of *Pelmatohydra oligactis* and was convinced that the individual animals tended to die between 20 and 28 months. Schlottke (*48*), however, made very careful cytological studies and, moreover, suggested that David's histological sections were heavily parasitized. Schlottke's observations can be summarized as follows: There appears to be an aging process in ectodermal cells which is characterized by nuclear changes, e.g., picnosis. He noted that the cells move from the ectoderm into the endoderm after they degenerate and observed the appearance of what he called "guanine deposits" as the remains of cells which had been resorbed into the endoderm. He also followed the degeneration of nematocysts and their subsequent migration into the endoderm.

Schlottke's early view is essentially identical with that of Brien (49) who, in 1953, published evidence based upon marking experiments, that there is a continual formation of new cellular elements in the region around the hypostome or mouth and that this is followed by a movement of cells down over the surface of the column of the *Hydra* body to the foot where death and resorption take place. The gradual movement of cells from the hypostome to the tentacles and base is even more elegantly shown by the radioautographic studies of Lenhoff (*125*) (see Fig. 2). The anticipated presence of lytic enzymes in the foot region and in the tips of the tentacles was recently demonstrated by Brock and Strehler (*50*) (see Fig. 3).

It certainly seems well established that a process of clonal aging is not a regular feature of coelenterates. Lines of *Hy-*

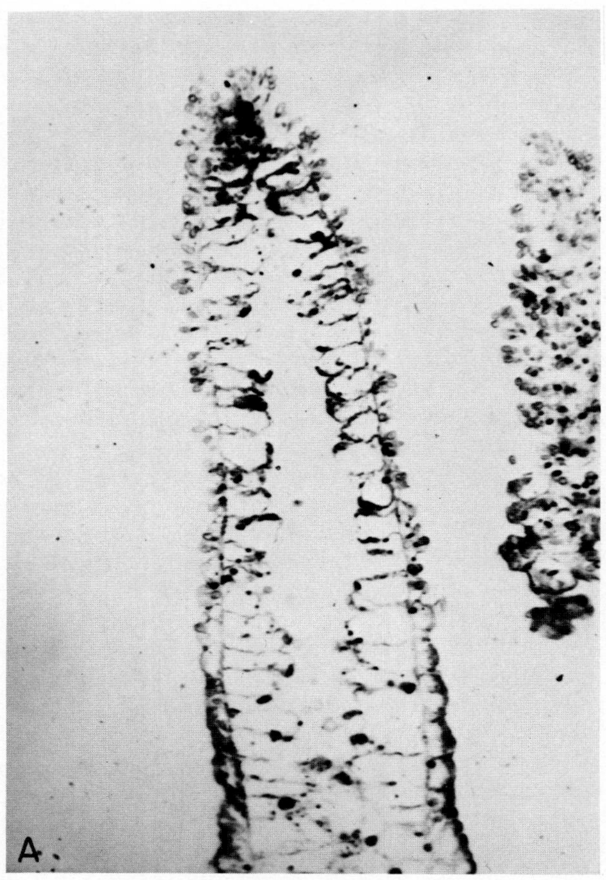

FIG. 3.A. *Acid phosphatase activity in the tips of the tentacles of* Hydra *(from Brock and Strehler, unpublished). This enzyme is characteristic of lysosomes and areas of cellular death. Gomori stain, magnification × 400.*

dra have been kept for decades without sexual crossing, the only means of propagation being the budding process. In our own study of *Campanularia flexuosa,* a colonial hydroid (*51, 52*), we have kept a clone going vigorously in the

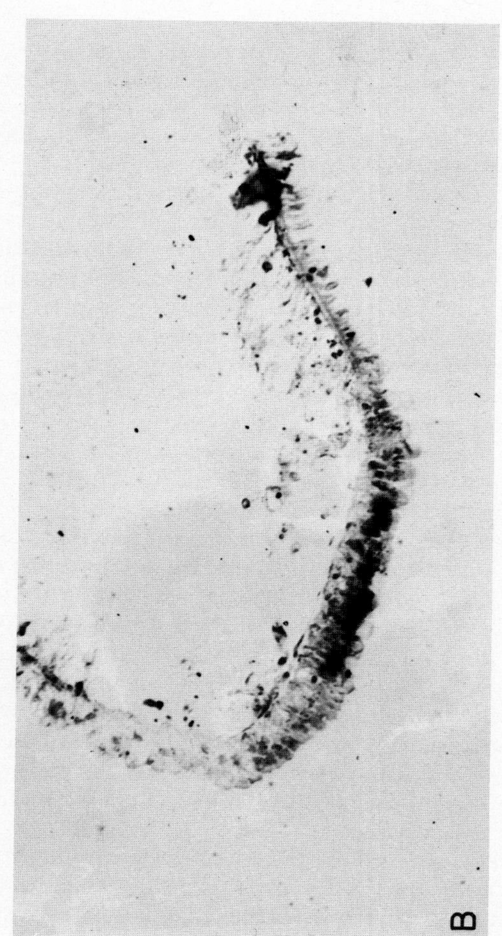

FIG. 3.B. *Acid phosphatase activity in the pedal disc of Hydra (from Brock and Strehler, unpublished).*

laboratory over the last three years on an artificial medium without sexual crossing. This strain was obtained earlier from Crowell (*53–55*), who had likewise kept it and perpetuated it as a clone for a number of years.

Although, in the opinion of most recent investigators, certain Hydrozoa such as *Hydra* do not undergo individual aging, there are closely related species such as *Obelia commissuralis* and *Campanularia flexuosa* which do undergo a clear and most remarkable aging process.

The details of the senescence and death of *Campanularia* hydranth is currently being investigated in our laboratory. The life history of this species, excepting the medusoid generation, is approximately as follows: The animal grows by sending out a rootlike structure called a "stolon" which grows on a hospitable substratum, either rock, piling, or even in some cases on an algal surface (e.g., fucus). At periodic intervals upright branches appear as shoots from the main stolonic growth. These proceed upward for a certain distance, acquire a series of annulations, the most distal of which eventually enlarges into a bulblike structure. This primitive structure then elongates, acquires a rhythmic muscular contractility, lays down a protective covering shield or chitinous perisarc, develops tentacles at the upper end, hollows out and finally perforates a mouth in the center of the tentacles (see Fig. 4). For four or five days, this hydralike animal, growing on a branched stalk, catches crustacea or other suitable prey with the batteries of nematocysts in its tentacles, ingests them, and dissolves their contents, which are taken up by a phagocytic process into the endodermal cell layer or transmitted back down along the branching rootlike stolon to other individuals in the colony or to the region of apical growth.

After three to seven days of active food gathering, digestion, and transmission to the rest of the colony, the individual hydranth suddenly contracts its tentacles and its hypostome and proceeds to dissolve internally. The particulate soup resulting from the self-digestive process is transmitted back into the rest of the colony, presumably to be used elsewhere, leaving only the chitinous exoskeleton as a reminder of the former inhabitant.

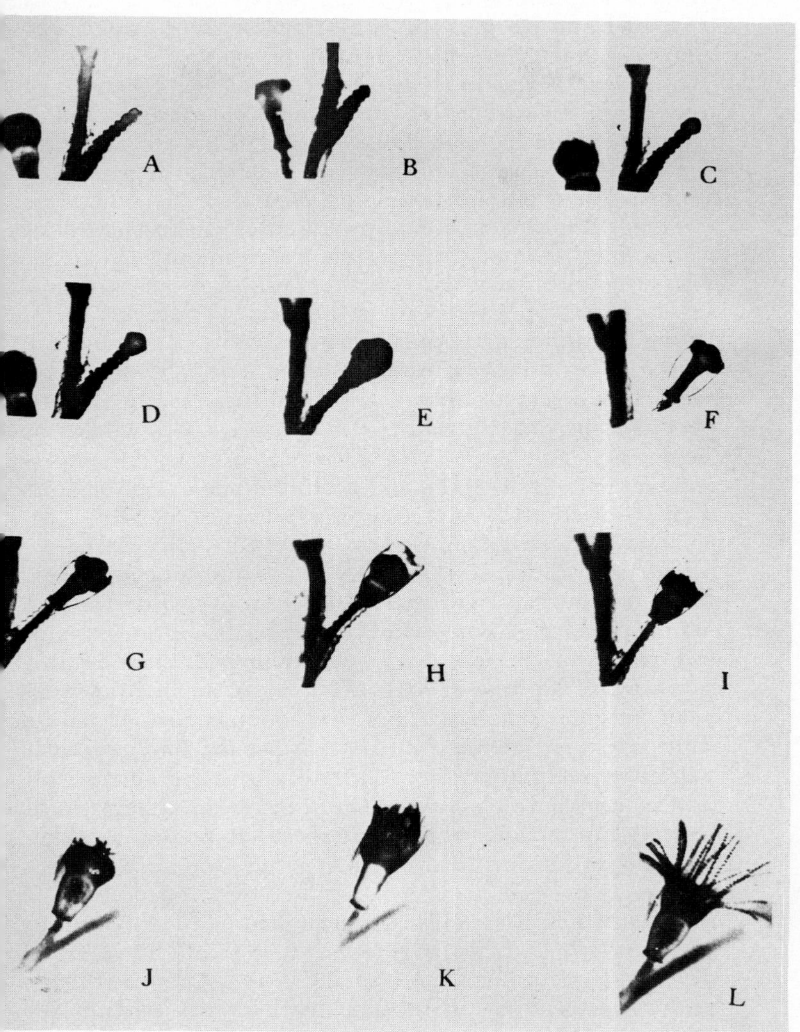

FIG. 4. *Development of a* Campanularia *hydranth (taken from a time-lapse sequence).*

This sequence of events, illustrated in Fig. 5, is truly aging and death on a relatively regular schedule.

Strehler and Crowell (*56*) have recently shown that there is no measurable impairment in either the food-catching or food-digesting capacity of the individual hydranths as they grow chronologically older. In view of the fact that under a restricted food regimen the hydranths in the apical region of each upright are dominant with respect to regenerative capacity, these authors have suggested that the systematic senescence of *Campanularia* and similar hydrozoans is of evolutionary advatnage in forcing the colony to evaluate its food supplies on a fairly regular schedule. In the presence of a meager supply of prey there is clearly an advantage to having a thin circumferencial layer or umbrella of feeding hydranths on a colony, whereas in times of plentiful food supply, feeding hydranths would be distributed in the less advantageous lower positions of the uprights as well as at the apices. Senescence in this form may well be an adaptation that serves the species as a device for achieving the most efficient distribution of feeding individuals.

Closely related colonial hydrozoans (*57*) such as *Bougainvillia,* which can also be cultured inland, do not appear to undergo a similar senescence cycle. However, the developmental pattern in *Bougainvillia* also contrasts quite markedly with that in *Campanularia.* The hydranths in this case arise at the tips of long filamentous stems, branching in an irregular manner. They are not fully formed before beginning their feeding functions, as are the *Campanularia* hydranths, but rather they continue to increase in size and even in number of tentacles for some days after the hydranth becomes functional. In consequence, they possess considerably less uniformity in size than do the *Campanularia* hydranths.

Clytia, which bears a close morphological resemblance to *Campanularia* and *Obelia* as far as the individual hydranths are concerned, differs, however, from the latter in that it hardly ever possesses more than one hydranth per upright stem.

With the hypothesis of the evolutionary basis of *Campanularia* senescence described above in mind, we have re-

FIG. 5. *Regression of a* Campanularia *hydranth (taken from a time-lapse sequence). A: Normal adult hydranth. B: Beginning of regression: tentacle shortening. C: Further contraction. D and E: Liquefaction of interior. F–I: Return of contents to colony.*

cently examined the longevity of *Clytia* and find mortality to be essentially first order with respect to time. This would not appear to be in contradiction to the hypothesis since we would not expect the members of a colony containing only apical members to undergo senescence. *Clytia,* however, differs from *Campanularia* and *Obelia* in one other very important respect. This is the fact that new hydranths are of varying sizes, depending upon the food supply. During periods of poor food supply the newly formed hydranths are smaller in size, presumably adapting the individual to smaller prey. Senescence of *Clytia* then, if it occurs, may be a means of adjusting the size of the hydranth to the food supply.

Generally, the calyptoblastic hydroids (that is those possessing chitinous shields over the hydranths and stolons) appear to be characterized also by a regular senescence cycle, whereas, the gymnoblastic hydroids do not exhibit any such regular senescence as a rule. We have already mentioned the absence of a systematic senescence in *Bougainvillia.*

Another species, somewhat different in appearance, and undergoing a modified regression process under unfavorable conditions is *Pennaria.* Time-lapse studies of this species have indicated a slow resorption of the individual animal into the colony under adverse conditions. The change is not nearly so dramatic as that occurring in the gymnoblastic hydroids, although the final result may be quite analogous.

In summary then, among the coelenterates, we encounter some of the most varied examples of behavior with respect to aging. There are probably nonaging species, such as the anemones, animals which may not undergo a regular senescence such as *Hydra* and possibly *Bougainvillia,* animals which undergo a resorption under unfavorable conditions such as *Pennaria,* and finally, animals which quite regularly and systematically die as individuals, their contents being returned to the colony. Among these latter are *Obelia, Campanularia,* and *Clytia.*

4. *Flatworms*

The most thoroughly investigated of the flatworms with respect to senescence are the free-living forms called *Pla-*

naria. Studies by Child (*58–61*) in the first decade of this century contributed to our understanding of the aging and rejuvenation processes in these animals. Using the species *Planaria dorotocephala* and *Planaria velata,* Child established the following: Although sexual reproduction can occur in these animals, old flatworms of the latter species occasionally fragment and then encyst; after a period a "young" worm emerges from the cyst. Child made the very interesting observation that this encystment could be prevented by starving the flatworms. Removing a portion of the worm and allowing the animal to regenerate also appeared to promote rejuvenation. Starvation, which caused a shrinkage of the animal to a fraction of its initial size, would cause rejuvenation to become apparent in the animal when it was re-fed. Child also noted that small pieces of the planarian seemed to produce more youthful animals than the large ones. From all of this he concluded that there was no necessity for sexual reproduction in order for rejuvenation to occur in a species. He concluded that senescence is due to a loss of functional capacity which is, in turn, due to a decrease in metabolic rate, which decrease ultimately is caused by the accumulation of inhibitory substances and possibly changes in permeability. Whether or not his speculations are in exact accordance with facts, as we know them, is not nearly as important as the fact that he made wide-ranging observations on a means of "rejuvenating" animals. Starvation he viewed as simply a substitute for section of the animal since the period of starvation and atrophy was followed by a period of cell division and regrowth.

Twenty years after Child's studies, Sonneborn (*62*) examined another species of flatworm, *Stenostomum incaudatum.* This species of flatworm is proportionally longer than are the planaria which Child examined, and they undergo an interesting type of fission which also contrasts with that exhibited by *Planaria dorotocephala.* In brief, the animal fragments transversely into four to six pieces, and each of them develops into a full animal. Sonneborn kept the head portions separate from the more rear parts, which, of course, subsequently developed heads. He discovered the interesting fact that the clones of animals retaining the old head parts eventually senesced and died out, whereas those derived from the more posterior portions of the parent animal develop new heads and retained their juvenile character. Clearly a prerequisite for the juvenile condition in the flatworms as well as in the coelenterates and Protozoa is a regular replenishment of all the parts of the animals. *Animals containing old cells or old tissues will eventually age and die. Animals constructed or treated in such a manner that they gradually replace their parts may remain young.*

5. *Rotifera*

Another group of animals which have received considerable attention from gerontologists because of the ease of their culture and other properties are the wheel animals or rotifers. This small phylum includes species whose life spans vary from several days to two months. The life cycle consists of a period of growth which takes place generally through increase in cell size. The nuclear number is said to be fixed. After attaining adult size rotifers enter a period of senescence which is characterized by a decrease in activity, degeneration of cells, deposition of pigment, and finally death. There is considerable literature on the external appearance of senescent Rotifera. Generally, the animals become sluggish in behavior and their reaction to stimuli, the tissues and cuticle shrink and become less transparent or more granular in appearance. They become more sessile and pigment accumulates in the gut, digestive gland, and mastix.

There have been numerous studies of rotifer senescence, most of which are outlined in the bibliography. It appears that, contrary to many species of animals, it is possible to influence the length of life of subsequent generations of rotifers by short-term selection processes. Thus, Finesinger (*63*), in 1926, and more strikingly, Lynch and Smith in 1931 (*64*), showed that poor food conditions decreased egg production and also affected longevity adversely. Moreover, the eggs produced under poor food conditions tended to produce more short-lived individuals than were obtained from well-fed strains. These results are highly reminiscent of Lansing's (*65, 66*) later "orthoclone" studies in which he showed that there was a cumulative, non-heritable and reversible factor in the rotifer, *Philodina citrina*. His experiments consisted essentially of selecting offspring of young mothers and offspring of old mothers, for a number of successive generations, using the offspring from young eggs as further sources of young clones, and similarly employing the old line as a source of subsequent generations of old clones. He found that the old orthoclones gradually or even suddenly died out, whereas the young orthoclones remained healthy.

In light of the studies by Lynch and Smith, which indicated that unfavorable conditions, particularly inadequate food, resulted in the production of unhealthy offspring, one wonders whether the Lansing results, rather than reflecting a premature aging, simply indicate a cumulative effect on egg viability due to a poor maternal environment which finally results in the abolition of the line. In this case the orthoclone experiments may have more relevance to the induction of developmental abnormalities than to gerontology. These experiments certainly deserve to be repeated with other species of rotifers and with larger numbers of animals.

6. *Mollusca*

We have already mentioned the extreme longevity of certain molluscs (*25*), including the common edible clam, *Venus mercenaria*. Crozier (*66*), in 1918, made one of the first systematic actuarial studies of molluscs. He studied the primitive species, *Chiton tuberculatus*. On the basis of the size of specimens collected in the field and of shell markings, he was able to show that there was very little death up until about three years, but that thereafter there was an approximately first-order death of the animals. He found that chitons lived for about twelve years maximally.

Szabó (*67*) has made important studies of histological and pathological changes occurring in gastropods, particularly in the nudibranch molluscs, such as the land slug, *Agriolimax*. He noted a number of different types of pathological lesions and also called attention to the accumulation of pigment within the cells of slugs. He considered these pigments as possibly related to the age pigments that occur in other animal species, including man. He noted the pigmentary accumulation in other gastropods as well and wrote a stimulating review of the senescence of invertebrates. A more recent review of the literature on age and aging of molluscs is given in Haskin's paper of 1954. A life table for *Agriolimax,* the comomn land slug, is given by Pearl and Miner (*45*) and is shown in the accompanying figure. Pearl also presented a life table for the rotifer, *Proales.*

7. *Arthropoda*

Aside from the vertebrates, the phylum whose members have been most thoroughly studied with respect to a variety of factors influencing the aging process and life duration is the phylum Arthropoda. This fact is probably due to the tremendous variety of living forms of insects and crustacea and to the fact that they include species whose longevities and whose ease of culture have attracted a considerable number of workers. Only two of the six classes of arthropods, the insects and the crustacea, have received extensive attention experimentally or observationally with respect to aging. The most studied group among the crustacea are various of the water fleas, such as *Daphnia longispina* and *Daphnia magna.*

In the late 20's and early 30's Terao and his co-worker Tanaka studied certain physiological properties of the water flea, *Moina macrocopa* Strauss. They found (*68*) that the duration of life of this species reached a maximum at a temperature of about 15°C. and that it decreased progressively on either side of that value. This is shown in the Table V. These workers also studied the rate of respiratory activity of these animals as a function of age corrected for body volume and found that it slowly decreased between the ages of 6 and 15 days. Finally they showed that the sensitivity to anesthesia as measured by the time required for the animals to become completely anesthetized in 1/50*M* chloretone gradually decreased with age.

About ten years later, Ingle *et al.* (*69*) gave their attention to another water flea, *Daphnia longispina.* They showed that this animal's life span was almost doubled by starva-

TABLE V

EFFECT OF TEMPERATURE ON LIFE DURATION OF *Moina macrocopa* Strauss

Temperature °C.	Days
5	4.2
9	11.1
15	14.3
21	9.2
27	6.5
33	4.7

tion, and that the heart rate was considerably slowed in starving animals. These results are reminiscent of the effects which Child noted in flatworms (*58, 59*), which Rudzinska noted in *Tokophrya* (*40*), and which McCay (*70*) has described in the laboratory rat.

Banta and Wood (*71*) extended the investigation to a study of some genetic aspects of these species which are capable of reproducing either parthenogenically or by sexual means. In a very interesting paper entitled "The Accumulation of Recessive Physiological Mutations during Long Continued Parthenogenesis," they noted that the offspring of a vigorous clone of *Daphnia longispina,* which had been made to reproduce sexually after 279, 378, 442, 477, and 570 parthenogenic generations, decreased in viability, although the parthenogenic individuals at these various times seemed quite vigorous. This decreasing viability was possibly due to the accumulation of recessive mutations.

Schechter (*72*) briefly reported on some effects of heparin and vitamin K on the life span of *Daphnia magna;* a slight decrease in the survival capacity accompanied immersion of unfed animals in solutions of vitamin K. The presence of heparin in solution seemed to increase survival. These observations should probably be repeated.

Another arthropod which has been investigated (*73*), particularly with respect to its regenerative capacity as a function of age and size, is the isopod crustacean, *Asellus aquaticus.* It was shown that the occurrence of regeneration repeatedly in a given locus tends to deplete a store of an unknown substance, since the rate of regeneration tends to slow down with repeated amputation. However, this was not the case if the amputations were repeated but in another locus; for example, if another leg were removed. These results are reminiscent of some findings of Liebman (*74*) on Annelida; he studied the competition between the capacity for regeneration and the occurrence of sexual reproduction. Primitive cells called eleocytes occurring in a structure called the chlorogogue give rise both to sex cells and to cells used for regenerative purposes. Their use for

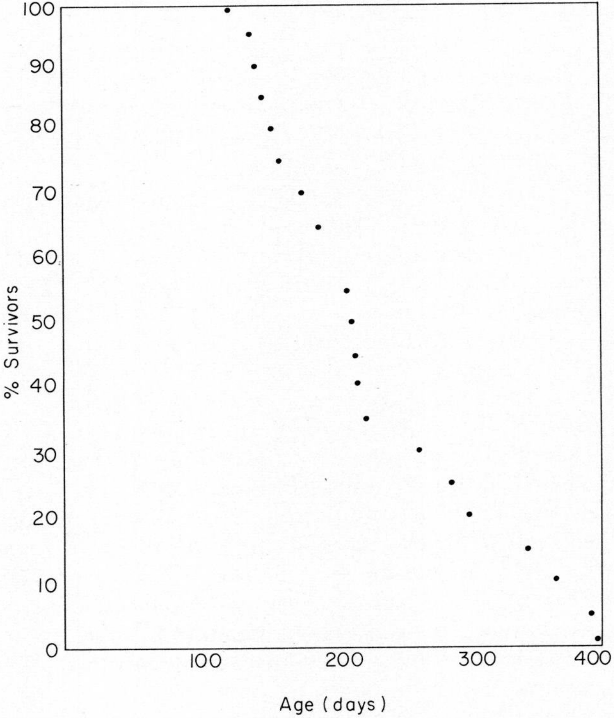

FIG. 6. *Survivorship of the roach,* Periplaneta americana *L. Per cent of survivors versus age in days (from data of Griffith and Tauber, ref.* 78).

one of these purposes reduces the number available for the other. Thus the fertility of the animal is lowered if it has been caused to regenerate parts and, alternatively, its ability to regenerate is much reduced if the eleocyts have been used for the production of sex cells.

Only a few species of insects have been extensively studied but they include representatives of several orders. The life duration of the beetle, *Pinus tectus* Boie, was shown by Ewer and Ewer to be affected both by temperature and by humidity (*75*). This appears to be the case for a number of insects and other invertebrates. The American roach, *Periplaneta americana* L., which has been used extensively by Bodenstein (*76, 77*) for basic studies of the mechanism of hormone action in insects, is one of the longest lived of this class of animals. Griffiths and Tauber (*78*) have collected some information on the duration of life for females after the final molt. The maximum age they obtained for the last instar female was 398 days while the shortest life duration was 120 days. The survival curve derived from their paper is shown in Fig. 6. They also showed that the higher fertility females appeared to have shorter lives. Virgin females lived up to 50% longer than the fertile ones, a fact which probably indicates a depletion of reserve materials and general hardship associated with egg-laying.

Recently Clark and Rubin (*79*) have made some interesting studies of the longevity of a *Habrobracon* species. They have shown that somatic mutation is probably not the cause of senescence in this insect, since the longevity of haploid and diploid males and females is quite similar, whereas their radiosensitivity differs in the expected direction.

Another hymenopteran, the honey bee, has been studied with respect both to the influence of dietary factors, particularly of the content of royal jelly, on longevity and also with respect to histology of aging. Hodge (*80*), in a poorly controlled study in the late 1800's, reported changes in the numbers and appearances of nerve cells of the brains of honey bees. His method of choosing old individuals, however, was not particularly admirable. He picked those individuals which looked old, moribund, or which had recently died. A more recent and careful study by Rockstein (*81*) has demonstrated that there is a substantial decrease in the total cell number of the brains of honey bees with age, and that there is a concomitant increase in the total cholinesterase. By far the most intensively studied arthropod with respect to aging is the fruit fly, *Drosophila,*

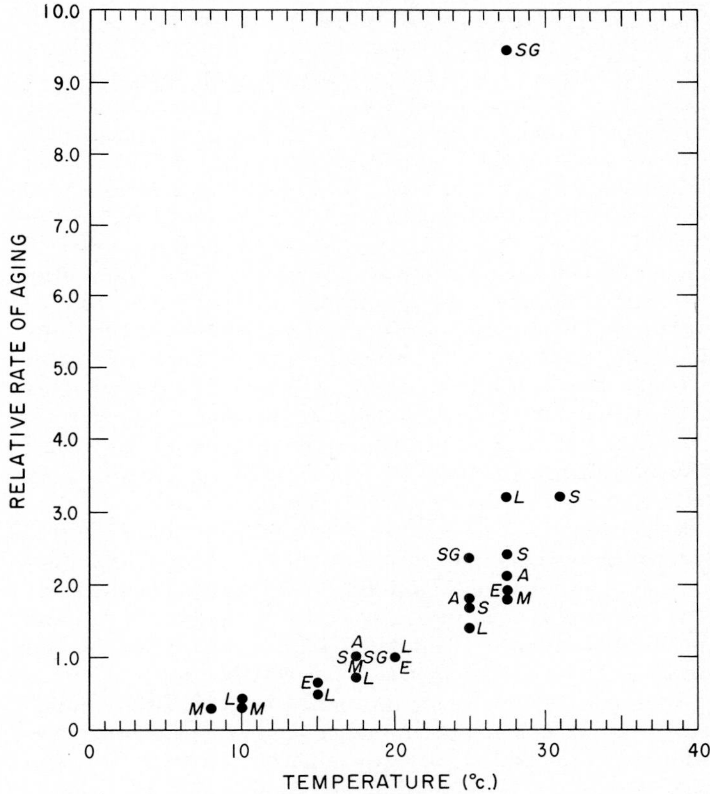

FIG. 7.A. *Relative rate of aging of a number of species of invertebrates versus temperature. L* = Drosophila melanogaster [*Loeb and Northrop* (82, 83)]; *A* = Drosophila melanogaster [*Alpatov and Pearl* (84)]; *S* = Drosphila melanogaster *(Strehler); MS* = Drosophila subobscura (*Maynard-Smith*); *E* = Pinus tectus *Boie* (*Ewer and Ewer*); *M* = Daphnia magna (*MacArthur and Bailley*); *SG* = Drosophila (*Strehler, Gompertz plots*). *Rate of aging was calculated as the reciprocal of the mean longevity and normalized to 20°C.*

whose excellence as a tool for genetic studies has led to its application in a number of different gerontological investigations.

An early application of *Drosophila* in gerontological studies was reported in the now classic papers of Loeb and Northrop (*82, 83*). They showed a clear dependence of the life span on the temperature at which the animals were kept during the imago stage. This temperature dependence is shown in Fig. 7 which also demonstrated the effect of temperature on the longevities of a number of other species of animals. Loeb and Northrop thus demonstrated that the

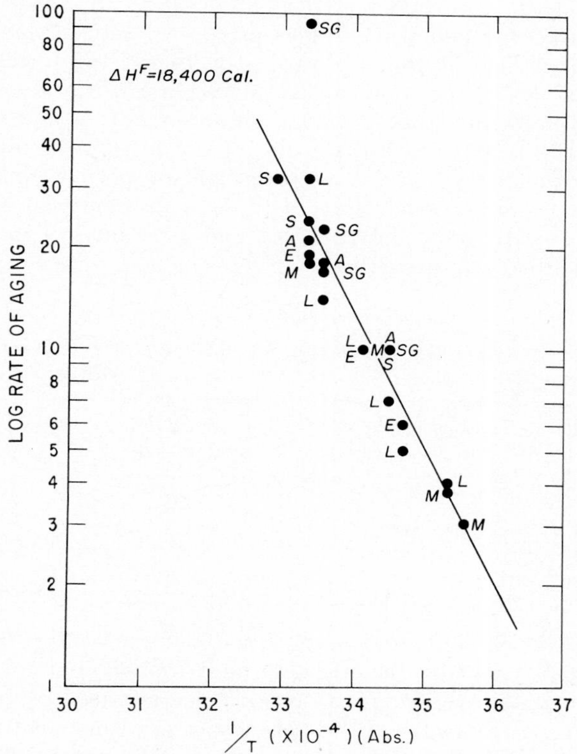

FIG. 7.B. *Some data as in Fig. 7A given as an Arrhenius plot (from Strehler, ref.* 98).

manipulation of the environment of a higher metazoan could produce a considerable increase or decrease in the life expectancy of the animal. Their classic investigations were followed by an extensive and imaginative series of studies by Pearl and his associates, Alpatov, Miner, Parker, and Gonzales (*84–90*). These studies are still among the most careful and controlled probings into the nature of factors controlling longevity. Alpatov and Pearl (*84*) extended the studies of Loeb and Northrop to the effect of temperature during the developmental, or larval, period of *Drosophila melanogaster* on the duration of life of the imago or adult. They found that flies reared at 18°C. not only were somewhat larger than flies reared at 25 or 27°C., but that they also lived for somewhat longer periods of time. Northrop (*91*) also showed that starvation of the larval forms for various periods of time caused an increase in the duration of development (that is, larval development is slowed by starvation). By contrast, the life of the imago was not appreciably affected. Thus, even though the period from egg to pupae was varied from 8 to 17 days, the life span of the imago varied only between 10.5 and 11.9 days. Table VI shows this correspondence.

TABLE VI

EFFECT OF RATE OF LARVAL DEVELOPMENT INDUCED BY STARVATION ON LIFE DURATION OF *Drosophila*

Egg-to-pupae interval (days)	Imago life duration
8	11.3
12	11.5
15	10.5
17	11.9

Crozier *et al.* (*92*) studies variations in the mortality rate of *Drosophila* during the life span and found what they believed to be several critical periods characterized by higher than usual mortality rates. These observations have never been confirmed and their statistical significance is open to question.

Among the other factors which have been studied for their effect on life duration in *Drosophila* are the following: radiation, successive etherizations, maternal age, genetic constitution (including hybridization, mutant character, and chromosomal balance and structure), population density, thermal shocks and rearing the animals at different temperatures for different parts of the life cycle, alcohol, starvation and the addition of various nutritional factors, anoxia, hyperoxia, and heavy water. A few of these factors will be analyzed in the following pages.

TABLE VII

EFFECT OF POPULATION DENSITY ON LONGEVITY OF *Drosophila*

Flies per bottle	Mean duration of life
Medium A	
2	32.79
4	31.71
8	32.50
16	32.72
32	35.94
64	31.71
128	26.09
256	12.95
Medium B	
5	35.98
25	41.91
50	41.60
75	37.01
100	33.07
200	17.91
300	13.77
400	12.60
500	10.98

Pearl, Miner, and Parker (*85*) investigated the effect of population density; their results are shown in Table VII. These authors also studied the rate of reproduction as a function of population density and showed that it dropped from a value of about 22 flies per day to around 1 fly per day when the density was increased from ca. 5 flies per bottle to ca. 90 flies per bottle. The equation relating rate of reproduction to population density was found by empirical fit to be

$$y = 34.53e^{-.018x}\ x^{-.658}$$

where y is the progeny per female per day and x is the number of flies per bottle.

Regarding the effect of various chemical factors in the environment on longevity we have already mentioned the fact that starvation during the larval period does not affect appreciably the length of life of the imago. Loeb and Northrop (*83*) had also showed that the duration of life of the imago was relatively unaffected by the presence or absence of a complicated complete growth medium since their animals lived just as long on a so-called "glucose-agar" medium, which, however, contained a much more complex mixture of substances than glucose and agar. As was to be expected, completely starved *Drosophila* died considerably sooner than did fed individuals. Pearl and Parker (*87*), however, showed that, although there is a considerable difference in *Drosophila* between the life spans of the mutant, vestigial, and the wild type under normal feeding conditions, there was practically no difference between the longevity of starved wild type and vestigials.

More recently, Gardner (*93, 94*) has shown that addition of RNA (ribonucleic acid) pyridoxine and yeast extract to the culture medium increases the longevity of *Drosophila* by about 10% over the longevity of similar flies reared on a minimal medium. When pantothenic acid was added to his mixture, however, he obtained an increase in life span as great as 46% over the controls. Gardner was led to these studies in an attempt to discover the factors in royal jelly which increase the longevity of flies. One of the most potent factors was pantothenic acid which, even in the absence of the other factors, caused as much as a 26% increase in longevity.

Pearl and Parker (*88*) showed that repeated etherization did not appreciably affect the longevity of *Drosophila*.

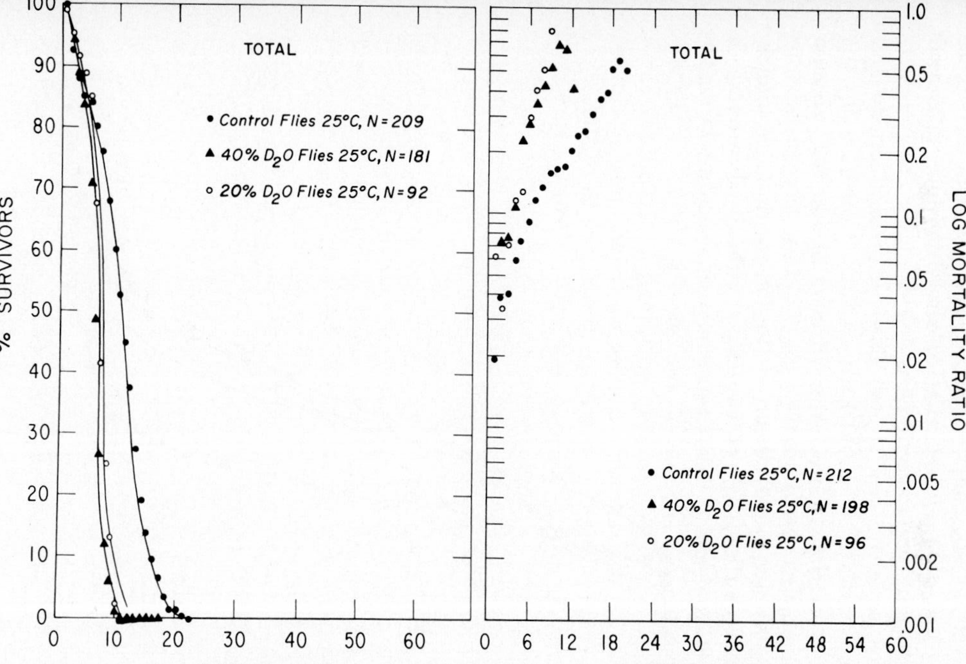

FIG. 8. *Effect of heavy water on mortality of* Drosophila melanogaster. *Flies were reared on regular corn meal medium containing indicated amounts of* D_2O *and were kept in individual cages (Strehler, unpublished).*

Their regularly etherized flies lived for an average of 51.6 days, whereas the control flies, which were very rarely etherized, lived for 49.78 days on the average. On the other hand, Pearl *et al.* (*89*) showed that alcohol tolerance decreased exponentially with age in *Drosophila.*

It has recently been shown that flies reared on 20 and 40% heavy water (*95*) and kept on such a medium for the duration of their adult lives will live about 50% shorter lives than the control flies (see Fig. 8). Low oxygen tensions (1% O_2) during the duration of the imago increases longevity, whereas 100% oxygen causes a significant shortening of life span (see Fig. 9). The sensitivity of the adult *Drosoph-*

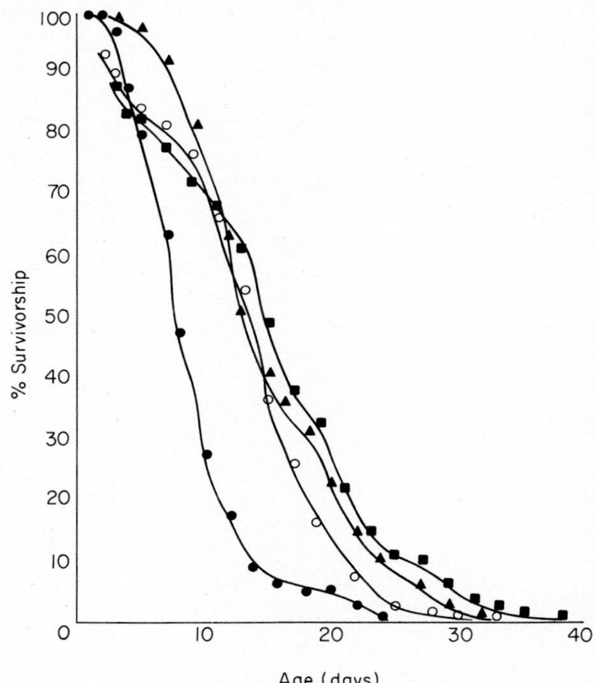

FIG. 9. *Effect of O_2 tension on survival of* Drosophila melanogaster *(Strehler, unpublished).* ●—*100% O_2, N = 402;* ○—*20% O_2, N = 888;* ▲—*2% O_2, N = 247;* ■—*1% O_2, N = 240. Remainder of gas mixture consisted of N_2.*

ila to ionizing radiation is remarkably low. In fact, under certain conditions, exposure to 5000 röntgens will actually increase the longevity of the exposed flies (*95*). Sacher has reported (personal conversation) that even dosages as high as 50,000 röntgens do not appreciably shorten the life of these animals. Sacher (*96*) notes, "Fruit flies were given daily doses of x-rays throughout their lives from emergence onward. Under these circumstances flies that received about 1.5 to 3.0 kr per day throughout life lived more than 30% longer than their controls, and at the same time manifested a markedly decreased variance." That such insensitivity is due to the nondividing character of the cells of adult *Drosophila* is suggested by Ulrich's studies, which demonstrated a considerable sensitivity to X-rays in *Drosophila* eggs. This sensitivity decreased as the eggs underwent cleavage.

More recently we have examined the conditions under which the X-ray prolongation of life becomes manifest and have found that although there is about a 30% increase in longevity when the flies are exposed to the X-rays under non-sterile conditions, the same exposure (5000 rads) of flies grown under sterile conditions and maintained on absolutely sterile culture media shows about a 10% decrease in longevity as a result of exposure to X-rays. That sterile flies live for longer periods than do nonsterile individuals was substantiated by a separate test.

The physical mechanisms underlying the differences in life expectancy of *Drosophila* and other cold-blooded animals when they are exposed to different environmental temperatures has been recently investigated on somewhat different theoretical grounds by Maynard-Smith (*97*) and by Strehler (*98*). Maynard-Smith was concerned with whether or not there were a number of different mechanisms of aging or whether the process in *Drosophila* is a unitary one. His experiments consisted essentially of measuring the life expectancy of flies which had been exposed for a considerable fraction of their normal lifetimes to high temperatures and then cultured for the remainder of their lives at lower temperatures. Maynard-Smith concludes that there are different processes producing death at temperatures above about 31°C. and at temperatures below that value. He uses this observation as an argument for multiple mechanisms of aging without, however, demonstrating that the processes occurring above 31°C. actually occurred to any extent at all in the normal physiological range of these animals. Indeed, one may question whether changes occurring at these elevated temperatures bear any resemblance at all to the normal aging process of these organisms. It seems likely that these deaths are a measure of the rate of denaturation of certain sensitive structures.

Our studies were designed to evaluate the possible contribution of high activation energy processes, such as thermal protein denaturation, to the normal aging process of *Drosophila* at physiological temperatures for this species. We subjected our animals to a short (1 hour) exposure to a carefully controlled series of temperatures between 36 and 39°C. We then measured the subsequent mortality behavior of the animals. Although flies exposed to 38.5°C. showed about a 50% mortality within 5 days after the exposure, those flies which recovered from the short-term effects of the thermal shock did not subsequently show any increased probability of death over that of the controls which had been maintained throughout life at 25°C.—the control temperature (see Fig. 10).

From these studies, we have concluded that the factors producing death in *Drosophila* as part of the normal sequence of senescence are not processes such as protein denaturation, because animals which have been subjected to a treatment that clearly causes considerable denaturation are not substantially "aged" by this treatment. Thus, although our results are consistent with those of Maynard-Smith, we disagree with his interpretation, since we do not believe that the processes responsible for death at high temperatures contribute substantially to the normal senescent process in these organisms. We have recently shown that short exposure to high temperature *will* produce a slightly increased age specific mortality rate of exposed flies as compared to control animals, if the media on which they are kept are regularly replaced.

It is a truism that the length of life is genetically determined. The difference between a turtle and a *Drosophila*

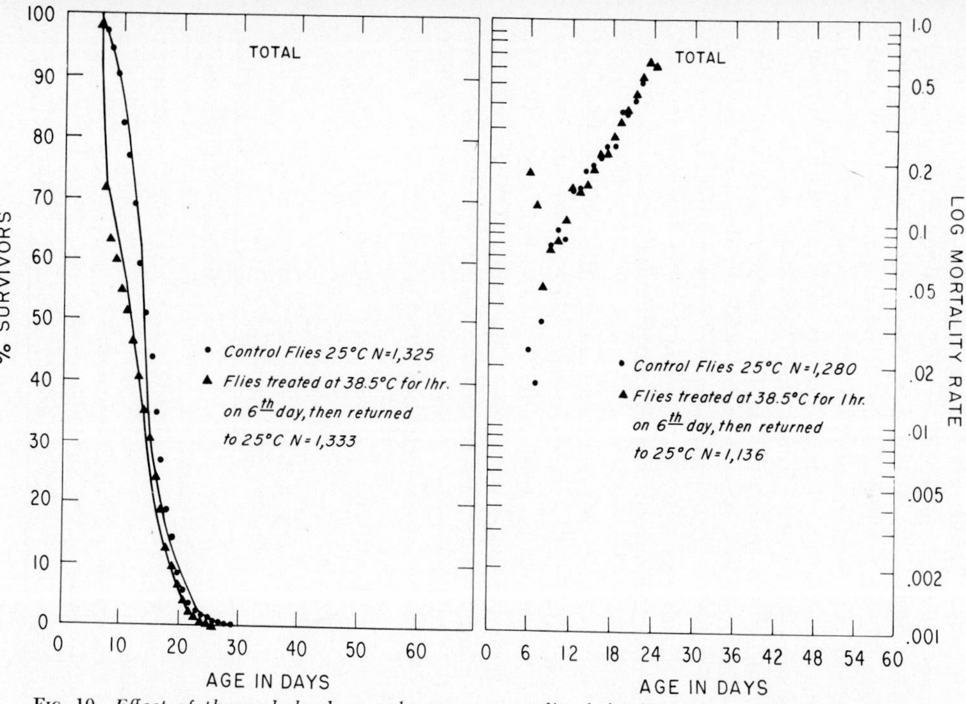

FIG. 10. *Effect of thermal shock on subsequent mortality behavior of* Drosophila melanogaster *(from Strehler, ref 98).*

is, of course, a consequence of differences in the genes which the cells of *Drosophila* and of turtles contain. There are a number of different kinds of genetic deficiencies outlined earlier which could result in the occurrence of an aging process. However, only one of these, the effect of mutant genes (i.e., of genes resulting in development of less than optimal structures or functions) is susceptible to direct genetic investigation. Contradictions between gene function, inadequacies of gene function, or omissions in the evolved genome which simply fail to take account of certain types of failure are not directly susceptible to the usual type of genetic study. It is only errors in gene replication in the germ line or possibly in certain dividing lines of somatic cells that are susceptible to experimental examination at present.

The first and still most elegant studies on the effect of genetic constitution on longevity were those reported by Pearl *et al.* (*90*) beginning in 1923. In these early studies, two parent stocks, a wild-type strain called "Old Falmouth" and a homozygote for five mutants called "quintuple" were used. The longevities of the parent stocks and of the F_1's derived from various reciprocal crosses are shown in Table VIII.

TABLE VIII

Length of Life of Parent Stocks and Hybrids of *Drosophila melanogaster*

Stock	Mean age at death (days)
Old Falmouth	46.26 ± 0.44
Quintuple	14.08 ± 0.23
Old Falmouth (male) × quintuple (female)	51.12 ± 0.84
Quintuple (male) × Old Falmouth (female)	51.73 ± 0.57
All F_1's	51.55 ± 0.47

Note in this case that the F_1's had an even greater average longevity than the wild-type stock from which they were partially derived. Similar, although in some respects more striking, results have recently been reported by Clarke and

Maynard-Smith (*99*), who crossed two geographically isolated strains of *Drosophila subobscura.* Maynard-Smith (*100*), apparently unaware of Pearl, Parker, and Gonzales' pioneering work, notes, "Our interest in aging originated with the discovery that the hybrid between inbred lines lived for longer and are less variable in life span than their inbred parents. These findings have been confirmed by later work although we are perhaps fortunate that the particular pair of inbred lines originally available for study showed the effect in a particularly striking manner. But later work has shown that, in addition to genetic variance due to heterosis or overdominance, much of the genetic variance of longevity is due to genes with sex-limited effects, i.e., to genes with different effects on the longevity of males and females." A tabulation of the longevities of some of the lines and of hybrids derived from them as studied by Clarke and Maynard-Smith is shown in Table IX. These results indicate

TABLE IX

EFFECT OF HYBRIDIZATION ON LENGTH OF LIFE OF *Drosophila Subobscura*

Line	Females (life span)	Males (life span)
K	17.2	31.2
NFS	40.7	42.4
B	33.3	25.8
F_1 hybrids		
K-NFS	55.9	67.4
B-K	61.5	61.6

that there occur within such highly inbred lines of flies deleterious recessive characters which considerably reduce the longevity of the offspring. In some cases these mutants may be recognizable because of their effects on other characters of the anatomy or physiology of the fly such as, for example, the original study of the vestigial mutant arising spontaneously in Pearl's *Drosophila melanogaster* cultures. The apparent hybrid or heterotic vigor, displayed in the studies of Maynard-Smith, probably represents a covering-up of certain nonvisible mutants in the F_1 generation.

By far the most intensive study of the effect of specific mutant genes and gene combinations on longevity in an experimental animal was that reported by Gonzales in 1923 (*101*) (see Table X). Gonzales crossed the F_1's resulting from

TABLE X

EFFECTS OF FIVE SPECIFIC RECESSIVE MUTATIONS ON LENGTH OF LIFE OF *Drosophila melanogaster*

	Mean duration of life (days)		
Phenotype	Female and male	Male	Female
Wild	39	38	40
Quintuple	10	9	12
Black (b)	40	41	40
Purple (pr)	24	27	21
Vestigial (vg)	18	14	20
Are (a)	26	25	28
Speck (sp)	42	46	38
Bpr	27	30	24
Bvg	20	16	24
Ba	21	20	23
Bsp	31	32	29
Prvg	15	11	19
Pra	33	36	31
Prsp	23	23	22
Asp	36	38	34
Bpra	32	35	30
Bprsp	27	31	24
Basp	30	33	26
Prasp	39	38	40
Vgasp	18	12	25
Prvgsp	10	9	12
Bprvga	18	14	22
Bvgasp	16	13	19
Bprasp	22	22	23

a quintuple versus wild-type cross and isolated the progeny according to their respective phenotypes. The quintuple stock contained the following mutants: black (b), purple (pr), vestigial (vg), Arc (a), Speck (sp). Thus, the work of Gonzales (*101*) demonstrates without question that the abnormalities in structure induced by the presence of mutant genes in a homozygous condition also, as a general rule, cause a decrease in longevity.

Another study of the effect of genetic constitution on longevity was initiated through a series of ingenious and painstaking experiments reported by Gowen (*102, 103*) in 1931. These experiments were designed to test the then-current hypothesis of Rubner (*104*) that length of life is inversely proportional to the rate of metabolism. Gowen prepared a number of different stocks of *Drosophila* which, in contrast to Gonzales' strains, did not contain visible mutant genes but which possessed varying ratios of autosomes to sex chromosomes. In *Drosophila,* where sex determination hinges on the balance between autosomes and X-chromosomes, it is possible not only to obtain normal males and normal females, but also triploid females and a variety of middle-sex intergrades in which the ratio of autosome to X-chromosome lies somewhere between the normal male ratio of two autosomes to one X-chromosome and the normal female ratio of two autosomes to two X-chromosomes.

Gowen found that there were slight differences between the average length of life of the normal males and females but that the triploid female lived for very nearly the same lifetime as did the normal diploid female. The mid-sex intergrades, on the other hand, averaged about one half of the average lifetime of the normal males, females, and triploid females. The total metabolism per milligram of body weight per day averaged about three times as high for the mid-sex intergrades as it did for the normal males, and about twice as high as for normal triploid females. Although the total CO_2 produced per lifetime by normal males and females and triploid females was quite similar, the mid-sex intergrades ranged from less than 50 to about 70% of the metabolism which the normal animals produced.

These results, then, are inconsistent with the simple Rubner hypothesis; in addition, they furnish another kind of evidence that the senescence of *Drosophila* cannot be due to accumulation of recessive somatic mutations since they should be extremely rare in the triploid females. Nevertheless, these individuals have the same longevity as their diploid sisters.

Another interesting observation made by Gowen is that the intersexes appear to die by a first-order process since the log survivorship versus age plot gives an essentially straight line, whereas the normal males, females, and triploid females give evidence of the so-called rectangular survival curves, i.e., curves indicating a mortality rate which increases with age. Table XI summarizes the above results.

TABLE XI

EFFECT OF PLOIDY AND SEX INTERGRADES ON LONGEVITY AND METABOLISM

Type of fly	Length of life	CO_2 produced/ mg./24 hours	Relative CO_2/lifetime
Male	28.9 ± 0.8	9.9	4.3
Female	33.1 ± 0.6	15.9	4.8
Triploid female	33.1 ± 0.8	11.2	4.5
Mid-sex intergrades		27.9	3.2
Female sex intergrades	15.0 ± 3.0	21.5	2.0
Male sex intergrades		24.3	3.2

There have been reported, in addition to the above, several experiments dealing with the stability of the genome of *Drosophila* as a function of age of the parent. Stern (*105*) in 1926 and Bridges (*106*) in 1927 studied respectively the frequency of cross-over in the first and in the third chromosomes of *Drosophila melanogaster* as a function of age and of temperature. Stern's results showed that animals reared at 30°C. until hatching showed a higher cross-over frequency by about 50% until the eggs which were undergoing mitosis during the exposure to high temperature had been removed. After this the frequency dropped to the lower value consistent with the 25°C. temperature. In the third chromosome of *Drophilila* Bridges found in initially high and then a somewhat lower rate of crossing-over versus age, followed again by a rise. No explanation was given for these observations, nor is there an evaluation of the reliability of the measurement. Hannah *(107)* in 1955 reported that there is a decrease in the sex ratio from about 50% females to about 42% females after 21 days of aging at 18°C. The stocks that she used were exotic ones and the general significance of this finding is also difficult to evaluate.

Comfort *(108)* in 1953 showed that there was no Lansing effect in *Drosophila subobscura,* i.e., that the offspring of young mothers taken for repeated generations did not live appreciably longer after repeated inbreeding than did the stocks from which they originally came. Table XII shows

TABLE XII

ABSENCE OF LANSING EFFECT IN *Drosophila subobscura*

Stock	No. of flies	Mean life expectancy	Sampling error	S.D.
F_1	72	23.95	1.15	9.65
F_2	77	24.18	1.15	10.12
F_4	95	22.31	1.18	1.55
F_8	129	24.69	0.877	10.13

these results. Glass *(109)* has recently reported that longevity of *Drosophila* is affected by the selection regimen employed in establishing young or old orthoclones.

The information available on invertebrate aging is sparse by comparison with that which is available on vertebrates, particularly on laboratory animals such as the rat and mouse, and on human beings. Much of the information in the remainder of this monograph will be drawn from the observations made on man and his mammalian relatives. In the following we shall enumerate some of the mortality data which subsequent discussions of structure and function will clarify.

CHAPTER IV

Ultimate effects of cellular aging–mortality–a review of theories of mortality

THE MOST SALIENT feature of the aging process is the fact that, in animals which show aging, the probability of death increases with age. This fact is illustrated for a number of different species in Figs. 11 and 12, which illustrate a logarithmic or Gompertz plot of mortality versus age for three species of mammals: thoroughbred horses, the laboratory rat, and human beings in various national environments. The fact that the mortality rate of humans is a logarithmic function of age was first noted by Gompertz *(110)*. The aging which we see is, most observers would agree, a result of an organism's decreasing ability to function optimally in carrying out his vital functions. This decline in function can also be viewed as a decreased adaptation of the organism to his environment. Such decreased adaptation is in turn, reflected in an increased mortality rate.

One must distinguish between the mortality rate of an individual and of a species. For the individual, the mortality rate is constant (zero) until the time of death—at which time it becomes, for an instant, infinite. The individual mortality rate is then a useless index for the study of the aging of individuals. On the other hand, if we assume that the average vitality of a population of a given age does not differ greatly from that of the individuals making up the population or, stated otherwise, that the process of aging produces changes in individuals which parallel to a considerable extent the average age correlated changes in a population, it follows that the mortality rate in a population must be related to the physiological age of individuals in that population. We postulate, therefore, that it should be possible to deduce certain facts about the physiological condition of populations or of individuals in populations from a study of the mortality behavior of such populations.

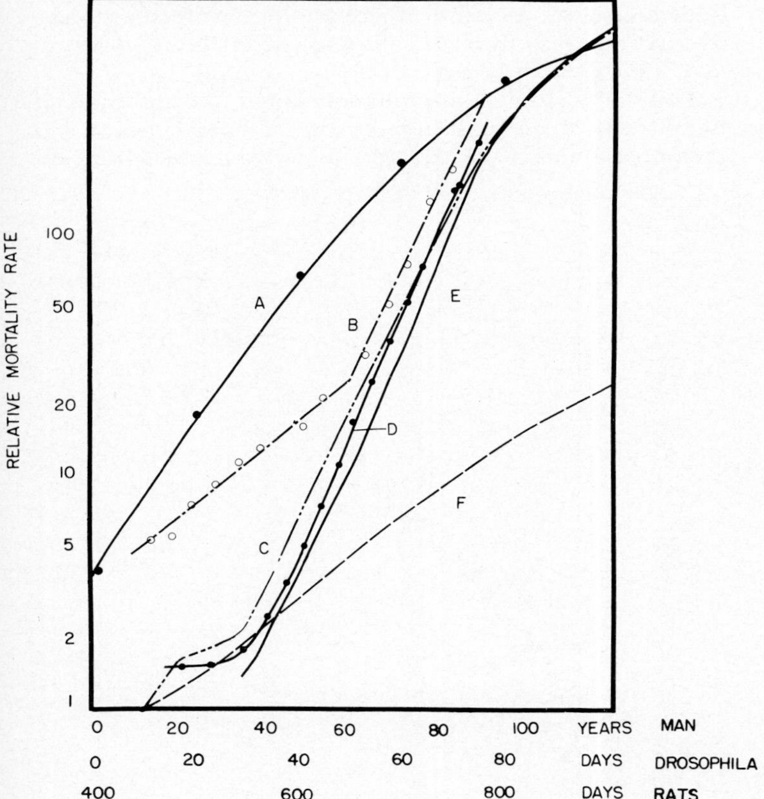

FIG. 11. *Gompertz plots of mortality behavior of a number of species and of humans in different environments. A = male rats (from Simms and Berg, ref.* 120). *B = male humans (Egypt); C = male human, white, (U.S.), North Central Division, 1949–1951; D = male human; E = female human, white, North Central Division, 1949–1951; F =* Drosophila melanogaster (*Pearl and Parker, ref.* 87). (*See Strehler,* 10)

The basic question in the biology of aging, of course, is the relationship between chronological age and structural and physiological properties. Of all of the properties of organisms and particularly of human beings that have been studied with respect to age, the mortality rate is probably the most carefully, exhaustively, and accurately recorded. It is generally a simple matter to tell whether a human being is alive or dead; moreover, there are in most modern societies accurate records of the dates of the birth and death of individual human beings.

This large store of information about the duration of life of individuals and large groups of human beings has prompted a number of attempts to derive mathematical ex-

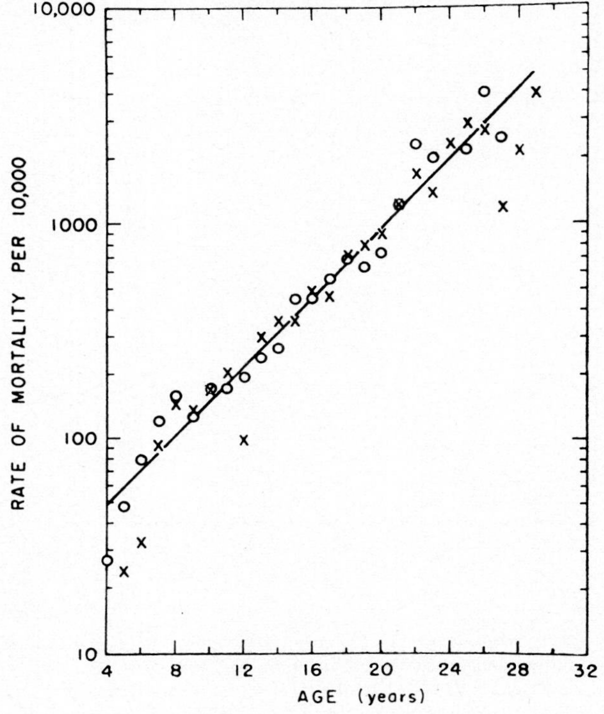

FIG. 12. *Rate of mortality of thoroughbred mares. From Sacher (ref.* 96) *(after the data of A. Comfort,* J. Gerontal. *13: 342–390, 1958).*

pressions to account for its general features. The human mortality curve is characterized by a number of distinct phases. The first of these is a rapid decrease in death rate during infancy and childhood. This is followed by a period roughly between 10 and 30 years of age during which there is a constant or a slowly increasing mortality rate. The third portion of the actuarial description of human beings consists of a period of logarithmic increase in death rate—the so-called Gompertzian period which extends from about age 35 to age 90 in a variety of different human populations. In most countries the time required for the probability of an individual's dying to double is about 8 years in the Gompertz region. Following the Gompertz phase the mortality rate increases more slowly on a semilogarithmic scale than it did during the preceding 50 to 60 years.

Mortality statistics may, of course, be expressed in a number of ways, of which three deserve special mention. The

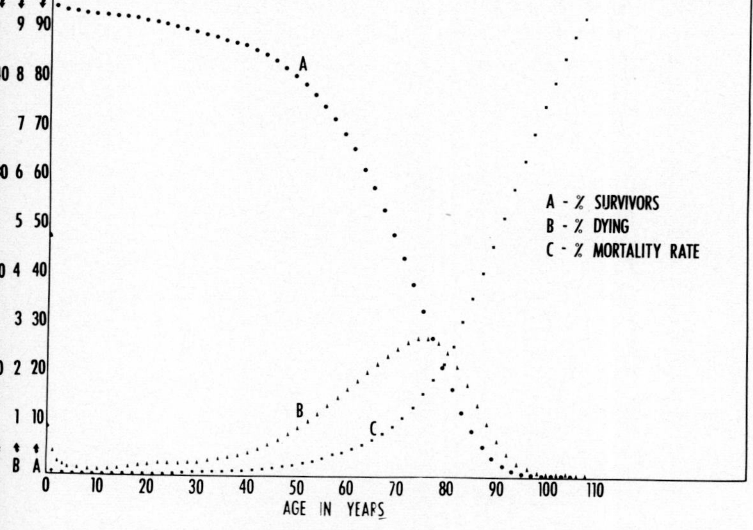

FIG. 13. *Three different presentations of the same mortality data of U.S. white males, 1939–1941 (from Strehler, ref. 11). A: per cent survivorship versus age; B: per cent of original population dying/year/ versus age; C: per cent mortality rate/year versus age.*

first of these is age versus the fraction of the original population dying during a given time interval; the second is age versus the fraction of the original population surviving, i.e., a survivorship versus age curve; the third is age versus mortality rate, i.e., the fraction of those surviving to a given age dying during the next time interval. Figure 13 illustrates these three methods of presentation.

The theories of mortality which have been developed are based on one or another of these means of expressing the data. For example, Pearl's theory (*14*) as well as a recent theory of Szilard and of Benjamin (*111*) make use of the number of individuals dying at each age as the primary observation. Curve *B* in the figure can be approximated (as was first shown by Pearson) as the sum of a number of different normal distribution curves of appropriate amplitudes, means, and standard deviations. Physical theories based upon this type of mathematical formulation generally have assumed that individuals in a population die when they run out of some biological commodity such as "vitality" or when they have accumulated a sufficient amount of damage to reduce their viability below the critical level neces-

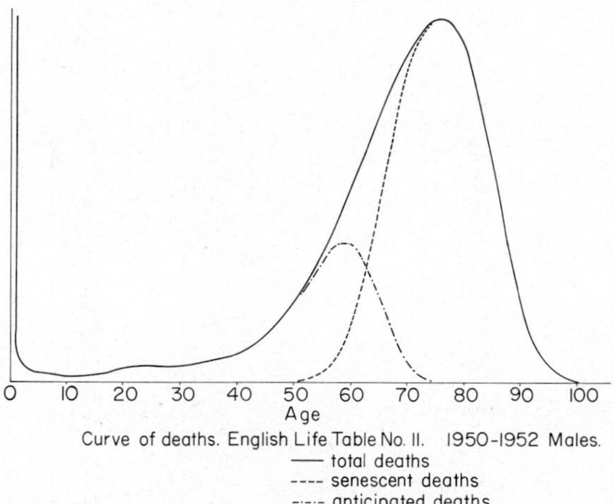

FIG. 14. *A representation of total deaths at any age as the sum of several overlapping distributions (after Benjamin, see ref.* 111).

FIG. 15. *An illustration of the "Class of Theories" represented in Fig. 14 (original drawing by Dr. Joseph Falzone).*

sary for life. In Pearson's (*112*) and Pütter's (*113*) theory and in Pearl's extension of it, life was attended at its various epochs by various kinds of death which produced affliction and demise in a given part of life but which did not generally extend into other portions of the life span. The infectious diseases of early childhood are one example; the mortality attendant upon the bearing, rearing, and support of children is a second source of death during a given period of life. The existence of still other factors causing death at specific ages is discussed in detail in a recent paper by Benjamin (*112*). Figure 14 shows a theoretical curve formulated according to the above assumptions. The essence of the theories postulating a number of different kinds of death, including death from senescence, is depicted in the accompanying drawing by Dr. Joseph Falzone of the Gerontology Branch, National Heart Institute (see Fig. 15).

Szilard's theory (*17*) is not primarily concerned with the fit of a mathematical function to the over-all distribution of ages at death, but rather deals specifically with the period from about 70 to 90 years of age during which the majority of deaths occur. Szilard assumes that death occurs when the amount of damage (he assumes genetic damage) that has accumulated reaches a lethal bound. The reason that different individuals reach the lethal bound at different periods of life, thereby giving rise to the observed distribution of ages at death, is that they start off with different amounts of genetic damage. Szilard's theory is depicted in Fig. 16 in which a population of individuals with different amounts of internal damage begin a journey across a tightrope stretched over an abyss. Some individuals lose their capacity to stay on the tightrope early in life because of the large number of faults they have within their genomes; others get along for quite a distance before their hereditary burdens plus the burdens imposed by their own life processes exceed the lethal bound and they fall off. Szilard's theory has been criticized recently by Glass (*114*) and also by Maynard-Smith (*115*). Glass' criticism will be quoted *in extenso:* "Szilard has not attempted to relate his theory of the ge-

FIG. 16. *A representation of the Szilard theory (original drawing by* **Dr.** *Joseph Falzone). Death occurs when some factor is exhausted.*

netic mechanism of aging to the Gompertz relation. Instead he has assumed a distribution of ages at death that depends upon a random (Poisson) distribution of genetic faults in the population. These faults are either those produced by 'aging hits' on the chromosomes or of those inherited from the past, since 'the main reason why some adults live shorter lives and others live longer is the difference in the number of faults they have inherited.' The somatic cell is assumed to become non-functional whenever both homologous chromosomes carry a similar fault, i.e., when ever an aging hit affects a chromosome, the homologue of which has either been hit previously or carries an inherited fault in some one of its active genes; but only one-fifth of the genes are supposed to be important for the functioning of the cells of the adult. (This last mentioned assumption appears to be entirely gratuitous, and is adopted to keep the calculated spontaneous mutation rate of the haploid set of vegetative genes conveniently low.) The mean number of faults per person (N) is related inversely to the critical surviving fraction of somatic cells (F^*). Thus for $N = 2$, $F^* = 1/4$ and for $N = 4$, $F^* = 1/12$. Since it seems unlikely that the critical surviving fraction of cells could be as low as 1/12, one is forced to assume that N is less than 4. Szilard has made many assumptions in order to keep the theory consonent with known relationships and existing data; but he appears to have overlooked a major difficulty just here. The analysis of Morton *et al.* indicates that the average genetic load of the human population amounts to some four 'lethal equivalents,' i.e., four recessive lethals or a larger number that are detrimental but not lethal genes collectively doing an equivalent amount of harm. To avoid this difficulty, Szilard's theory would have to assume that most of these lethal and detrimental genes are for some reason not among the vegetative genes required in the somatic cells of the adult. There is little evidence to bear on this question but what does exist, from the study of cell lethality of lethals in *Drosophila melanogaster* indicates that a majority of all lethals are cell lethal in effect; i.e. to say, they are requisite for the life of the individual adult somatic cell."

Maynard-Smith (*115*) on the basis of his own studies of

Drosophila takes issue with Szilard's theory. Szilard (*116*), on the other hand, dismisses conclusions about the mechanism of mammalian senescence based on a study of *Drosophila*. The general applicability of Szilard's theory to a variety of different kinds of animals is certainly in doubt. Its applicability to human beings would also seem to be in doubt on this basis: much of the change associated with aging in vertebrates appears to center around alterations in such nondividing cell lines as nerve, muscle, adrenal, etc., which do not have appreciable sensitivity to mutagenic agents. The complexity of the quantitative assumption relating mortality to age, as well as the dismissal of environmental factors as important determinants of death, are also possible weaknesses in the Szilard theory.

Most of the recent theories of mortality have used the Gompertz function as one of the prime observations to be explained. Four general groups of such theories will be discussed here. These are (*a*) the Brody-Failla theory (*117–119*) (*b*) the Simms-Jones theory (*120, 121*) (*c*) the Simms-Sacher theory (*122, 123*) and (*d*) the Strehler-Mildvan theory (*124, 18*). In analyzing these theories, two criteria have been used. They are:

1. Does the theory require assumptions which are qualitatively or quantitatively inconsistent with observation?

2. Does the theory make predictions which are qualitatively or quantitatively inconsistent with observation or natural law? A third criterion is the mathematical or physical parsimony of the theory. Mildvan and Strehler (*18*) have outlined a number of observations with which any mathematical theory of mortality should be consistent or incorporate into its postulatory structure. Among them are:

1. *The Gompertz Function*

A number of species of animals exhibit an approximately exponential increase in their mortality rate with age (see Figs. 7, 11, and 12). This relationship, which was first pointed out by Benjamin Gompertz in 1825, can be expressed mathematically as follows:

$$R_m = -\frac{1}{n} \times \frac{dn}{dt} = R_0 e^{\alpha t}$$

where n = number of individuals at time t and α and R_0 are constants. The last-named constant is the hypothetical extrapolated mortality rate at $t = 0$. Makeham (*127*) has pointed out that many mortality rate curves which depart from simple Gompertzian kinetics at early ages can be fitted by including an additive constant A in the mortality rate expression thus:

$$R_m = R_0 e^{\alpha t} + A$$

This constant, A, is presumably due to age-independent causes of death.

2. *Loss of Function*

As will be discussed in detail in later sections, it has been shown that although the change in physiological functional capacity of human males from age 30 on shows a great deal of individual variation, the decade averages exhibit a slow decline in function with time that is very nearly linear.

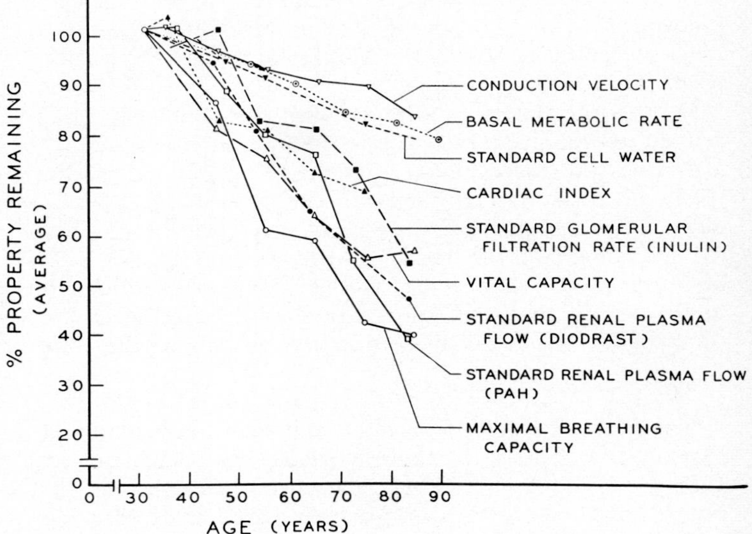

FIG. 17. *Composite diagrams of the per cent of various (human) functional capacities or properties remaining at various ages. Data from Shock and collaborators (from Strehler, ref.* 10).

The rate constants for this linear loss have been evaluated by Strehler and Mildvan (*18*) in several different ways and appear to be about 0.8 to 0.9% loss per year of the functional capacity existing at age 30 (see Fig. 17).

3. *Relationship between Gompertz α and R_0*

The Strehler-Mildvan theory predicted that there should be an inverse correlation between the log of R_0 and the Gompertz slope. In other words, countries with a low standing death rate (presumably good environments) should possess Gompertz plots whose slopes are greater than those of poor environments. The relationship between Gompertz slope and intercept for males is shown in Fig. 18, taken from Strehler and Mildvan (*18*).

Although there are a number of other observations which were listed by Mildvan and Strehler (*126*) in their "Critique

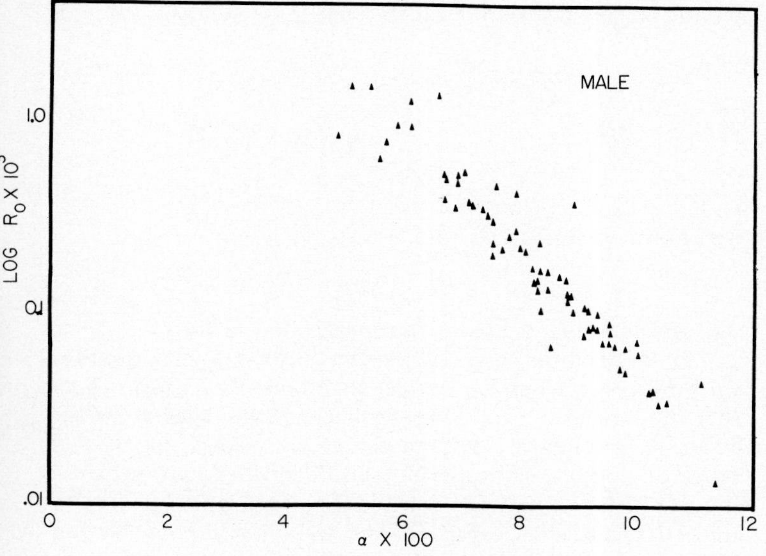

FIG. 18. *Relation between Gompertz slope* (α) *and log mortality rate extrapolated to age at birth for various national environments. Data from United Nations Yearbook for 1955 (from Strehler and Mildvan, ref.* 18).

of Theories of Mortality," they are subsidiary to the above. A brief critique of each of these theories is given below. A more detailed analysis is contained in the above-mentioned article.

STATEMENT AND CRITIQUE OF THEORIES

1. *Brody-Failla Theory (117, 118)*

The Brody-Failla theory proposes that the mortality rate is inversely proportional to vitality, a physiological property which decays by an amount proportional to its own amount, i.e., as a first-order decay process. Now it can easily be seen that the vitality at any time is equal to the vitality at zero time times $e^{-\alpha t}$ or

$$V = V_0 e^{-\alpha t}$$

If the mortality rate (R_m) is equal to a constant k times the reciprocal of vitality, it follows that

$$R_m = \frac{k}{V} = \frac{k}{V_0 e^{-\alpha t}} = \frac{k}{V_0} e^{\alpha t}$$

or if we define:

$$R_0 = \frac{k}{V_0}$$

we obtain the mortality rate:

$$R_m = R_0 e^{\alpha t}$$

This is a statement of the Gompertz relationship.

The theory thus correctly predicts the Gompertz relationship; however, when we inspect the above equations, we see that the mortality rate increases between the ages of 30 and 80 by approximately 300. It therefore follows that the vitality during the same period should decrease to one-three hundredth of its value at age 30. The theory is thus in contradiction with two aspects of the second basic observation. First, it predicts a logarithmic rather than the linear decrease in function which is observed and, second, it predicts a rate of loss of function which is much greater than that actually observed. For these reasons and also because the theory, in order to account for the third observation, would necessitate a lower rate of loss of function in a bad environment than in a good one, it is apparent that it must either be discarded or be considerably modified in order to be consistent with observation.

2. *Simms-Jones Theory*

A second theory, which was stated in outline form by Simms (*120*) in 1940 and more recently expounded by Jones (*121*), suggests that the exponential form of the mortality curves might be due to an autocatalytic accumulation of damage and disease. Jones, for example, says, "We may regard the lessening of vitality as the accumulation of damage. The rate at which damage is incurred is proportional to the damage that has already been acquired in the past." In other words, $V = V_0 - cD$ where $D =$ damage at time t. The theories also state that the change in damage

$$\frac{dD}{dt} = \text{a constant, } \alpha \text{, times the amount of damage}$$

Integrating, we obtain

$$V = V_0 - cD_0e^{\alpha t}$$

Assuming that the mortality rate R_m is proportional to the damage (i.e., is equal to kD), we obtain $R_m = k\mathrm{D}_0e^{\alpha t}$ and defining $k\mathrm{D}_0 = R_0$, we obtain $R_m = R_0e^{\alpha t}$.

The theory, thus stated, is consistent with the first observation that it predicts. On the basis of the theory, it is not possible to estimate the remaining vitality since the vitality is equal to $V_0(1 - ce^{\alpha t})$. However, the rate of loss should increase exponentially, which is in conflict with the second observation. The most serious objection to the theory, however, consists of the fact that it is in basic conflict with the third observation. In a bad environment one should certainly expect the rate of increase of damage to be greater than it is in a good environment, since the total rate of increase of damage is a function both of the growth rate of the damage itself and of environmental factors which also produce harmful effects. However, the correlation between the Gompertz slope and harmfulness of environment is a negative one. Consequently this theory, like the Brody-Failla theory, is not sustained by independent observations.

3. *Simms-Sacher Theory*

Sacher (*123*) has recently greatly expanded, evaluated, and tested a theory which was stated in rough outline by Simms in 1942 (*122*). Simms' original theory was based upon his measurements of the capacity of rats of various ages to recover from bleeding. He found that the number of grams of blood which could be removed per 100 g. of rat without killing it decreased from 4.35 g./100 g. at 50 days of age to 3.40 g./100 g. at 824 days of age (the values at 100 days were 3.9 g./100 g. and at 357 days were 3.72 g./100.). In an effort to explain the 16-fold increase in mortality rate which occurs over the same interval, on the basis of a 12% change in vitality (as measured by resistance to bleeding) Simms suggested that death occurs when the stability of the animal's innate physiological condition was disturbed by a fluctuation lying at the extreme of a probability distribution.

Simms did not develop his theory in detail nor did he explore the exact mathematical assumptions which were necessary to develop it fully. Sacher expanded the theory and incorporated the concept of a linear decay of mean physiological state into the postulates of the theory. He suggested that although the mean physiological state declines at a constant rate with time, random or Gaussian displacements occur continually about this mean. Death occurs when a displacement of the physiological state exceeds a certain limiting value. He postulated that the probability of death increases with age because, as the mean moves toward a lower limiting value, more and more of the random displacements exceed the limiting value. It should be noted particularly that the mean physiological state must never closely approach the limiting value, for otherwise the approximations required to fit theory to Gompertz kinetics would not be valid. The theory can be derived as follows:

Definitions:

L = lower limit of physiological state (constant)
M = mean value of physiological state at time t

M_0 = mean value of physiological state at time $t = 0$
$\lambda = M - L$ = difference between mean and limit
$\lambda_0 = M_0 - L$ = initial difference between mean and limit
$\Delta\lambda = \lambda - \lambda_0 = M - M_0 = \Delta M$
α and σ are constants
R_m = mortality rate
B = linear decay constant of mean physiological state $= -\dfrac{\Delta\lambda}{\lambda_0 \Delta t}$

Mathematically, using the above postulates, definitions, and basic probability considerations, the following equation has been derived by Sacher for the rate at which members are removed from the population as a function of the difference λ between their mean physiological state and the limiting physiological state.

$$R_m = \frac{g}{\sigma}\lambda\left(\frac{2}{\pi}\right)^{1/2} \exp -\frac{\lambda^2}{2\sigma^2} \tag{1}$$

In order to fit Gompertzian kinetics (observation 1), the following steps, which were taken by Sacher, are here expanded for clarity.

$$\lambda = \lambda_0 + \Delta\lambda \tag{2}$$

$$\lambda^2 = \lambda_0^2 + 2\lambda_0\Delta\lambda + \Delta\lambda^2 \tag{3}$$

If $\Delta\lambda \ll \lambda_0$, the following approximations can be made:

$$\lambda^2 \doteq \lambda_0^2 + 2\lambda_0\Delta\lambda \tag{4}$$

$$\lambda \doteq \lambda_0 \tag{5}$$

$$R_m = \left[\frac{g}{\sigma}\lambda_0\left(\frac{2}{\pi}\right)^{1/2}\right] \exp -\frac{(\lambda_0^2 + 2\lambda_0\Delta\lambda)}{2\sigma^2} \tag{6}$$

$$R_m = \left[\frac{g}{\sigma}\lambda_0\left(\frac{2}{\pi}\right)^{1/2} \exp -\frac{\lambda_0^2}{2\sigma^2}\right] \exp -\frac{\lambda_0\Delta\lambda}{\sigma^2} \tag{7}$$

It is postulated that:

$$\Delta M = -k\Delta t \tag{8}$$

Therefore,

$$\Delta\lambda = -k\Delta t \tag{9}$$

$$R_m = \left[\frac{g}{\sigma}\lambda_0\left(\frac{2}{\pi}\right)^{1/2}\exp-\frac{\lambda_0^2}{2\sigma^2}\right]\exp\frac{\lambda_0 kt}{\sigma^2} \tag{10}$$

Let $$R_0 = \left[\frac{g}{\sigma}\lambda_0\left(\frac{2}{\pi}\right)^{1/2}\exp-\frac{\lambda_0^2}{2\sigma^2}\right] \tag{11}$$

Let $$\alpha = \frac{\lambda_0 k}{\sigma^2} \tag{12}$$

Therefore, $$R_m = R_0 e^{\alpha t}$$

Now, just how closely does this theory fit the observations outlined earlier? It certainly does give to the Gompertz function a high degree of accuracy particularly if the fraction of functional loss is small. The theory also correctly predicts observation (3) (an inverse relationship between Gompertz slope and intercept). The theory assumes a linear rate of loss of vitality which is in qualitative agreement with observation (2) but inconsistent with it in that the quantitative rate of loss of physiological function (vitality) which it predicts appears to be considerably smaller than that actually observed. This shortcoming of the theory may be demonstrated as follows in which the actual change in mean physiological state is evaluated according to Sacher's theory's postulates:

$$k = -\frac{\Delta\lambda}{\Delta t}$$

Therefore, $$\alpha = -\frac{\lambda_0}{\sigma^2}\frac{\Delta\lambda}{\Delta t} = \left(\frac{\lambda_0^2}{\sigma^2}\right)\left(\frac{-\Delta\lambda}{\lambda_0\Delta t}\right) \tag{13}$$

Let $B = (-\Delta\lambda/\lambda_0\Delta t)$ = the linear decay constant of the mean physiological state

Therefore, $$\alpha = \frac{\lambda_0^2}{\sigma^2}B \tag{14}$$

$$\frac{\alpha}{B} = \frac{\lambda_0^2}{\sigma^2} \tag{15}$$

$$\lambda_0 = \sigma\left(\frac{\alpha}{B}\right)^{1/2} \tag{16}$$

Substituting equation (16) into equation (11), we have:

$$R_0 = g\left(\frac{\alpha}{B}\frac{2}{\pi}\right)^{1/2}\exp-\frac{\alpha}{2B} \tag{17}$$

Taking logarithms $\ln R_0 = \ln g \left(\frac{\alpha 2}{B\pi}\right)^{1/2} - \frac{\alpha}{2B}$ (18)

Differentiating equation (16) with respect to α:

$$\frac{d\,(\ln R_0)}{d\alpha} = \frac{1}{2\alpha} - \frac{1}{2B} \tag{19}$$

Therefore, from a plot of $\ln R_0$ versus α for various countries we can evaluate B thus:

$$-140 \leq \frac{d(\ln R_0)}{d\alpha} \leq -75$$

Therefore,

$$0.0035 \leq B \leq .0058 \quad \text{or} \quad 0.0035 \leq \frac{-\Delta\lambda}{\lambda_0 \Delta t} \leq 0.0058 \tag{20}$$

These values are somewhat lower than the decline constants of observation (2).

Further, by setting $\Delta t = 70$ years, one obtains

$$-0.25 \geq \frac{\Delta\lambda}{\lambda_0} \geq -.41$$

Since the mean physiological state, as measured, may decrease by as much as 25 to 41% of the total difference between original state and limiting value in 70 years, we may conclude that the approximations made in equations (4) and (5) are not justified.

Thus, although the theory is qualitatively consistent with several key observations, it requires assumptions which are in quantitative disagreement with other observations.

4. *Strehler-Mildvan Theory (124, 125)*

According to this theory, an organism is considered to be composed of a number of subsystems which are continually subject to displacement by internal or external factors or stresses. These displacements call for the expenditure of energy by the organism, which work is generally directed toward the reestablishment of the original steady-state condition. The maximum rate at which such energy can be expended to restore the original condition of a subsystem is called the vitality of that subsystem and the vitality of the organism as a whole may be viewed as a sort of weighted average of the vitalities of all the subsystems. Death occurs whenever the rate of work output demanded surpasses the maximum rate at which the subsystem can do work. This causes the environment of this and other subsystems to change until they, in turn, are incapable of meeting the demands placed upon them. Thus, the system loses its ability to recover.

The central assumption of our theory is that the fluctuations in demand for energy expenditure are due principally to more or less random fluctuations in the internal and external environment of the organism. These stresses are moreover assumed to be distributed exponentially as is a Maxwell-Boltzmann distribution of kinetic energy among gas molecules. Thus, the frequency of stresses of a certain magnitude increases exponentially as the rate of energy expenditure required to offset them decreases linearly. The death rate is thus proportional to the frequency with which stresses surpass the ability of the subsystems to restore initial conditions. This latter assumption and observation (1) are the basis of the Strehler-Mildvan theory, which is stated briefly as follows: Since the rate of death (R_m) is proportional to the frequency of stresses that can kill (X), we have the following:

$$R_m = CX = CK'e^{-\Delta H/RT}, \quad \text{if} \quad X = K'e^{-\Delta H/RT} \qquad (21)$$

ΔH = size of energetic fluctuation just sufficient to kill = vitality, RT = average size of energetic fluctuation. C, K, and K' are appropriate constants.

Combining this assumption with observation 1 (Gompertz kinetics), we obtain

$$R_m = R_0 e^{\alpha t} \doteq CK'e^{-\Delta H/RT} \doteq Ke^{-\Delta H/RT} \qquad (22)$$

which is the basic equation of the theory from which all other relationships are derived.

FIG. 19. *A representation of the Brody-Failla theory. The width of the ski slide (vitality* = V) *decreases exponentially with time; mortality rate, which is assumed to be inversely proportional to vitality, therefore, increases exponentially in Gompertzian fashion (original drawing by Dr. Joseph Falzone).*

Fig. 19

Critique

(a) The theory assumes observation (1) and, hence, is consistent with it.

(b) The theory predicts a linear decline of vitality with age, thus:

If
$$R_m = R_0 e^{\alpha t} = K e^{-\Delta H/RT} \tag{23}$$

solving for vitality (ΔH) as a function of time, letting $\Delta H_0 =$ vitality at time 0, we obtain

$$\Delta H = \Delta H_0 \left(1 - \frac{\alpha t}{\ln \dfrac{K}{R_0}}\right). \tag{24}$$

Since α, K, and R_0 are constants, we may set

$$\frac{\alpha}{\ln \dfrac{K}{R_0}} = B \tag{25}$$

which is the linear decay constant of vitality. Thus,

$$\Delta H = \Delta H_0(1 - Bt) \tag{26}$$

The theory permits two independent calculations of the rate of loss of function (B) purely from mortality statistics (*see below*). The values thus calculated are, moreover, in good quantitative agreement with the B values given in observation (2) (see Fig. 6 also).

(c) The theory predicts an inverse relationship between α and $\ln R$ and is thus consistent with observation (3). Thus, by substitution of

$$\Delta H = \Delta H_0(1 - Bt) \tag{26}$$

in equation (22), we obtain

$$R_m = K e^{-\Delta H_0/RT}\, e^{\Delta H_0 Bt/RT} = R_0 e^{\alpha t}. \tag{27}$$

FIG. 20. *A representation of the Sacher theory. Individuals move toward the lethal limit (the edge of the cliff at the right) along rather irregular courses determined primarily by physiological fluctuations superimposed on a linear decrease in mean physiological state (the straight line). When a random fluctuation carries an individual beyond the lethal limit, he is removed from the population (original drawing by Dr. Joseph Falzone).*

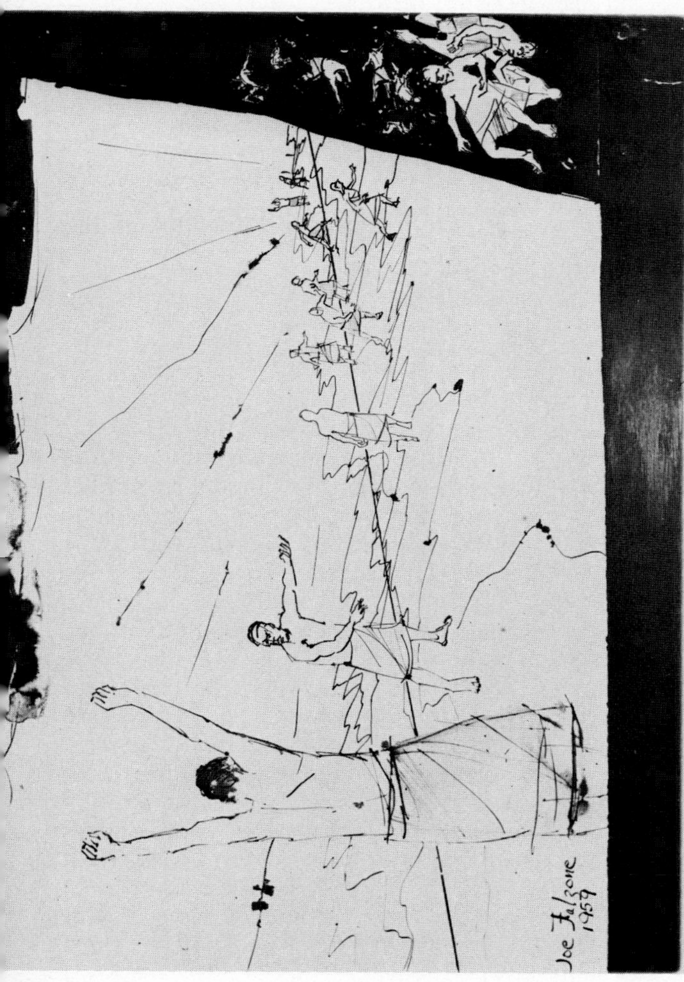

FIG. 20

Setting

$$t = 0, \quad R_0 = Ke^{-\Delta H_0/RT} \tag{28}$$

Solving for α, we have

$$\frac{\Delta H_0}{RT} B = \alpha \quad \text{or} \quad \frac{\alpha}{B} = \frac{\Delta H_0}{RT} \tag{29}$$

Substituting for $\Delta H_0/RT$ in equation 28 and taking logarithms, we obtain

$$\ln R_0 - \ln K = -\frac{\alpha}{B} \tag{30}$$

Differentiating, we have

$$\frac{d \ln R_0}{d\alpha} = -\frac{1}{B} \tag{31}$$

This is qualitatively consistent with observation (3).

Plotting α against $\ln R_0$ for various countries, one obtains values of B, according to equation (31), ranging from 0.0093 to 0.013/year. Alternatively (since $0.6 < K < 2.0$), making the independent and reasonable assumption that K, the maximum possible observable mortality rate, is $\cong 1$, one may calculate $B = 0.0097$.

Both of these calculated B values are in good quantitative agreement with observation (2). The Brody-Failla, Sacher, and Strehler-Mildvan theories are graphically depicted in Figs. 19, 20, and 21. Figure 22, taken from Mildvan and Strehler, shows a comparison of observed and theoretical time courses of physiological function according to the four theories and observations.

In summary, then, of the six theories of mortality discussed above, four of them could be treated in a quantitative

---

FIG. 21. *A representation of the Strehler-Mildvan theory. As a consequence of aging, there is a linear decrease in functional capacity (this may take place at different rates in different individuals) which brings individuals closer to the lethal limit. Environmental and internal fluctuations produce challenges of varying magnitudes (symbolized by the jagged edge of the abyss). The probability of intercepting a fluctuation capable of causing a fatal displacement increases according to age and the shape of the cliff (the distribution of challenges). If the challenges are Maxwell-Boltzmann, the mortality rate will increase in Gompertzian fashion (original drawing by Dr. Joseph Falzone).*

Fig. 21

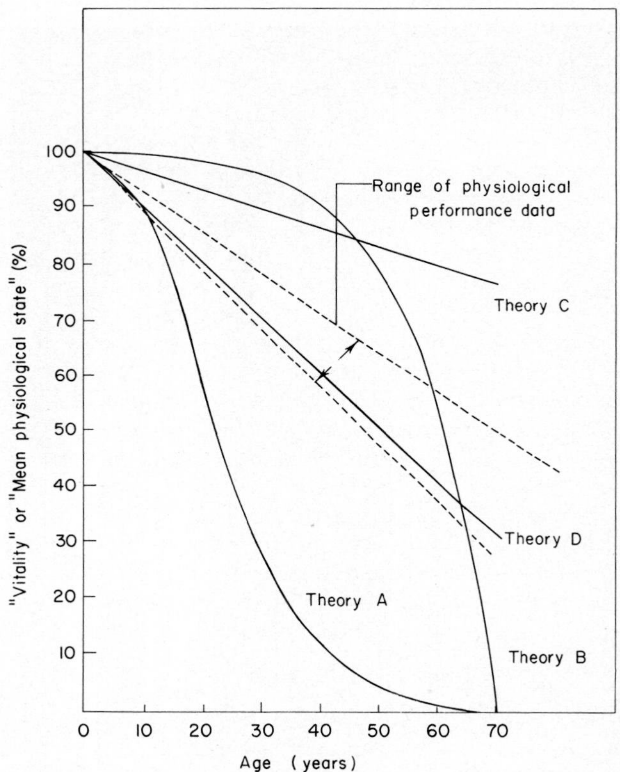

Fig. 22. *Representation of relationship of kinetics of physiological decline and predictions of the various theories discussed. Theory A—Brody-Failla theory; Theory B—Jones theory; Theory C—Sacher theory; Theory D—Strehler-Mildvan theory. The range of physiological performance is taken from the data in Fig. 17 (see Strehler, ref.* 18, *for discussion*).

fashion particularly as regards the relationship between mortality behavior and physiological function. However, although three of the theories make certain predictions which are in keeping with observation, they are not completely consistent with certain other primary observations relating time, physiological function and mortality. The Strehler-Mildvan theory fits the Gompertzian mortality kinetics and assumes a linear decay of physiological function at a rate consistent with observation. Finally, it predicts the quantitatively inverse relationship between Gompertz slope and intercept which has been observed.

In many respects there is a similarity between the Strehler-Mildvan theory and the Simms-Sacher theory. The difference between the two theories lies in the shape of the distribution of fluctuations, stresses, challenges, or displacements, as the case may be. We assume a primary exponential distribution both because this simplifies the rest of the theory and because it seems to us that the appropriate dimensions of the physiological functions in question are work output per unit time (power). There is probably a more direct correlation between the energy expended upon an organism and the power demanded in order to correct it than between the magnitude of the displacement and the energy required to compensate for it. The Sacher theory may be made to coincide with most of the elements of the Strehler-Mildvan theory if a square function of a normal distribution is taken as the fundamental variable operating on the living system rather than the Gaussian distribution itself. By analogy, the distribution of velocities of molecules of the gas is a Gaussian one but the distribution of kinetic energy (a square function of velocity) is Maxwell-Boltzmann and the probability of reaction, perhaps like death, is a function of the energy expended rather than of the velocity of the disturbing object.

CHAPTER V

Proximate effects of cellular aging

A. PHYSIOLOGICAL DECLINE

It is self-evident that organisms die because they are incapable of overcoming challenges to their continued existence. The forms which these challenges take vary from the necessity to overcome an invasion by microorganisms, as in the acute infectious diseases, to the ability to perceive, outwit, or outrun a tiger; from the ability to withstand long periods without food or water, exposure to cold or heat, to the ability to regenerate lost structures or to accommodate to the loss, through a vascular accident, of a portion of the circulatory system.

The ability to survive a challenge depends upon two factors, at least. The first is the absolute magnitude of the challenge; the second is the magnitude of the resources available to the organism to offset the disruptive effects of the challenge.

Williams (*9*) has pointed out that if there were a particularly predominant source of failure of organisms prior to the achievement of reproductive age there would be strong selection against this deficiency and development of devices and capacities to overcome the dominant source of selective disadvantage within the species. *On the basis of this general argument, when an organism inhabits an environment similar to that in which it has evolved, it would not be expected that there would be a single or predominant site of physiological failure and death.* In a relevant attempt to ascertain whether the human animal was weaker in one organ system than another, Raymond Pearl undertook to analyze the causes of death according to the organ system and even according to the embryological germ layer from which various tissue types are derived (*128*). His conclusions, which are no longer applicable because of the conquest of major sources of infectious disease, illness, and death since his studies were made, were that the endodermal derivatives were the cell systems most likely to give rise to

TABLE XIII

THE TEN LEADING CAUSES OF DEATH IN THE UNITED STATES IN 1900 AND 1959[a]

Rank	Cause of death	Death rate per 100,000 population	Per cent of deaths from all causes
	1900		
1	Pneumonia and influenza	202	11.8
2	Tuberculosis	194	11.3
3	Diarrhea and enteritis	143	8.3
4	Diseases of the heart	137	8.0
5	Cerebral hemorrhage	107	6.2
6	Nephritis	89	5.2
7	Accidents	72	4.2
8	Cancer	64	3.7
9	Diphtheria	40	2.3
10	Meningitis	34	2.0
	1959		
1	Diseases of the heart	364	38.6
2	Cancer and other malignancies	148	15.7
3	Cerebral hemorrhage	108	11.5
4	Accidents	50	5.4
5	Certain diseases of early infancy	39	4.1
6	Pneumonia and influenza (except of newborn)	33	3.5
7	General arteriosclerosis	20	2.1
8	Diabetes mellitus	16	1.7
9	Congenital malformations	12	1.3
10	Cirrhosis of liver	11	1.2

[a] After Spiegelman. (*129*).

terminal illness. The change in the principal site of failure from the endoderm to the mesoderm between the years 1900 and 1959 is shown in Table XIII. The table lists the causes of death in order of their frequency and also as per cent of the deaths from all causes (*129*). A composite figure showing the Gompertz plot of the cause-specific death rate in the United States in a recent year is shown in Fig. 23.

The data available on the decline in various functional capacities in humans (*130–140*) is much more complete than on any other animal species (see Fig. 17). A few qualitative observations have been made on the change in heart rate with age in *Daphnia* and on the metabolic rate per unit mass, as discussed elsewhere in this review. The change in the wingbeat frequency in *Drosophila,* as a function of

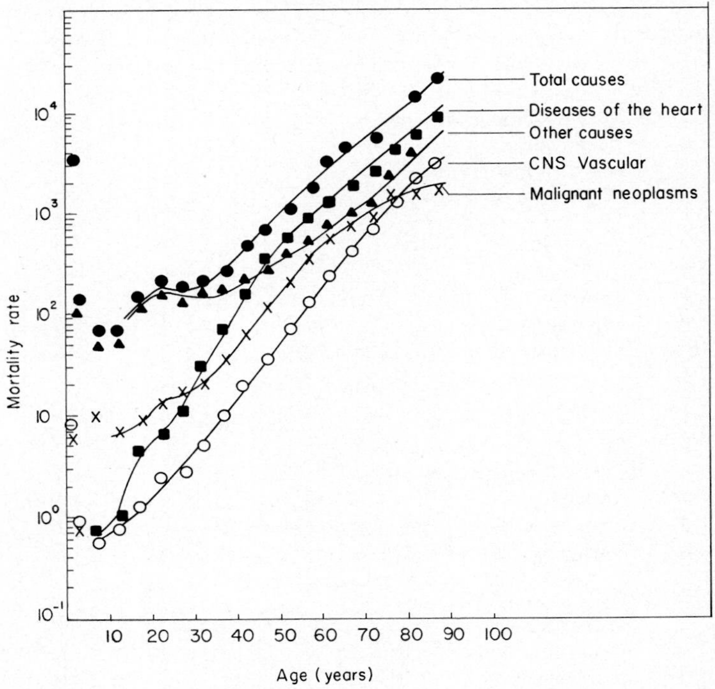

FIG. 23. *Gompertz plot of cause-specific mortality rates. (from Strehler, ref.* 18).

age, was measured years ago by Williams (*141*). We have recently studied food catching and digesting capacity in *Campanularia* of various ages. But generally speaking, no good or extensive analysis of maximum physiological function in invertebrates has been undertaken.

Somewhat more is known about the ability of vertebrates and particularly of mice and rats to respond to various stressful situations. Simms (*122*), for example, has measured the volume of blood which a rat may lose before he succumbs; a number of studies of the maze-learning ability of rats have been undertaken by Verzar, McDougal, and others (*142–148*); various measures of spontaneous activity and maximum work rate, e.g., maximum swimming time or ability to resist cold or anoxia as a function of age, have been reported. Sensitivity to radiation (*149*) and to various toxic substances (*150*) has also been studied as a function of age. These studies have, by and large, yielded little of an unexpected nature. In general, there is a gradual decrease in an organism's ability to do work or withstand stress as he ages.

Shock (*151, 152*) emphasizes the point that physiological function estimates should be based upon studies of animals or humans that are required to perform at their maximum rate. Many functions, particularly those concerned with homeostasis of the circulatory system, such as blood pH, osmolarity, sugar, etc., are maintained at nearly identical levels by young and old individuals. However, if subjects are exposed to a strong displacing factor, there readily become apparent differences in the rates at which displacements are counteracted by young and elderly individuals.

Although a detailed account of the changes occurring in the various organ systems and tissues of the body lies beyond the scope of this survey, we shall in the following pages summarize some of the salient, relevant information currently available on the subject. The evaluation of such physiological data as is represented by the following is made doubly difficult by the fact that practically no old individuals are exempt from the hidden or delayed effects of exposure to disease and accidents. There is no exact method, at present, for partitioning out that fraction of functional decrease which is due to intrinsic processes and that fraction which is a result of earlier avoidable mishap.

B. DIFFUSE CHANGES AFFECTING THE FUNCTION OF A VARIETY OF ORGAN SYSTEMS

Throughout the organism a number of changes occur which may have far reaching consequences affecting a variety of specific organ systems. There appear to be changes both in the network of fibers and gel which support the functional cells of tissues, the parenchymal cells, and in the connective tissue elements represented by the vascular tree. Such changes occur particularly in the walls of the larger arteries and arterioles. These changes in the circulatory system were once believed to be an intrinsic part of the aging process but most authorities now regard vascular changes—at least those which are most definitive and disastrous in their effects—as consequences of a less than optimal environment and diet. This view is summarized by Bortz (*153*) in a background paper on research in gerontology prepared for the recent White House Conference on Aging in the following terms: "Atherosclerosis is a pathologic condition of blood vessels characterized by the deposition of fatty substances in the walls of the arteries. This is the basic process which causes diminished blood supply to many vital organs including the heart and the brain. As the causal process in coronary artery disease and cerebral vascular disease, it is ultimately responsible for most strokes and heart attacks which take a large toll of human life. Atherosclerosis was formerly thought of as a normal process in aging, but it is now conceptualized as a result of abnormal fat metabolism."

Other changes that may be diffuse and pervasive of many organs or cell types include atrophy due to a gradual death and loss of irreplaceable cells and the accumulation of the possibly noxious fluorescent substances known as lipofuscin in many nondividing cell lines such as brain and muscle.

As will become apparent from some of the illustrative material shown in the next portion of this review, there also appears to be an increase in the degree of inhomogeneity from cell to cell and also a decrease in the orderly relationship of cell to cell.

The extent to which many of these changes are causal of the physiological failure or physiological functional decrease characteristic of aging and to what extent they are the products of more basic underlying processes cannot now be evaluated. For the present, the relation of all except the most obvious changes at the microscopic and biochemical level to age and function is on a tenuous logical basis. Most circumspect writers do not extrapolate from the more basic visual and analytical observations to the effects on cells and whole organ systems, but rather are content to enumerate certain of the changes in maximum physiological function which have been observed. In the following we make apparent our desire to join their number.

C. FUNCTIONAL CHANGES IN SPECIFIC ORGAN SYSTEMS DURING THE AGING PROCESS

1. *Skin and Its Appendages*

One of the most generally reliable and widespread clues we have to the age of individuals is the appearance of the skin during the aging process. The main visible changes that occur are a general increase in irregularities such as wrinkles, roughness, pigmented areas, warts, moles, etc. These visible signs are accompanied by a change in the texture of the skin due to a loss of cells, of subcutaneous fat, and to the decrease in elasticity as the connective tissue elements are altered. A third change of note is the loss of hair from many areas, particularly from the head and face in men. Some of these changes are summarized by Olansky (*154*) in his background paper for the White House Conference on Aging: "Certain families display changes in the skin which are premature to the average about them . . . Exposure to sun, wind and weather seem to hasten the aging process, particularly in certain groups such as those with a Scottish-Irish background. The covered areas of the skin, as a general rule, show changes with aging more slowly than the exposed parts. Old skin is wrinkled, dry and tends to show a sallow, gray or yellow coloring. It shows diminished elasticity in many areas, increased pigmentation and often seborrheic warts. There is an increase in malignant tendencies in the older skin. The atrophy is reflected in the diminished size of epithelial pegs and dermal papillae, the size and differentiation of epidermal cells, changes in collagen and elastic fibers. The thickness and volume of the epidermis decreases with advancing age. The blood vessels tend to thicken and there is a decreasing number of glomus units which are important in temperature regulation and in conservation of body heat. Sweat glands may show diminished function with age. The aging skin heals more slowly and insults to it last considerably longer. There is a drop in oxygen consumption of and carbon dioxide diffusion through the skin and a tendency for less lipid secretion on the skin in old individuals. Facial hair decreases in old men and increases and becomes coarser in old women. There are increases in calcium, magnesium, sodium and potassium content but the silicon content drops with age. Sulphur also decreases with age. In addition to these general changes, there are a number of diseases of the skin to which elderly individuals are more susceptible."

2. *Digestive System*

The most obvious change in the digestive system during the aging process is the deterioration or loss of teeth. The changes in the teeth are perhaps the best example of the "wear-and-tear" hypothesis of aging. Dentists are of the opinion and it has been verified statistically that the loss of teeth over age 35 is primarily due to peridontal disease, which is itself a result of inflammation and degeneration of the soft and hard tissues that support the teeth. This disease is initiated and aggravated in many instances by the accumulation of calcified material or tartar around the bases of the teeth. Over an extended period of time, the tissues around the teeth may become painful and the teeth themselves loosen in their sockets.

With advancing age, there is a diminished sensitivity to taste and smell which interferes with the normal pleasures of eating. The secretion of gastric hydrochloric acid and

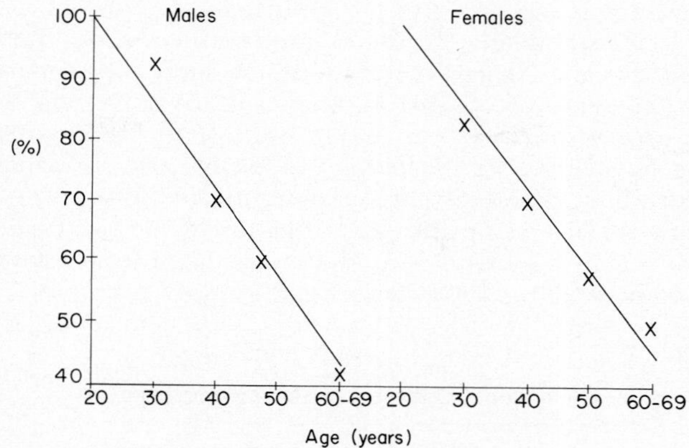

FIG. 24. *Change in acid secretion in response to a test meal versus age (from Ivy, ref.* 159). *When volume of secretion is considered, the secretion of total acid decreases with age in both sexes. If acidity alone is considered, then a decrease appears to occur in males only.*

digestive juices also tends to decrease. Studies by Polland (*155*) have shown that the total rate of gastric secretion decreases linearly in both males and females at a rate of about 12% per decade (see Fig. 24). According to Bloomfield and Polland (*156*), the incidence of achlorhydria in response to an Ewald test meal changes as a function of age (Table XIV).

TABLE XIV

AGE VERSUS ACHLORHYDRIA INCIDENCE

Age (years)	Incidence (%)
20–24	5.3
30–39	9.5
40–49	16.7
50–59	24
Above 60	35.4

Age changes in the small intestine are not marked, whereas there is a gradual decrease in the weight of the liver, according to a study by Edith Boyd (*157*) on victims of accidental death. In the large intestine, one of the most characteristic changes with age is the increasing frequency of occurrence of the disease known as diverticulosis, which consists of outpocketings of the wall of the large intestine due to changes in its connective tissues and musculature. These out-pocketings may become infected and give rise to more serious complications. The incidence of diverticulosis is shown in Table XV: data were taken from a study by Kocour (*158*) on 7000 consecutive autopsy cases.

TABLE XV

Age Incidence of Diverticulosis

	Incidence (%)	
Age (years)	White male	White female
20–31	0	1.9
31–40	0	1.0
41–50	0.8	1.5
51–60	1.9	2.8
61–70	6.4	6.9
70 and up	7.1	15.2

According to Ivy's extensive review (*159*) of age changes in the digestive system, "Death in the aged is apparently only rarely due to a wearing out of the organs of the digestive system. Most elderly persons die with a digestive system that is capable of functioning beyond the ordinary life span." Atrophic changes, as a consequence of aging or of injury by external agents, cause death or serve as a contributory cause.

3. *Circulatory System*

Failure of the circulatory system, particularly due to diseases of the heart and to the effects of interference with cerebral blood flow, is the chief cause of death in the human being. The main changes that occur are a decrease in the cardiac output, a change in the elasticity of the large arteries, a change in the distribution of the circulating blood

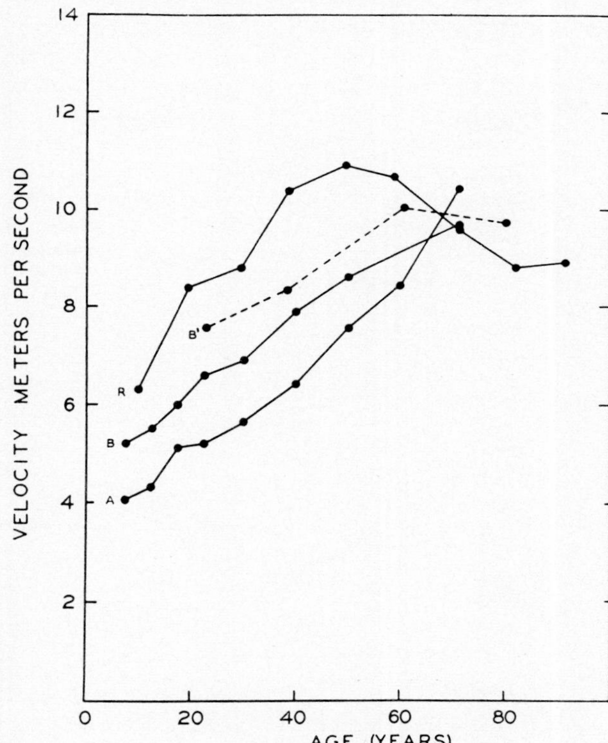

FIG. 25. *Pulse-wave conduction velocity in different arterial segments versus age (from Landowne* et al. *ref.* 160). *A: aorta; B: radial carotid; R: radial brachial; B′ = radial carotid.*

among the various organs and particularly the deposition of fatty substances, such as cholesterol, in the walls of the large arteries followed by the deposition of insoluble calcium salts. The change in cardiac output with age is illustrated in Fig. 17, whereas Fig. 25, taken from the work of Landowne (*160*), illustrates the effect of elasticity changes on the pulse-wave velocity in individuals of various ages. Figure 26 shows schematically the agewise changes in body and organ vascularity in man as a function of age (*161*). The conductance in various organ systems is expressed in

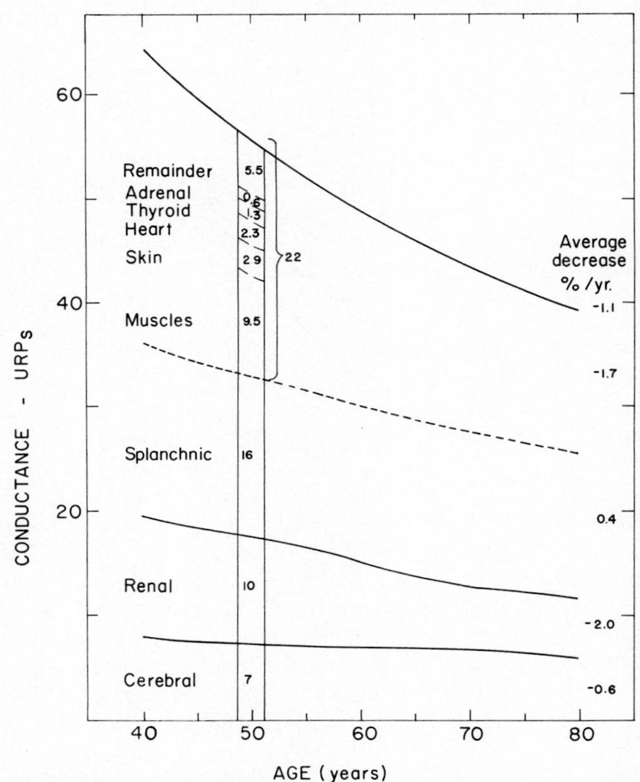

FIG. 26. *Change in amount and distribution of circulation to various organ systems versus age (from Landowne, ref.* 161).

reciprocal peripheral resistance units as milliliters per millimeter of mercury per minute.

Changes in the capillary network supplying the aorta of experimental animals of different ages have been described by Woerner (*162*). According to this author, capillaries are practically never found within the normal intima. Considerable thickening and fibrosis and other evidence of atherosclerotic change are present when capillaries are found either in the intima or in the inner third of the media. Apparently, the normal aorta and coronary arteries are supplied with oxygen and nutrition by diffusion through the endothelium and intima. It thus appears that the extension of the vasa vasorum to the inner portions of the large arteries is a response to the preexisting pathological lesion rather than a portion of the normal aging process.

The contribution of cellular pathology within the endothelial lining of the vascular system is discussed in some detail by Zweifach (*163*). At present, it is not possible to evaluate the importance or lack thereof of changes in the structure, permeability, and function of the endothelial cells of the circulatory system. Zweifach speculates that the differentiation process may have progressed further in the endothelial layer of the larger vessels than in the capillary endothelium which may retain a more embryonic condition enabling it to grow, continue to differentiate, repair itself, etc. He remarks that: "In the large blood vessels, the endothelial cells would appear, as in the case of the smooth muscle and connective tissue constituents of the vessel wall, to have undergone further differentiation. With time, this process may continue to the point of no return and then lead to cellular pathology. Aging as a general phenomenon in relation to vascular endothelium may therefore be concerned with an ever-increasing differentiation until even the capillary endothelium loses many of its basic attributes and falls prey to invasive elements." Interesting as this speculation is, there does not appear to be any direct evidence on the basis of which a critical evaluation of the concept may be based.

The degeneration of the vascular tree, particularly of the large vessels, and of the coronary arteries, appears to involve certain mechanical factors, such as areas of flexure or the existence of high blood pressure over a period of years. Also implicated appears to be the presence of higher than normal amounts of blood cholesterol. Fatty plaques are laid down in certain areas of the aorta and larger arteries as an early phase of the process. Whether this follows a local injury to the endothelium or the underlying connective tissue or whether the deposition of the fatty materials is the primary lesion has not yet been clearly established. Following the deposition of the fat, however, there appear to be changes in the underlying connective tissue; processes of fibrosis and invasion by the capillaries of the vasa vasorum appear to be important parts of the succeeding process. Eventually calcium and other metallic ions are bound in the regions of fibrosis. These then may act as sites around which clots, subendothelial lesions, or hemorrhages may occur with increasing frequency. As fibrosis of the arterial wall continues, its elastic properties change, a process which further decreases the efficiency of the aging circulatory system (see Fig. 27).

4. *Kidneys*

Changes in the glomerular filtration rate and other kidney functions versus age are illustrated in Fig. 17.

5. *Nervous System*

a. *Conduction Velocity*

Figure 17 also shows the speed of conduction of the nerve impulse as a function of age as measured by Norris *et al.* (*164*). It should be emphasized that, although these figures represent the maximum velocity of nerve conduction, it is not clear whether this decrease is a result of a change in the average properties of the surviving nerve fibers or whether it is a consequence of a gradual selective loss of the more rapidly conducting axons as time passes.

TABLE XVI

Age versus New Cases of Impaired Hearing

Age (years)	Cases/10^5/yr.
Under 5	0
5–14	33
15–24	6
25–34	13
35–44	49
45–54	52
55–64	143
65–74	444
75 and over	1014

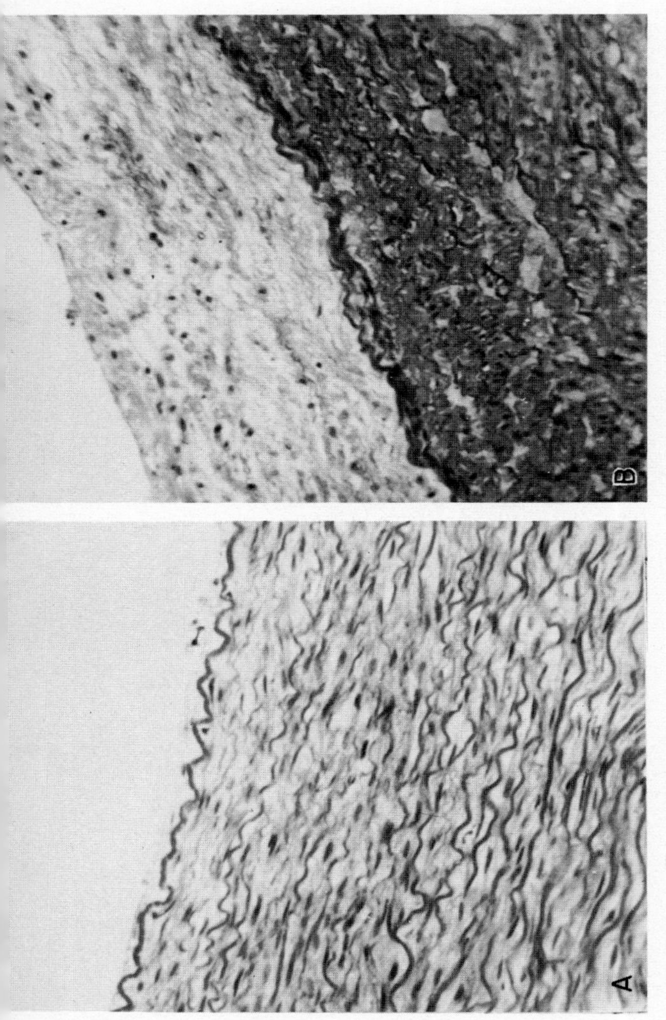

FIG. 27. *Section of (A) young (infant) and (B) old aorta. Note the very thin intimal layer in the young aorta and the great thickening of the old intimia. The heavy line is the elastica which demarcates intimia from media.*

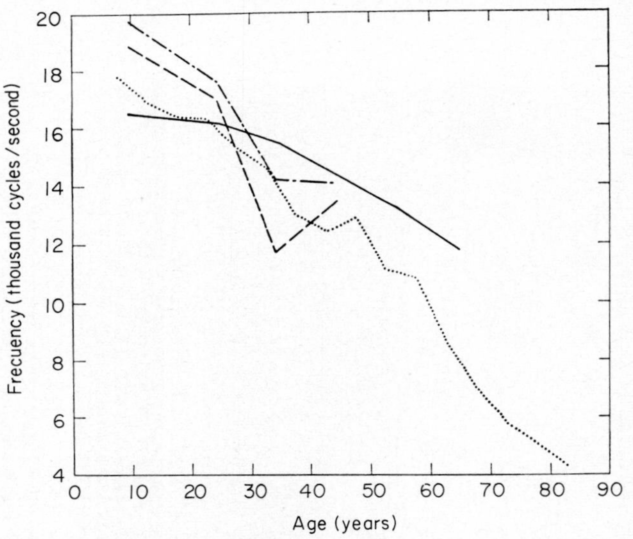

FIG. 28. *Maximum frequency of sound capable of being heard versus age (from Weiss, ref. 166). Key:* ——, *Ciocco;* . . . . ., *Schober;* — — —, *Gildemeister (air);* - - - -, *Gildemeister (bone).*

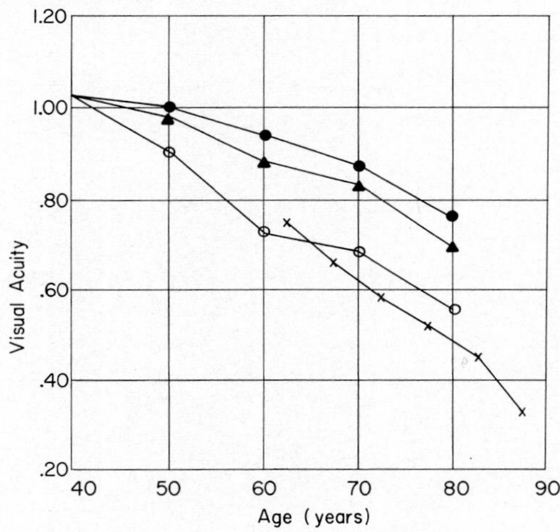

FIG. 29. *Visual acuity versus age (from Friedenwald, ref. 167).*

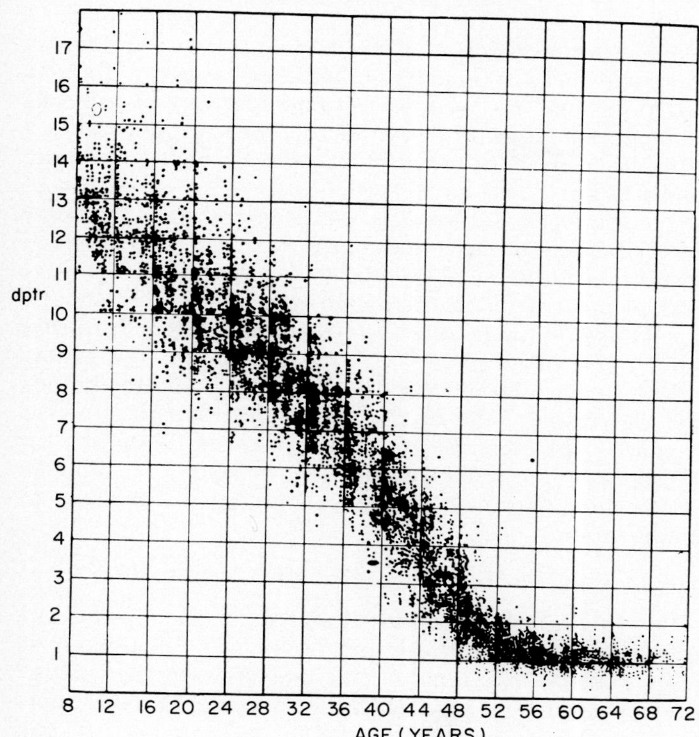

FIG. 30. *Accommodation capacity of the human eye versus age (from Duane, ref.* 168).

Sensory Functions

Changes in sensory function with age have been measured for a number of the sense organs. The relative rate of occurrence of new cases of deafness of males versus age (*165*) (any stage of impaired hearing) is shown in Table XVI. These numbers represent the number of new cases of hearing difficulties per 100 thousand of population at that age. Figure 28 shows up the upper frequency limits of hearing as a function of age (*166*).

According to Friedenwald (*167*), visual acuity falls gradually with age (see Fig. 29).

The relation between age and the accommodation of the

eye in 4000 cases studied by Duane (*168*) is shown in Fig. 30. Note that the accommodation capacity decreases linearly with time, that the spread of values decreases as the accommodation capacity decreases, and that it approaches a steady level of about one diopter, below which it does not appear to go.

Bernstein (*169*) studied the variations in accommodative power of different individuals of the same age and compared it with their subsequent length of life. He found a positive correlation between the accommodative power and longevity. If these findings were confirmed, they might furnish a useful index of the degree of senescence of the individual. This decrease in accommodation powers is due to the fact that the center of the lens is more rigid than the outside. As aging progresses, the rigidification proceeds toward the periphery of the lens, making it more and more difficult for the musculature to deform it and thus to produce accommodation.

b. *Integrated Nervous Functions*

The literature on nervous function during aging is admirably and critically reviewed in Birren's "Handbook of Aging and the Individual." One measure of higher mental function versus age (*170, 171*) is shown in Fig. 31. The upper curve illustrates the average number of digit substitutions performed per unit time. The lower curve shows the incidental memory remaining after the first test. After completing a digit-symbol substitution series, the individuals tested were required to recall the combinations. This constituted a test of so-called incidental memory since the original tests had not been presented as a memory test. Note that although the curves are similar in shape, there is a much earlier peak for the incidental memory.

6. *Respiratory System*

Two gross indices of the functional capacity of the respiratory system in humans as they age are the vital capacity (that is, the maximum volume of air that can be taken in and expelled per breath) and, second, the maximum breathing rate (the maximum rate at which air can be taken in and

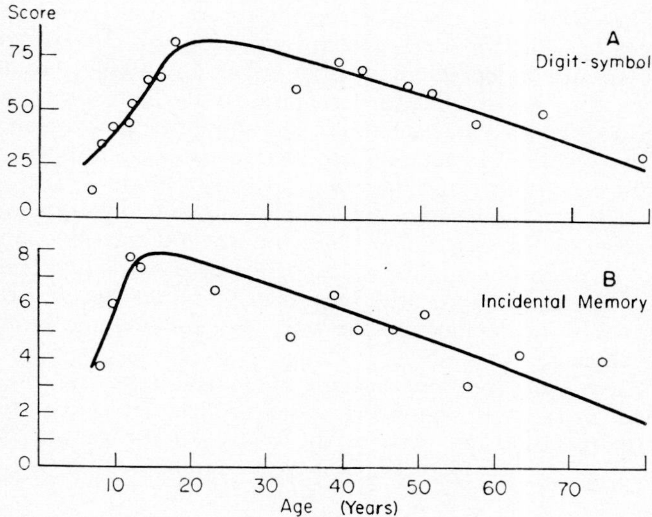

FIG. 31. *Change in two psychological capacities versus age. A: digit-symbol test scores versus age; B: ability to recall above associations versus age (no warning given beforehand that recall would be requested) (from Jerome, ref.* 170).

expelled). The latter is a function both of the lung capacity and the rate at which respiratory movements may be made. Data showing the values of these functions corresponding to various ages are given in Fig. 17 from the data of Shock *et al.* (*140*).

The vital capacity and maximum breathing rates represent one end of the oxygen consumption machinery. An index of the rate at which oxygen is actually consumed is, of course, given by the basal metabolic rate. Early studies had indicated that the basal metabolic rate declined as a function of time and recent studies have confirmed this. However, concurrent studies on total intracellular volume, as measured by total body potassium (*172, 173*), indicate that the basal metabolic rate and total intracellular volume decrease in a parallel fashion so that the rate of oxygen consumption per unit cellular water remains practically constant.

These later findings raise the important question of the extent to which the decreases in the various functional parameters are independent of each other and the extent to which they are related to a common underlying function. Presumably, the basal metabolic rate should be proportional to the volume of metabolically active tissue. Similarly, it might be argued that the rate at which blood is passed through the kidneys is dependent upon the long-term demand upon the system and, thus, the size and activity of the pool of nephrons might be proportional to the active body mass. In like manner, the liver may be under the indirect control of the demands of the body mass for fuel and building blocks.

These considerations suggest the possibility that there exists an over-all regulating system which determines the active metabolizing mass of the body. In the rabbit, the

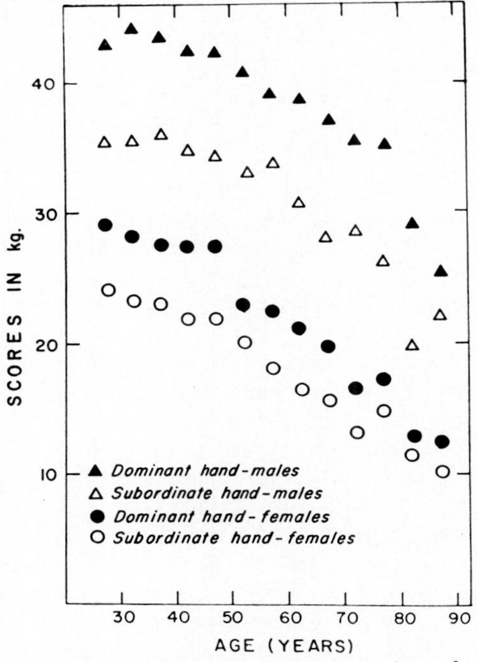

FIG. 32. *Grip strength versus age (from Norris* et al., *ref.* 278).

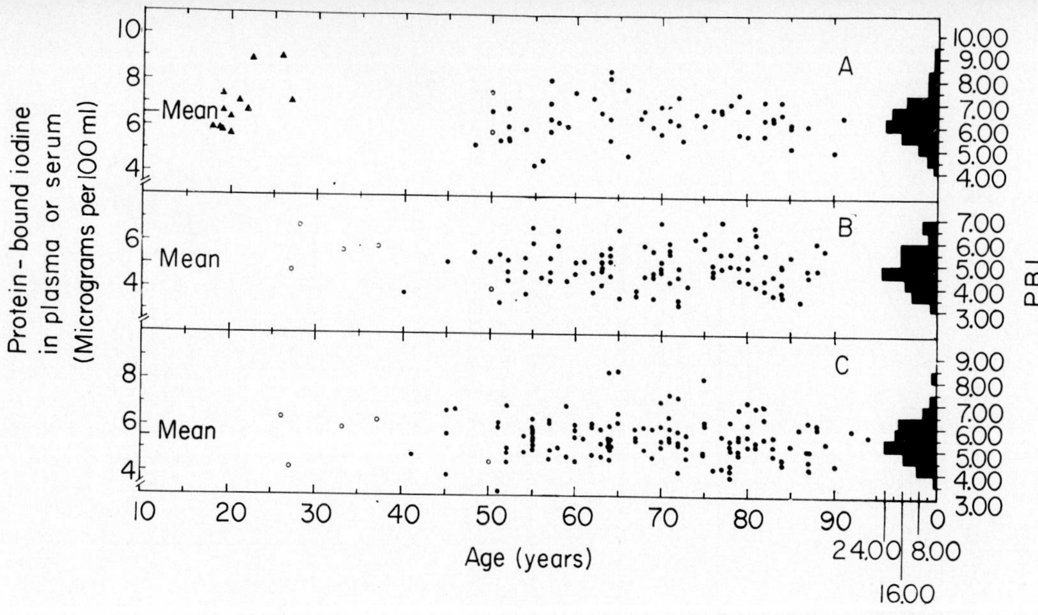

FIG. 33. *Protein-bound iodine versus age for three different groups. Top: determinations by O'Neal and Simms method; Middle: determinations by modified Baker, Humphrey, and Soley's method (at gerontology branch, Baltimore City Hospital); Bottom: determinations by Baker, Humphrey, and Soley's method (at Biological Science Laboratories). Frequency distributions are shown at right of the figure (from Gaffney* et al., *ref.* 178).

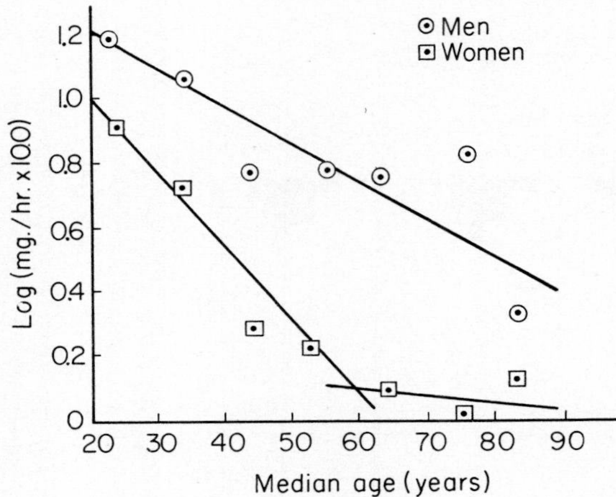

FIG. 34. *Androgen excretion by men and women versus age (from Pincus, ref.* 180).

size of the muscular mass can be altered by the injection of androgen *(174)*. Whether a change in the level of this or another hormone during aging is a causal factor or similarly

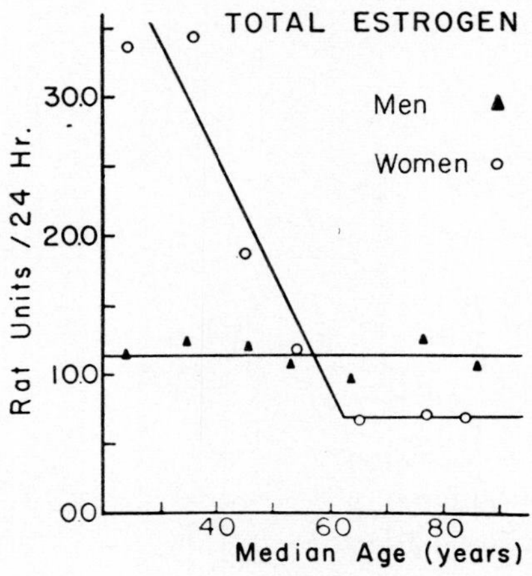

FIG. 35. *Total estrogen excretion in men and women versus age (from Pincus, ref.* 180).

a reflection of a more fundamental change in some other regulatory system is an intriguing question for the future.

7. *Muscular Strength*

The muscular strength of human beings, as a function of age, and measured by grip strength, maximum rate of work performance for short periods of time, and other indices (*175, 176*), is shown in Fig. 32. There appears to be a gradual decrease in muscular strength with age. Whether this is a primary age change or a response to decreased activity in turn due to psychological or sociological factors cannot be answered. Shock and his colleagues have measured, in addition to the maximum work rate of the arm musculature versus age, the efficiency with which oxygen consumption produces usable work as a function of age (*177*). They have found that the efficiency of old subjects at low work rates is somewhat lower than that of young individuals, whereas at high or maximum work rates the young and old groups are essentially identical. They have tentatively ascribed the

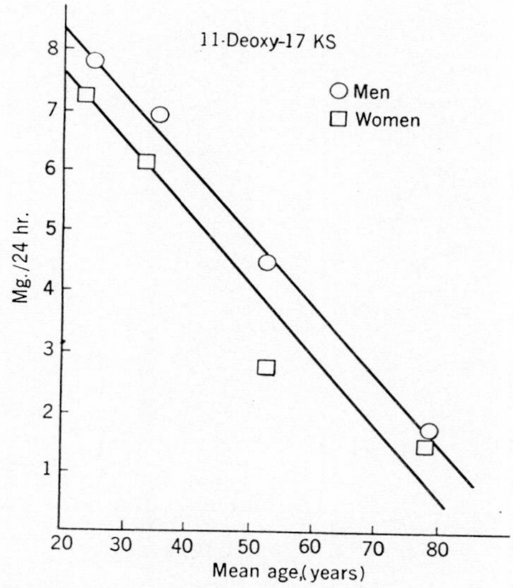

FIG. 36. *Excretion of 11-deoxy-17-ketosteroids in men and women versus age (from Pincus, ref.* 180).

inefficiency of the elderly individual to a less effective co-ordination of muscular movements (for example, the relaxation of opposing musculature at low work rates) rather than to intrinsic differences in the efficiency of the chemical machinery.

8. *Endocrine System*

Studies of thyroid gland activity, as a function of age, have been somewhat contradictory in the past (*178, 179*). Certain workers have found a decrease in the total rate of iodine incorporation into thyroxin or thyroglobulin; others have shown an essentially constant rate of turnover when the activity is related to unit body weight. Some relevant data are illustrated in Fig. 33.

Changes in the rate of steroid hormone excretion (*180*) in the urine is shown in Figs. 34 and 35. Data for 11-deoxy-17-ketosteroids are shown in Fig. 36. These decreases in steroid

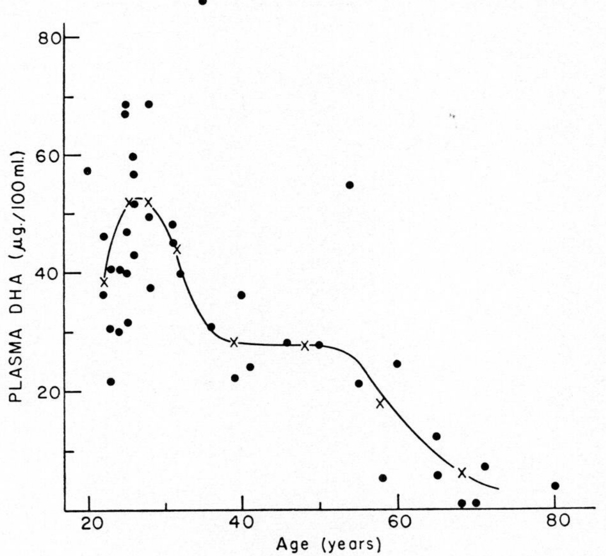

FIG. 37. *Plasma concentration of dihydroepiandrosterone versus age in adults (from Samuels, ref.* 181). *Key:* ●, *individual determinations; x, average values for periods symetrically distributed around x.*

excretion are, of course, much greater than the corresponding decreases in glomerular filtration rates or urinary volume and therefore undoubtedly are a reflection of a considerable change in the level of circulating hormone. A study by Samuels (*181*) of the change in conjugated dehydroepiandrosterone in plasma of adults with increasing age is shown in Fig. 37. Finally, in Fig. 38 is shown a scatter plot of 110 gonadotropin assays from premenopausal and postmenopausal women (*182*). Note that in contrast to the other hormonal factors discussed, which generally show a decrease with age, the gonadotropin assays show a tendency to increase with advancing age. Note also that there is an increasing scatter in the level after the menopause. Masters holds that there is a gradual decrease in gonadotropin, beginning about fifteen to twenty years after the menopause, suggesting that the initial increases represent a compensatory reaction due to the decreased responsivity of the target

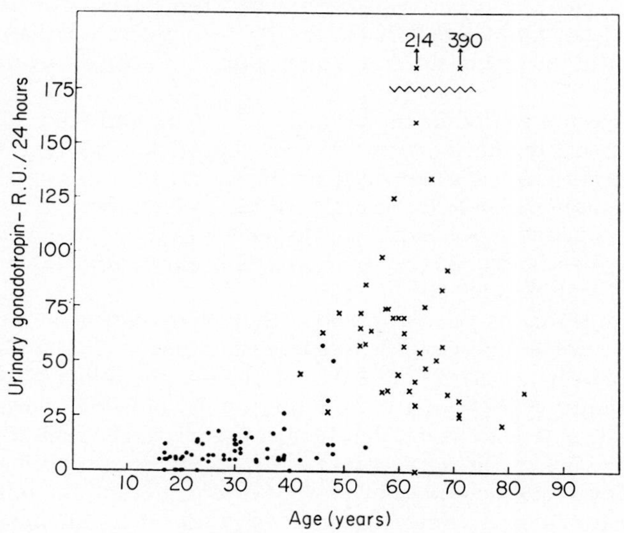

FIG. 38. *Excretion of gonadotropic hormone in women at various ages—note sharp postclimacteric rise (from Albert* et al., *ref.* 182). *Normal values of 110 females;* ●: *premenopausal (95% = 0–35, range = 0–100); x: postmenopausal (95% = 14–205, range = 0–390).*

organ. After a number of years the pituitary also decreases in its capacity to respond in this compensatory manner.

9. *Miscellaneous Stresses*

Measurements of the capacity of the immunological defenses of the body to respond to infection as a function of age are essentially lacking. Parfentiev measured the circulating levels of certain antibodies in normal elderly and young individuals and found no essential difference between them (*183*).

Verzar has discussed the capacity of rats of various ages to adapt to low atmospheric pressure as well as to cold and heat (*184, 185*). When animals, either young or old, are placed at an atmospheric pressure of 350 mm. of mercury, their body temperature declines by 4 or 5 degrees. After two or three days, the animals return to their original temperature by increasing their heat production. This change is followed by a decline in heat production to the normal level, yielding a new equilibrum between heat production and loss. Old animals have a very incomplete adaptation and do not regain normal temperature, even in six to nine days.

In other experiments, animals 2 to 6 months old were exposed for one hour to −2.5°C. These animals retained their normal body temperature. However, 14- to 16-month-old animals showed a temperature decrease of about 1°, and 24- to 26-month-old animals decreased by 3°. Young rats were also better able to adapt to high environmental temperatures (e.g., 38°C.).

From the above, it is obvious that many data have been collected on various physiological functions and organ systems with respect to the effect of age on physiological performance. Unfortunately, it is not usually possible to evaluate the extent to which the changes that have been observed are a part of the aging process (i.e., primary events in the sequence of senescence), or to what extent they are the reflections of changes elsewhere in the organism or even changes induced by altered environmental demand on the functional activity of the animal. Most of the sensory and neural measurements appear to be primary and not a function of use or disuse. The extent to which altered function is a property of the system being investigated and to what extent it is a function of intercellular interaction is a question that will be best answered by basic studies on tissue and organ interdependences in the normal animal, by studies on the fundamental changes in cells in response to hormonal and neural stimulation, by studies of changes in the cytoplasmic constituents and the nutritional relationships between cells, and finally, by continued careful studies of age changes in human beings and experimental animals, both longitudinal and cross-sectional, in which the contribution of disease and pathology to dysfunction can be partitioned out.

CHAPTER VI

Aging of cell aggregates and tissues

A. GENERAL CONSIDERATIONS

THE REMARKABLY COMPLEX and yet finely integrated organism which the metazoan represents may conveniently be viewed as a hierarchical system in which the individual functioning entity is the ultimate object of natural selection. In analogous manner, on the evolutionary scale, it is not so much the survival of the individual but the perpetuation of a line of organisms that is the result of natural selection. This evolutionary process has taken place primarily through the subordination of the simpler constituent parts of the organism, at least in the short run, to its broader aspects. At the individual level, the various organ systems are subordinated to the interests of the organism as a whole; the tissues are coordinated and integrated as specialized effector systems. Individual cells are sequestered in evolutionarily advantageous sites; subcellular organelles and enzymes are generally regulated and controlled in the interests of the cellular or organismic economy.

At each of these levels of organization, the potentiality of gradual structural and functional disorganization exists. The morphogenetic lines along which cells and tissues are laid down during the development of an individual, may set the stage for ultimate disorganization and discoordination. We have discussed the consequences of such deteriorative changes at the population level (mortality) and on the capacity of the specialized organ systems to perform work appropriate to their structures.

We cannot ascribe the failure of individual organ systems

solely to the properties of the cells of which they are made. In some instances, we do know of appreciable changes in the intracellular characteristics of old cells, but many of the most obvious features of aging at the microscopic level are manifest at the level of organization of tissues rather than of cells.

B. THE LOCI OF TISSUE CHANGES

A tissue, as a functioning entity or collection of cells, can conveniently be divided into three distinct components: the extracellular component, the supporting cellular structures, and the actual functioning cells characteristic of the tissue. These last are called parenchymal cells. We shall discuss the changes that occur in the three compartments in the succeeding sections.

1. *Extracellular Components*

The extracellular components of a tissue include the various nonliving entities, the water with its dissolved solutes (salts, various metabolites, waste products, etc.) and various fibrous and colloidal elements which give a texture or elasticity and form to the aggregate of cells.

Fibers are of three general types—the collagenous fibers, which are generally fairly nonelastic; elastic fibers, which are much less ordered in their electron microscopic appearance than the collagenous fibers; and reticular fibers, whose chemical and physical properties have been much less thoroughly examined than the other two. Photographs of the disposition of collagenous, elastic, and reticular fibers are shown in Figs. 27 and 39. Figure 40 shows the electron microscopic appearance of isolated collagenous fibers.

The collagenous fibers are generally found in those situations where a fair rigidity is required (*186–190*). They are major constituents of tendons and fascia and, as such, are admirably suited to the purpose of locomotion, transmission of force, etc., to which elastic fibers would be poorly suited.

Elastic fibers (*190–193*), on the other hand, are particularly useful in the frequently deformed portions of the body, such as the skin. They have the property of returning to

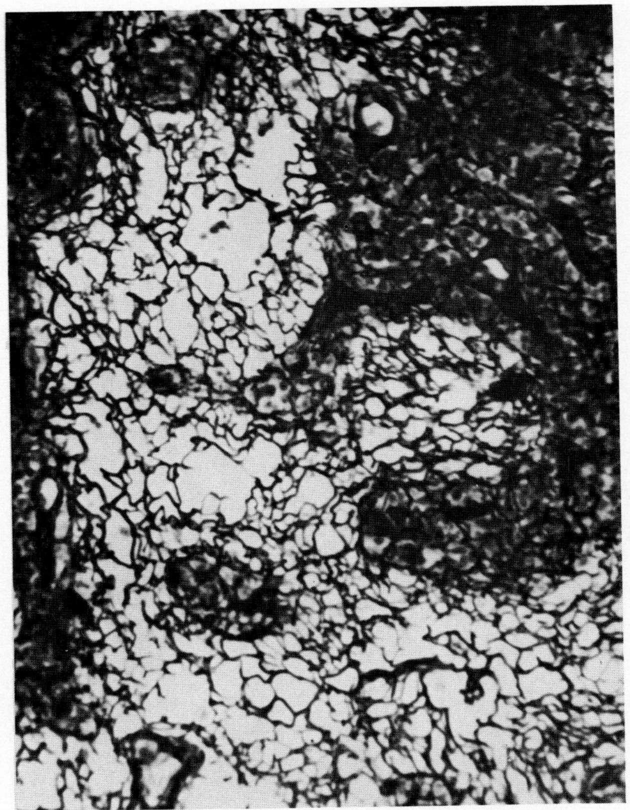

FIG. 39. *Reticular tissue. Magnification: × 500. Spleen: silver stain.*

the original shape after deformation and thus enable the organism to adapt itself to distorting forces, movement, etc., with a minimum of permanent damage. They are also useful in such structures as the large blood vessels, where elasticity is of value in conserving the potential energy generated by the contraction of the heart and stored temporarily as the hydrostatic pressure of the blood. Their deterioration or replacement by nonelastic fibrous connective tissue decreases the efficiency with which the work of the heart can be utilized to perfuse the tissues.

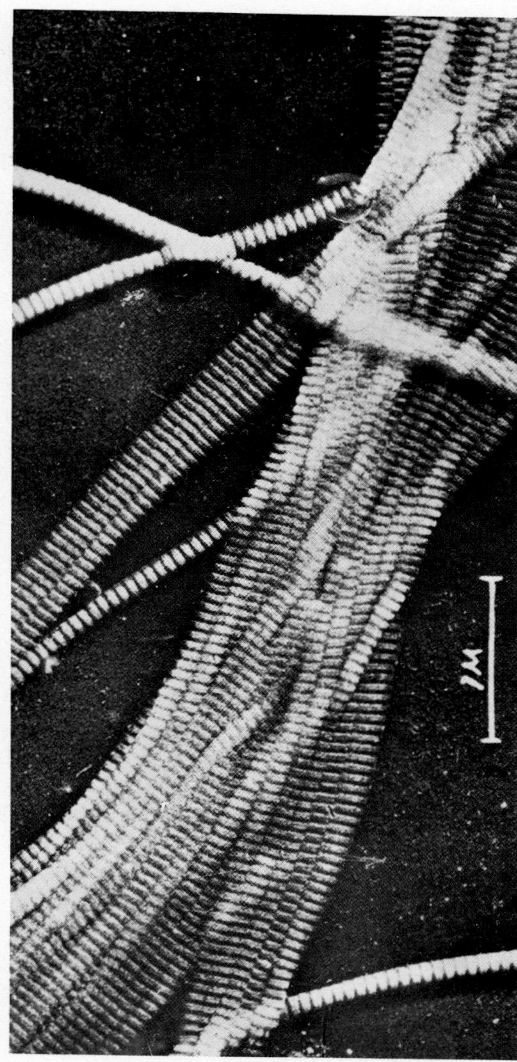

FIG. 40. *Electron micrograph of collagen fibrils (from Gross, ref. 186).*

Reticular fibers (*194*) are much finer than the collagenous and elastic fibers and seem to be involved in a much more intimate support of individual cells particularly in areas of continous membranes, such as the so-called basement membranes which underlie the typical epithelium. The chemical nature of reticular fibers has not yet been definitively settled. Some workers maintain that it is composed of considerable amounts of substituted sugar derivatives. Ham's comment summarizes current thinking: "It is possible, of course, that the sugars obtained by Leblond (*195*) and his group from reticular and collagenic fibers were derived fròm the fibers themselves, but it is also possible that they were the components of the material with which the fibers were intimately associated. In our present state of knowledge, this matter cannot be settled definitely, but the bulk of the evidence seems to suggest that there is material that is PAS positive, that is associated intimately and abundantly with reticular fibers and constitutes the major material in basement membranes and that this material is associated to a much lesser extent with collagenic fibers. This material, the precise chemical nature of which is not understood, must be very permeable."

In addition to the essentially solid materials arranged in the form of fibers, there also is within the extracellular space a jellylike substance (*196*) that coats the surfaces between cell and extracellular space and also probably pervades and lubricates the fibrous elements. Due largely to the brilliant studies of Meyer (*197, 198*), we now have some considerable insight into the chemistry of these amorphous, jellylike intercellular substances. They were usually described before his work as belonging to a chemically ill-defined group known as mucoids and were supposedly glycoproteins (i.e., proteins with a carbohydrate moiety attached to them). Meyer's work has shown that these should rather be called mucopolysaccharides, emphasizing the fact that they are essentially carbohydrate derivatives. According to Meyer, they consist of equimolar parts of hexosamine and glucuronic acid combined with a protein. The precise nature of the protein component has not yet been determined. The substances have the capacity to change from a sol to a gel and their concentration within tissues varies quite widely as a result of certain environmental effects or hormonal changes. Starvation, for example, results in a considerable decrease in both the mucopolysaccharides and in the soluble collagen fractions *(199)*.

Age Changes in Extracellular Connective Tissue Components

The observation that tissues of old animals contain larger amounts of collagen than young ones is commonplace to every housewife who has bought an old beefsteak. The quantitative estimate of the amount of collagen in various tissues during the aging process, as well as changes in other connective tissue elements, is a more recent subject of inquiry. One of the early quantitative measurements of the elastic properties of skin and subcutaneous tissues in young and old individuals was made by Kirk and Kvorning *(200)* in 1949. They showed that there is a greater resistance to deforming forces and a slower recovery of the original shape in old tissues than in young. Evans *et al.* (*201*) in studies of the aging of human skin, made the interesting observation that the change in elastic properties of skin may give rise to important histological artifacts. The lower degree of elasticity of old tissue as compared to young results, during fixation of skin biopsies, in a much less severe contraction from old than from young individuals. Since the young skin tended to contract more than the old, the artifactual impression was generated of a greater depth and folding of the young sections.

Kohn recently measured the uptake of water by pieces of heart tissue of various ages when they are subjected to solutions of various pH and tonicity (*202, 203*). He found a gradual decrease in the extensibility of heart autopsy specimens versus age, which he interpreted as a greater resistance of the connective tissue network to tissue deformation.

A particularly useful source of collagen upon which a quantitative comparison of the physical properties of collagen versus age can be based is the rat tail. Verzar removed small bits of tail tendon from intact rats under light anesthesia. When these are placed in a heated water bath, there occurs, after a characteristic period of time, a thermal shrink-

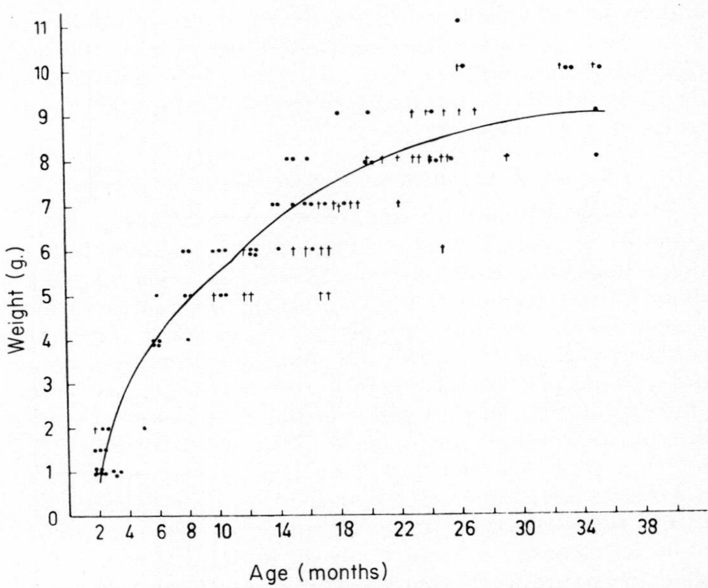

FIG. 41. *Weight required to prevent thermal contraction of rat-tail tendon collagen versus age (from Verzar, ref.* 205). ●: *healthy animals;* †: *animals died spontaneously.*

age (*204–206*). Both the shortening and the tension developed are characteristic of the age of the animal under standardized conditions. More recently, Chvapil and Hruza (*207*) have studied a similar change in the contractility of rat tail tendons versus age under the influence of perchloric acid solutions. Certain of the above experiments are illustrated in Figs. 41 and 42. Chvapil and Hruza also showed that McCay rats, i.e., animals fed on a restricted diet, possess tail collagen which is similar to that of chronologically younger animals fed an unrestricted diet.

Sinex (*208*) has attempted to see whether exposure of the tails of rats to ionizing radiation will cause premature aging of these structures. On the contrary, the irradiated animals possessed more youthful tails on the basis of the degree of epiphyseal closure. According to Sinex, 50,000 röntgens of cobalt 60 gamma radiation is required to lower the critical

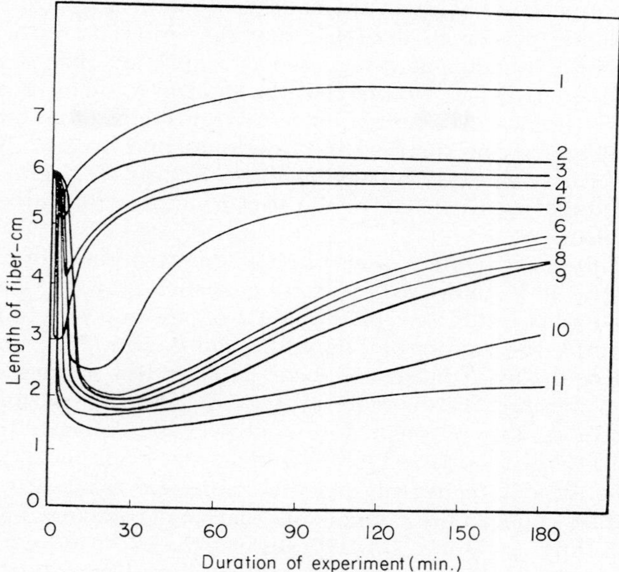

FIG. 42. *Time course of the contraction of rat tail tendon fibers of various ages in perchlorate (from Chvapil* et al., *ref.* 207). *Age (in days): curve 1 = 30; 2 = 60; 3 = 90; 4 = 120; 5 = 150; 6 = 180; 7 = 210; 8=260; 9 = 295; 10 = 320; 11 = 32 months.*

shrinking temperature of collagen one degree. In this case, then, radiation exposure does not mimic the effects of a normal passage of time.

Measurements of changes in the relative quantities of various connective tissue constituents have been made by Sobel and collaborators (*209, 210*), who have studied the hexosamine/collagen ratio of femurs and skins of rats as a function of rat age (as estimated by weight). The ratio in femurs dropped from about 4 to about 2% between the age of 50 to 400 days, whereas in the skin it dropped by about 50% from 1 to about ½%. These changes are generally attributable to a continued accumulation of the collagenous component rather than to a loss of the mucopolysaccharide component which remains essentially constant.

Whether the change in elasticity of the structures examined and the increase in the collagen content are factors in the aging process in the sense that they interfere with the optimum function of the animal is a question that is still unresolved. It may well be that the changes in quantity and properties of collagen mentioned are reflections of an adaptively useful continuation of a developmental process. The reader is referred to the basic studies of Gross (*187, 188*) for a stimulating discussion of the background of the collagen problem.

Collagen is a likely candidate for long-term deterioration because it is known from labeling studies that its rate of turnover is quite slow in the adult organism. The fundamental investigations of Thompson and Ballou (*211*), which will be discussed in greater detail later in this monograph, are particularly germane in this regard. Nevertheless, under certain conditions there does appear to be collagen turnover. Certain invasive types of tumors, for example, appear to be capable of hydrolyzing the connective tissue bed, including collagenous components (personal communication, R. Kohn). Jackson (*212*), who studied the effect of an algal product called carrageenin, reported that this substance, when injected beneath the skin, causes an injury that is followed by a replacement of the damaged component by fibrous connective tissue. However, following the deposition of collagen, there is a period of resorption of the newly deposited fibrils and their replacement by cells more characteristic of the damaged area. The replacement of collagen, although occurring at a low rate under normal conditions, may not be an irreversible process under sufficient local environmental conditions. The extensive studies of Busick and collaborators have also contributed substantially to the above concepts.

The possibility has been mentioned repeatedly that changes in the connective tissue matrix may act to change the diffusion barriers to the functioning parenchymal cells of the various tissues and organs. Attractive as is this speculation, there is no convincing evidence in the literature that substantially supports the hypothesis (*213*). The increase in the collagenous network between cells would hardly appear to be a sufficient barrier to affect in any serious fashion the access of nutrients and the egress of waste products. Changes in the gel properties of the mucopolysaccharide coatings of cells might alter selective barriers to certain molecules and permit the access of others. But the occurrence of such changes has yet to be definitively described.

If time and its effects on tissues and organs does produce cellular atrophy through a kind of starvation, then it appears much more likely that the initiating mechanism is the loss of capillary perfusion by a dropping out of capillary elements rather than by the interposition of a hypothetical diffusion barrier. Kirk and Laursen (*214*) have studied the changes with age in diffusion coefficients of solutes for human tissue membranes. The only change they noted in their studies was an increase in the rate of diffusion of certain substances with age, a finding which hardly supports the hypothesis.

The second major solid constituent of intercellular space is elastin. Elastin is chemically a more poorly characterized substance (*190–192*) than collagen. Among the methods used by Lansing (*193*) for its preparation was the digestion for 40 to 45 minutes of fat-extracted ligamentum nuchae with 1/10 *M* NaOH solutions. The resulting product gives the impression in the published pictures of a rather disordered, irregular collection of fibers. The substance contains a certain fraction of lipid and is dissolved by the enzyme, elastase. Lansing and collaborators have also studied the amino acid composition of arterial elastin as a function of age (*215*). They report that there is an increase in the concentration of dicarboxylic amino acids with age in elastin of the aorta but, by contrast, no such increase in that derived from the pulmonary artery, which incidentally is usually free of degenerative lesions. Studies by these latter authors have also demonstrated a gradual accumulation of calcium salts in the aorta during the aging process, particularly in the vicinity of elastin. It has been conjectured that the increase with age in dicarboxylic amino acids in the aorta but not in the pulmonary artery results in an increased binding of calcium ions which might effectively be bound by the negatively charged groups of the dicarboxylic amino acids.

Dribben and Wold have described structural changes in

the connective tissue of the adrenal glands of female rats during the aging process (*215*). In the capsule, reticular fibers give rise to collagenous fibers and there is a general thickening of the existing collagenous fibers. In the zona glomerulosa and fasciculata, there is a slow thickening of the reticular fibers, but no obvious transformation into collagenous fibers. In the zona reticularis, reticular fibers appear to thicken and collagenous fibers appear.

Studies by Smith (*216*) on argentophil fibers (reticular fibers) indicate that changes are most distinct in the aorta where the "fine argentophilic fibrous networks around the elastic membranes in the young animal becomes heavy, shaggy and brushlike coverings in the old animal." In another study, Smith reported a gradual increase of reticular fibers in the vicinity of blood vessels as aging proceeded.

Kirk and Dyrbye (*217*) have studied the hexosamine and acid-hydrolyzable sulfate concentration of the aorta and pulmonary artery in individuals or various ages. The changes noted here were not nearly so striking as the accumulation of cholesterol observed in the same study and the calcium concentration increase noted by other workers. Rasquin and Hafter (*218*) have observed changes in the interstitial tissue of the teleost, *Astyanax americanus*. Insoluble concretions occur in the testes of these fish by the age of 6 years or less.

Unfortunately, very little can be said concerning changes in the supporting cells—the connective tissue cells, such as fibroblasts, and the cells of the vascular system, as a function of age. The extent to which the cellular elements of the connective tissue are subject to a regular replacement regimen is not known. Similarly, although the major cellular constituent of the circulatory system, the circulating blood cells, particularly the anucleate red cells, are continually replaced, we do not know whether the vascular endothelium, either that of the capillary bed or that lining the large vessels, is regularly replaced. It is known that the ingrowth of capillaries is possible in the event of physical damage at the site of a wound or as part of a revascularization response to vascular inadequacy subsequent to a coronary occlusion.

These observations, however, do not have a direct bearing on whether there is or is not a regular replacement cycle of cells in the circulatory system or merely whether the capacity for such replacement exists provided that an adequate stimulus is brought to bear.

C. TISSUE DISORGANIZATION AND CHANGE

We may now turn to the central question: What changes occur in the gross aspects of tissues during aging, particularly in the parenchymal cells, the functioning cells of specific tissues. It is obvious that a direct comparison of the appearance of sections obtained from fixed autopsy specimens may show differences between young and old tissues that are not normal age changes. Changes in the connective tissue framework, as was already pointed out in the case of skin by the work of Evans and collaborators (*201*), may give a totally misleading picture of the disposition and arrangement of cells. The products of disease and the sequelae of long-continued illness may also give the impression of atrophic or other changes which are not necessarily a part of the normal aging process. Differences in nutritional habits and economic status of individuals of different ages may well be reflected in apparently systematic differences at the tissue level which are essentially artifactual. Despite these difficulties, there are presented in Figs. 43 and 44, photographs, side-by-side, of various tissues from young and old human beings. The reader may decide for himself which of the observable differences are significant. Nevertheless, certain generalizations appear to be possible. These include:

(*a*) *There is an apparent decrease in the regularity of arrangement of cells as an individual grows older.* For example, in the heart sections of young individuals, there is a comparative homogeneity in the size of the individual myocardial bundles, whereas in the old individuals, there is a greater diversity in their apparent size. Similarly, the regular spacing of cells in the adrenal gland, in the thyroid, but not so clearly in the liver or kidney, are features which appear reasonably consistent, at least to this observer.

(*b*) *Another change of some note is the greater variability*

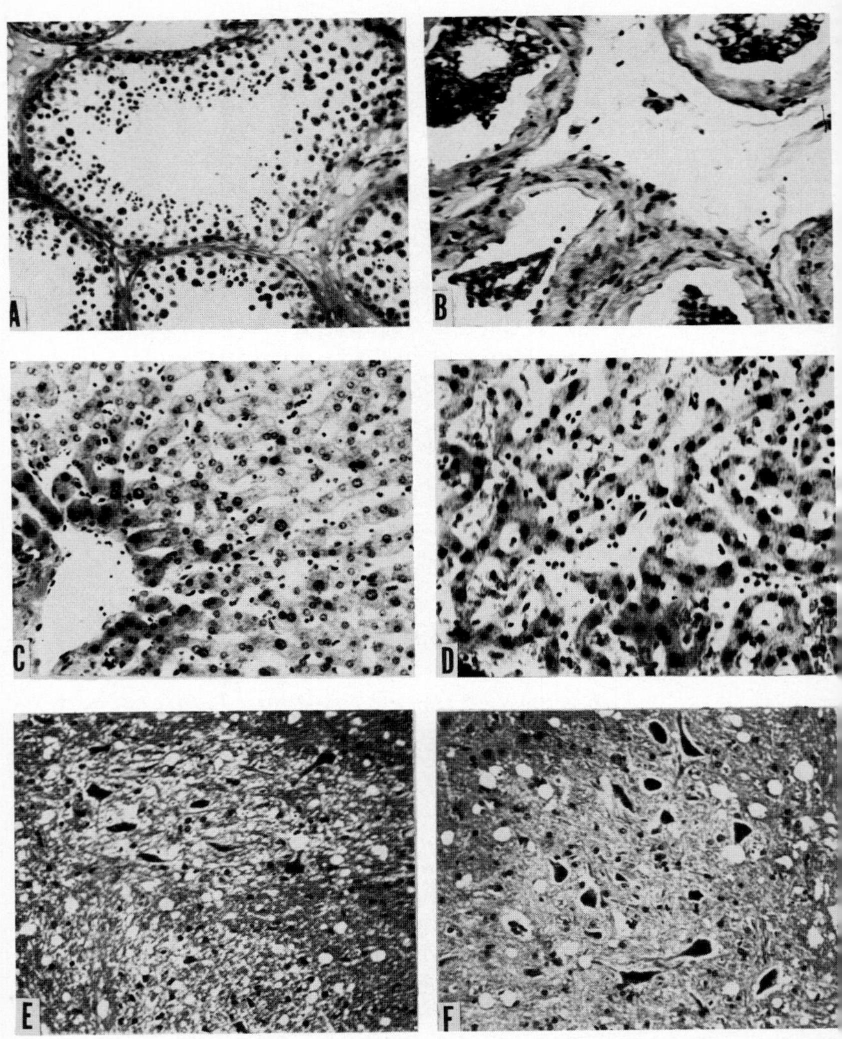

Fig. 43. *Histological comparisons of young and old tissues. A: young testis, human, about age 35; B: old testis, human, age 105; C: young liver, human, about age 35; D: old liver, human, age 105; E: young brain, mouse, age 13 months; F: old brain, mouse, age 39 months. Magnifications:* ×*480. H and E stain. These sections are chosen to represent the most "normal" old and young areas. In old tissues, it is, of course, usually possible to find many more diseased, disordered, or necrotic areas or areas of fibrosis.*

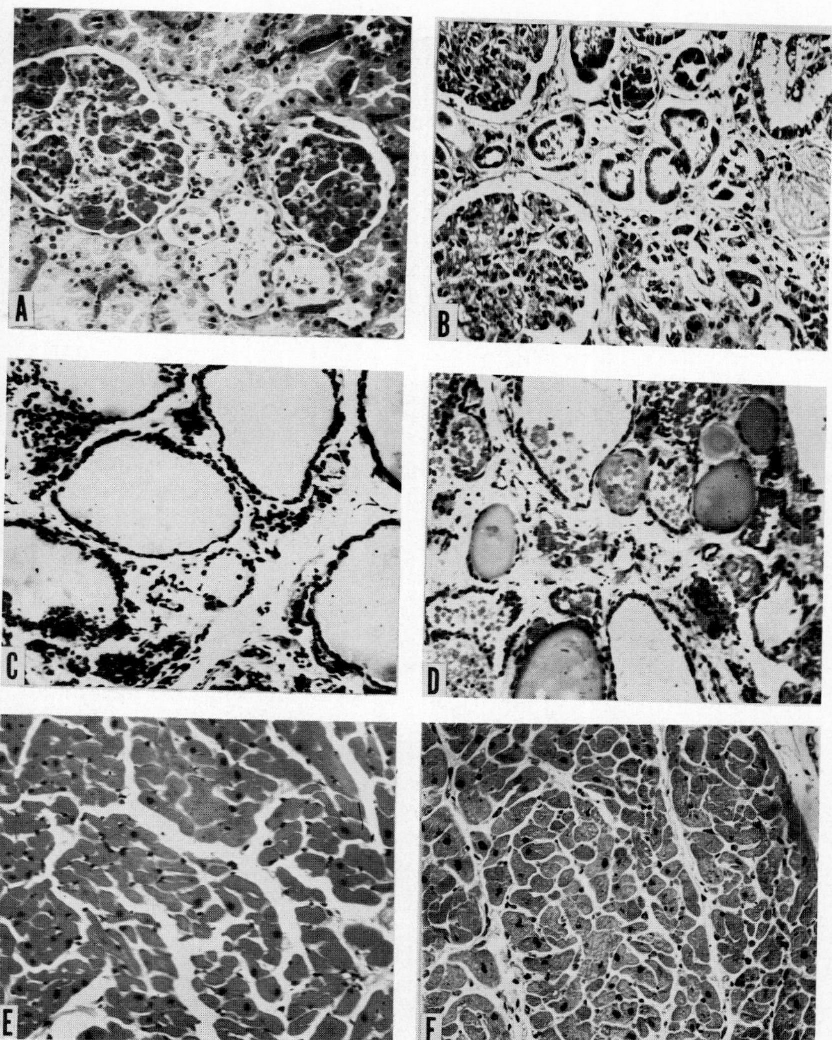

FIG. 44. *Histological comparisons of young and old tissues. A: kidney, human, age 25 years; B: kidney, human, age 93 years; C: thyroid, human, age 33 years; D: thyroid, human, age 93 years; E: heart, human, age 33 years; F: heart, human, age 89 years. Magnifications:* ×*480. H and E stain. Note age pigment in old heart section, variability of colloid in old thyroid, and "hyaline" glomerulus in old kidney section. Over-all comparison of Figs. 44 and 45 gives impression of disorder in old tissues.*

of nuclear size in aged individuals (*219*) and in the intensity of the staining reaction. By and large, there appears to be a decrease in the nucleocytoplasmic ratio in the older tissues, although the precise measurement of this variable under controlled conditions in a variety of tissues does not really seem to have been undertaken.

(*c*) *The appearance of the individual cells, particularly in the case of the heart, is more homogeneous in young individuals than in the old.*

(*d*) A fourth generalization, which will be treated in much greater detail in the next section, is the fact that *there is an accumulation of pigment in certain cell lines of aged animals* (*220*).

A further survey of changes in various organ systems follows, much of which is derived from the extensive studies of Andrew and his collaborators, both in rodent and human material. Andrew's studies of age changes in the skin of Wistar Institute rats (*221*) have indicated that proportionally more cells are present in the dermis of the very young rat than in middle-aged and old rats. The stratum corneum is closely packed in the old animals, whereas it is much looser in the young. Finally, the nuclei of the old cells appear to be more granular than the young.

In the spleen and lymphatic system (*222*), the following observations have been made: In the rat spleen the reticular architecture changes progressively to a more sinusoidal structure. Andrew's studies (*223*) of changes in the deep cervical lymph nodes of these same animals are excellent examples of the decreased regularity in arrangement of cells as animals age.

Gross changes in the kidney are not so apparent, but Andrew and Pruett (*224*) noted the presence of some aberrant cells containing several nuclei and the occurrence either of amitosis or fusion. The capillary boundaries appear to be more sharply defined in the aged individuals than in the young. In the liver, also, Andrew (*225*) reported that there is an increased frequency of so-called giant nuclei containing "inclusion bodies." Falzone *et al.* (*226*) has recently questioned the generality of this phenomenon and of a significant change in the ploidy class of nuclei during aging in the liver of rats. H. Tauchi's (*219*) studies of the fundamental morphology of senile changes stresses particularly an increased spread in the relative size of nucleus and cytoplasm during aging.

In the pancreas of Wistar Institute rats, Andrew (*227*) notes the formation of saculations around ducts instead of the relatively regular and solid alveoli characteristic of youth. He also noted changes in the islets of Langerhans, but these changes appear to be secondary to the cavity formation.

Payne (*228, 229*) has studied changes in the histological appearance of the pituitary of chickens and also in the adrenal cortex of fowl during the aging process. He noted the appearance of bodies of an uncertain origin in the acidophils of the pituitary. He also noted the accumulation of pigment in the anterior pituitary. A similar pigment accumulation occurred in the adrenal cortex. He reported that the characteristic vesicles of aged basophils of the pituitary may persist even after the cells in which they had formed had perished. Payne also indicated that there are changes in the appearance of mitochrondria of pituitaries, although the basis of their identification as mitochondria and their possible relationship to the vesicles mentioned above was not clearly set forth. Hunt (*230*) studied the occurrence of mitotic activity in the anterior pituitary of mature female rats belonging to different age groups and at different periods of the day. There was a gradual decrease in mitotic activity up to 300 days of age. The animals were treated with colchicine 9 hours before sacrifice. There also appeared to be a clear relationship to the estrus cycle. Hunt's work suggests a turnover of the chromophobes and acidophils of the pituitary during the life of the animal, whereas he could find no evidence for a turnover of basophils as measured by the occurrence of mitoses. Blumenthal (*231*) showed that other endocrine glands in the guinea pig are affected by hormonal treatment. Estrogen or progesterone will cause an increase in the mitotic activity in the thyroid, parathyroid, and adrenals of guinea pigs. These studies indicate that at least some of the cell types in these endocrine glands are capable of replacement under appropriate stimulation.

Andrew has devoted particular attention to the cytological changes occurring in various types of nerve cells during the aging process. In the trigeminal ganglion, spinal cord, and brain of the mouse, Andrew noted, for example, a decrease in the Nissl substance (*232*), an increase in basophilia, and a less regular cell outline. He also observed the accumulation of pigment in ventral root cells and vacuolar degeneration in the trigeminal ganglion. In Purkinje cells, the Golgi apparatus, according to Andrew (*233*), changes from a net-like structure to disconnected, disordered granules. Jancso, according to Andrew, feels that pigment degeneration is due to the alteration of the Golgi apparatus. In man, Andrew also noted a shrinkage of nuclei in Purkinje cells, a decrease in Nissl substance, and a concomitant increase in pigment. Nuclei, he reports, become less readily visible. However, Andrew differentiates between the decrease in Nissl substance that occurs during the muscular fatigue of younger animals, a change which mimics the changes occurring in old age. He notes that other changes characteristic of aged cells are not so apparent and even the changes in the Nissl substance are not so striking in exhausted young animals as in the old ones.

Andrew and Andrew could find no corresponding evidence of changes caused by fatigue in the cerebral cortex of mice. Age changes, however, included the loss of Nissl substance, a process known as satellitosis, in which small supporting cells gather around and eventually engage in the neuronophagia of degenerating or dead neurones.

The Andrews (*234*) called particular attention to the occurrence of nuclear profiles suggesting a process of amitotic division. More recently, Andrew (*235–237*) has proposed that amitotic division of nuclei may be a means of permitting cells to increase their chromatin content without a resort to normal mitotic processes. Since the arguments are based upon studies of fixed material, it is not readily appropriate to a time-sequence analysis. Other data related to the possible contribution of amitosis to multinuclear cell formation in developing muscle tissue strongly suggest that apparent amitosis can quite frequently be explained as a transitory, nuclear polymorphism rather than an active process of DNA (deoxyribonucleic acid) replication and segregation. A more definitive answer to the question might be furnished by a study of the ploidy of neurons supposedly undergoing amitosis. Studies by C. and O. Vogt (*238*) on age changes in neurones suggest that different portions of the brain age at different rates. Unfortunately, as is typical and necessary in histological investigation, much of this study is based upon subjective impressions of the investigators. In the absence of quantitative measurement of appropriate variables, including some index of what is meant by aging of a neurone, the acceptance of the rather far-reaching conclusions of the Vogts' should perhaps be postponed. These and many other workers have contributed substantially to additional information on tissue changes during the aging process. Unfortunately, even these presently discussed major contributions cannot always clearly be evaluated either as regards their representativeness or their freedom from some of the controllable sources of error outlined earlier in this discussion.

D. CELL DEATH AND CHANGES IN CELL NUMBER

In addition to the above-mentioned changes in the appearance of individual cells, their nuclei, the presence or accumulation of inclusion bodies, and the altered relationship of cells to each other and to the supporting vascular, cellular and acellular components of the connective tissue network, there appears to occur, at least in certain tissues, a loss of cells with the passage of time (*239–241*).

Whether the usual muscular atrophy, characteristic of aged individuals, is a result of cell loss or merely of cytoplasmic atrophy is not known at present. On the organismic scale, particularly in humans, the change in intracellular potassium, as well as the drop in basal metabolic rate and intracellular water, as estimated by antipyrine and thiocyanate space measurement, strongly suggests not only a decrease in the activity per unit volume but also a decrease in the number of functioning cells (*172, 173*). Direct measures of the occurrence of cell deaths is complicated by the fact that even where parenchymal cells die out they are frequently replaced by other cell types, particularly fibroblasts. Thus, a simple measurement of DNA/unit volume is not sufficient to answer questions relevant to parenchymal cell loss.

Measurements of the number of functional glomeruli versus age and particularly cell counts in the nervous system suggest that there is a small but gradual decrease in total cell number.

In the brain of the bee, there were early reports of a loss of cells during the aging process. These studies by Hodge *et al.* (*80*) were subject to some criticism, both because very few animals were examined and because the criterion of age of the bees was that they "appeared" to be aged or senile. However, Rockstein (*81*), in a recent careful study, has clearly shown that there is an unequivocal decrease in the number of cells in a representative cross section of a bee's brain. Figure 45 illustrates his findings. Brody (*242*) has

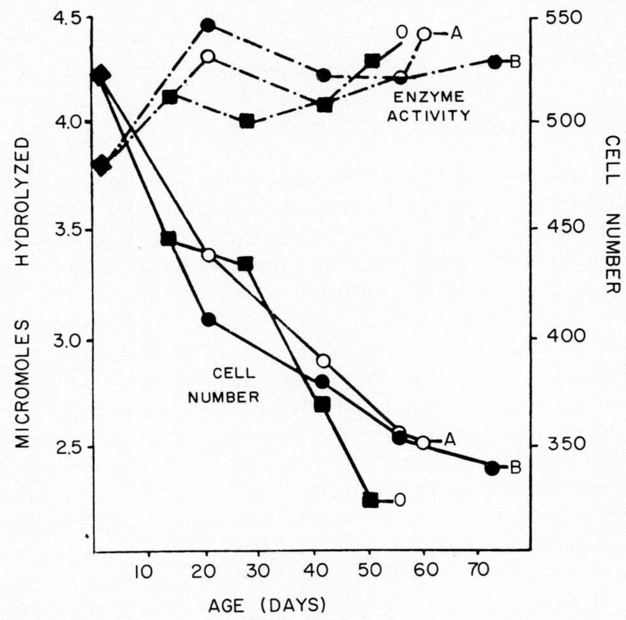

Fig. 45. *Change in number of cells and of total choline esterase activity in the brains of bees of various ages (from Rockstein, ref.* 81). *A and B: two lots of indoor caged bees; O: outside bees.*

recently counted nerve cells in four parts of the cerebral cortex of 20 human subjects. He reported decreases in the neuronal population, particularly in the superior temporal gyrus. Other areas showed lesser amounts of cell attrition. A large number of studies dealing with changes in cell number have made use of the Purkinje cells of the cerebellar cortex which may readily be counted because of their linear arrangement. A loss amounting to about 25% of the original number of cells has been reported by Ellis (*241*).

Gardner (*239*) has reported a loss of about one third of the total number of cells in the eighth and ninth thoracic spinal ganglion, whereas Corbin and Gardner (*240*) estimated the cell loss within the spinal ganglia by counting the number of dorsal and ventral root fibers contained in nerves originating in these two thoracic spinal ganglia. This report, however, is contradicted by a more recent study by Birren and Wall (*243*), who found no age difference in the number of fibers in well-fixed rat sciatic nerves.

In summary, then, *there appears to be little doubt that some cell death and loss is a general characteristic of the aging process in man and probably in other animals.* However, whether this is an important feature of the process, whether it is a major cause of dysfunction in other cells, or whether it is a result of fundamental events occurring in other cells or even outside of the organism are some of the basic questions still remaining unanswered.

CHAPTER VII

Aging of subcellular components

A. CELL TURNOVER

CERTAIN CELL TYPES, by virtue of their specialized function, are more exposed to the harmful effects of environment than others. In such cell lines the necessity for a replacement mechanism and regimen has led to the evolution of such an adaptation. Other cell types, particularly the neurones, portions of the musculature, etc., cannot be replaced on a simple schedule without grossly adverse effects on their contribution to the life of the organism.

1. *Normal Cell Death*

Perhaps the majority of cell species do not fall into either of these categories; they are neither rapidly damaged by environmental or functional factors nor is their persistence as individual cells of value to the organism. In all probability, endogenous, senescent changes are not typical of the main dividing lines of cells which cover the inner and outer surfaces of the body or which carry oxygen and CO_2 from place to place in the circulatory system. In the skin and its appendages, cell death is usually preceded by the transformation of the cellular structure into a protective keratinized coat. A detailed study of the biochemical changes accompanying the cell deaths preceding keratinization may furnish a model for more general concepts of cell death and disintegration. Figure 46 shows the regular progression of cell division, differentiation, and death that occurs in skin.

The digestive system is exposed to even more variable and extreme chemical conditions than is the skin. Appar-

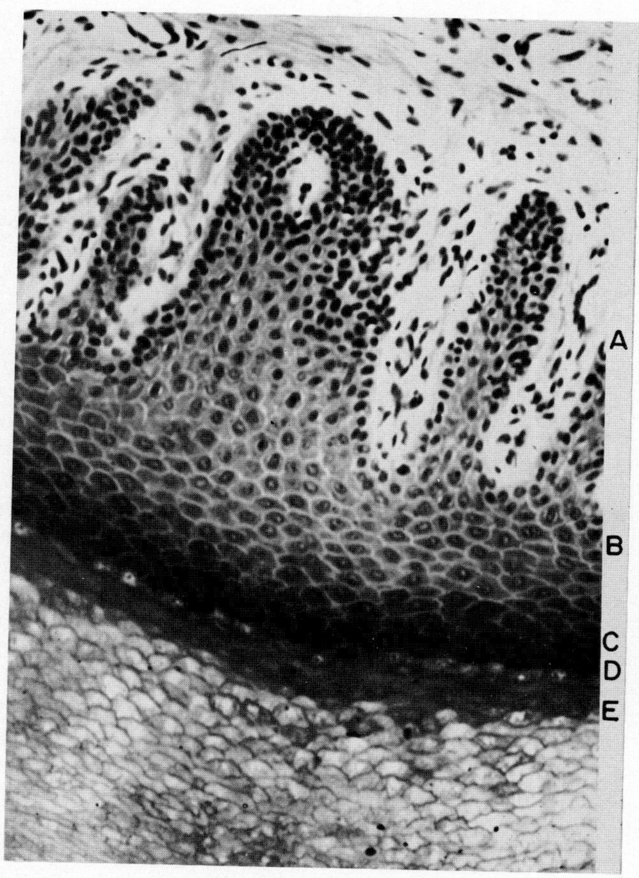

FIG. 46. *Section of thick human skin showing* (A) *germinal zone;* (B) *zone of differentiation;* (C) *granular zone;* (D) *zone of cell death;* and (E) *keratinized zone. Zone* (A) (*characterized by heavily stained nuclei*) *is arranged in folded sheets; zone* (C) *is the very dark area; zone* (B) *is between* (A) *and* (C); (D) *is represented by the row of cells with pycnotic nuclei just below zone* (C); *zone* (E) *shows transitions to the completely keratinized cells.*

ently there is a regular and rapid replacement of the cells lining the digestive system and probably of the associated lymphatic cells that resist the invasion of the circulation by potentially pathological organisms. The importance of cell replacement in the maintenance and defense of the digestive system is demonstrated by the fact that acute radiation sickness leads to death of two principle types, both related in all probability to the mitosis-inhibiting effects of radiation. Thus, damage to the vascular system, particularly the capillary endothelium, inhibition of red cell formation, and a breakdown of the intestinal barriers to infection are among the first and most serious symptoms of radiation sickness and causes of death (*244, 245*). Whether cell death precedes exfoliation in the lining of the gut or whether continual growth and abrasive loss counterbalance each other is not known.

The human red cell, which is, by virtue of the absence of a nucleus, a highly atypical cell and, in the view of some, essentially dead at the time of its release into the circulation, has nevertheless been an object for detailed studies of the effects of the age of cells on their physical and metabolic properties. Labeling studies have established that the average "life" of a red cell is approximately 120 days. At the end of this time, the cell is somehow recognized as an old cell, taken out of circulation and broken down into its constituent parts, some of which are reutilized by the next generation of red cells (*246, 247*). Experiments combining isotopic labeling and centrifugation techniques have demonstrated a change in the specific gravity of red cells as they grow older. Changes in their sensitivity to osmotic lysis and to mechanical disruptive forces have also been described by Marks and Johnson (*248*).

Brock (*249*) has studied the longevity of red cells in hibernating hamsters and changes in phosphate pools during such periods. Some of her results are illustrated in Fig. 47.

Gabrio, Huennekens, and their collaborators have made a study of biochemical changes occurring during the storage of red cells *in vitro* (*250–252*). Their findings, which may have general implications toward mechanisms of cellular death may be summarized as follows: The deterioration of

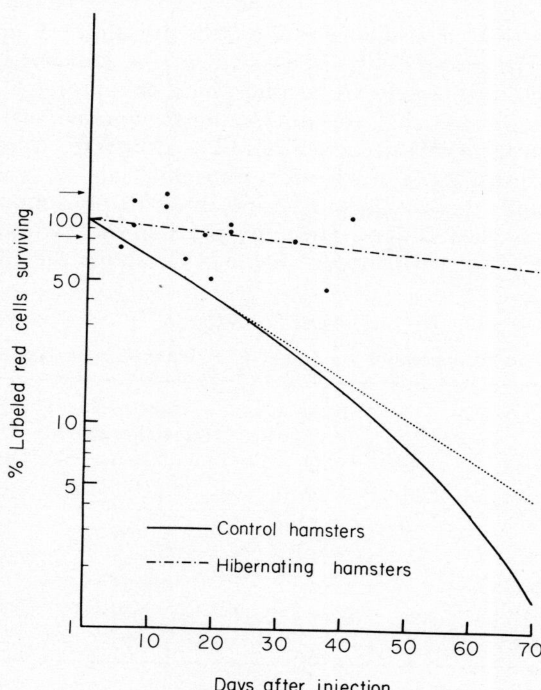

FIG. 47. *Turnover of red cells of control and hibernating hamsters (from Brock, ref.* 249).

red cells during storage is not due to simple environmental factors, since neither the manipulation of the gas phase nor alteration of the age and frequency of replacement of the suspending medium greatly affects the rate of the deteriorative processes. Analysis of changes in the various phosphate pools during storage indicated a gradual decrease in adenosine triphosphate levels and an increase in organic phosphate.

Most interesting is the fact that the rate of development of the lesion was decreased by the addition of adenosine to the suspension. There was a pronounced increase in the level of organic phosphorus compounds after the addition of this nucleoside. The fact that other nucleosides were also effective in promoting the accumulation of organic phosphorus compounds dispensed with the hypothesis that adenosine acts solely as a phosphate acceptor. Further studies indicated that the nucleoside functioned primarily as a source of readily metabolizable substrate, that it is broken down by a nucleoside phosphorylase to give the purine and ribose-1-phosphate and that this phosphorylated pentose is then broken down by the pentose dissimilative pathway of the erythrocyte. Table XVII shows the effect of

TABLE XVII[a]

EFFECT OF NUCLEOSIDES ON ORGANIC PHOSPHORUS OF RED CELLS

Factors added	Concentration (mmoles/100ml.)	Intact cells (μmoles organic phosphorus/100 ml. red cells)	Hemolyzed cells
None	—	400	229
Inosine	1.3	1305	917
Adenosine	1.3	1135	876
Guanosine	1.3	980	836
Xanthosine	1.3	894	687

[a] From ref. (*292*).

various nucleosides on the level of organic phosphorus/100 ml. of red cells. A purified enzyme preparation was practically inactive with adenosine and xanthosine. These compounds are apparently converted into the appropriate nucleoside (inosine) prior to reaction.

The extent to which other cell types turn over during the normal life span of an animal has not been subjected to highly systematic investigation. Thymidine labeling experiments would in many respects be ideal for such purposes but a safe means of getting information by such studies on human tissues has not yet been developed. Also germane would be studies of the mitotic index, the fraction of the cells in a given tissue showing mitotic figures. This is usually measured by counting the number of mitotic figures accumulating in a given tissue following the administration of colchicine some hours earlier. (Colchicine permits mitosis to proceed to metaphase and then arrests it.) The detection of the mitotic index of cells which are replaced once every 5 or 10 years (if there be such) would technically be a very difficult undertaking.

2. *Regeneration and Cell Loss*

Another experimental approach consists of the measurement of the capacity of cells to divide under certain artificial stimuli, e.g., after removal of a portion of an organ (e.g., liver). In rats there is generally a marked increase in the mitotic index of the liver within 24 to 48 hours after partial hepatectomy. Glinos' studies (*253*) have shown that one of the important factors controlling the mitotic rate in regenerating liver is a factor in blood serum. His analyses have indicated that a serum protein is one of the chief controlling factors.

According to Norris, Blanchard, and Polovny (*254*), there is a greater rate of regeneration in young rats than in middle-aged or old ones. In these studies "young" animals were defined according to weight as between 0 to 100 g., "middle-aged" animals weighed from 150 to 200 g., and "old" animals weighed 250 g. or more. If the growth rate of the young animals was higher than that of the larger individuals, the observed differences might well be a reflection, at least in part, of normal growth activity rather than a measure of the capacity for regeneration.

Bucher and Glinos (*255*) have reported that young, middle-aged, and old rats regenerate the liver mass equally well, but that old rats do not produce as many nuclei. It follows from this that the regenerated cells of old rat livers must be larger than those of younger animals. The classical studies of Bucher *et al.* (*256*) have demonstrated that the control of liver regeneration is due to a systemic factor. They used parabiotic animals in these studies (i.e., artificial Siamese twins) united so that there is a continual exchange of diffusible substances between their circulatory systems. If one of such a pair of animals, united so that they have common elements in their circulatory systems, is subjected to partial hepatectomy, it is found that the nonoperated individual shows an increase in the mitotic index of his liver after about 48 hours. The rate actually increases by about a factor of 10 (from 4.8×10^{-5} to 3.06×10^{-4}) in the operated animals. Glinos and Bartlett (*257*) studied the latent period preceding the onset of liver regeneration in the rat as a function of age. Although their studies are based upon small numbers of animals, there does appear to be an earlier onset of regeneration in young animals than in older ones.

Swartz (*258*) has used the technique of heteroplastic transplantation of intact and macerated kidney tissues of rats of various ages onto the chorioallantoic membrane of the chick. While these experiments probably involve immunological factors, as well as age variables, it is interesting that the tissues of very young rats implanted into the chorioallantoic membranes of chicks, survived for considerable periods of time whereas the older tissue implants died quickly. Whether these results reflect differences in division rates or adaptability of nondividing cells to a new environment is not entirely clear.

One of the most interesting demonstrations of the regenerative potency of tissues such as muscle, which are normally not considered to be of the regenerating type, was reported by LeGros Clark and Wajde (*259*). These authors showed that ligation of the blood supply of the gastrocnemius muscle of a rabbit will result in an essentially complete breakdown and resorption of the muscle. However, if the blood supply is restored, there ensues after the period of degeneration a phase of regrowth in which the muscle is regenerated, acquires appropriate innervation, and becomes functional nearly to the extent that it had been originally. Apparently an important factor facilitating regeneration is the intactness of the connective tissue framework upon which regenerating muscle can be laid down.

Recent studies by Konigsberg (*260*) have indicated that skeletal muscle explants from aged humans are also capable of producing outgrowths which proceed to differentiate into striated, contractile muscle fibers. Thus, even though there probably is not an extensive replacement of muscle tissue during the lifetime of an animal, there remains a capacity on the part of the cells or perhaps of primitive cell

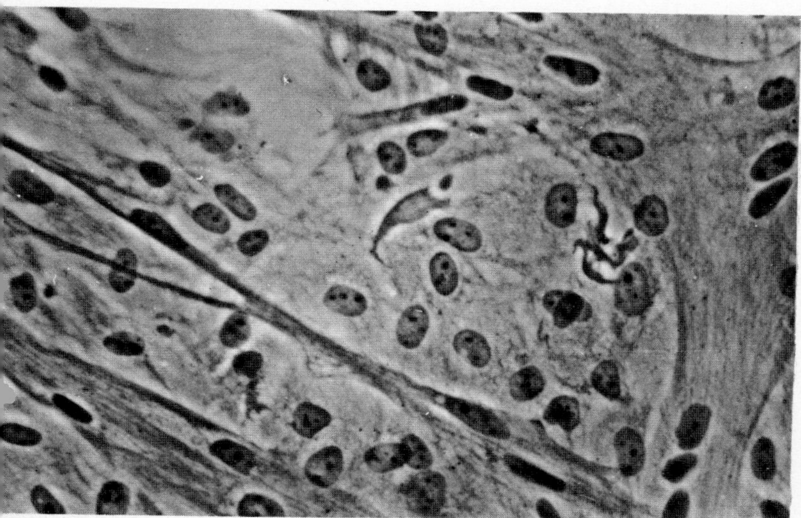

FIG. 48. *Multinucleate muscle fibers developed from explants of human muscle biopsy obtained from a 64-year-old woman. (Photo courtesy of Dr. I. Konigsberg)*

types that still remain in adult or aged muscle, under appropriate conditions, to give rise to new muscle (see Fig. 48). A systematic study of the factors controlling this outgrowth and differentiation *in vitro* is of importance both to theoretical and to more practical aspects of gerontology.

The question of cell replacement is related in an intimate manner to the general process of wound healing. DeNouy, in 1916, undertook one of the first semiquantitative studies of the process of wound healing (*261*). His investigations consisted essentially of measuring the rate at which wounds of a certain size heal in adults of various ages. The change in the diameter of the wound was measured as a function of time after the wound was inflicted, and from these successive readings an index of the rate of healing was derived.

Unfortunately, DeNouy's sample was extremely small and the scatter of the individual "cicatrization indices" was extremely high so that no clear age dependence was manifest. Howes and Harvey (*262*), some 20 years later, studied age as a factor in the velocity of the growth of fibroblasts in healing wounds. They found that young and old individuals differed, not so much in the rate of regrowth, but in the interval before the onset of regrowth. As in the case of Glinos' studies on regenerating rat livers, there appears to be a greater time lag before the onset of repair processes in old animals. A thorough reinvestigation of this question with more modern techniques is needed.

3. *Systemic Factors in Cell Division and Replacement*

The effect of the internal environment on cell growth and regeneration was first systematically studied in tissues of higher organisms some 50 years ago by Alexis Carrel and his associates (*263–268*). Carrel developed methods for taking sterile explants of organs and of measuring the effect of environmental factors and of the chemical medium in which they were incubated on their growth characteristics. His quantitation method was extremely time-consuming and consisted essentially of the measurement of the growth rate of the two equal halves of a chick embryo fibroblast culture under standard control conditions and in the presence or absence of another factor. One of his earliest observations was that a regular schedule of replacement of the medium in which the tissue cultures were growing resulted in their rejuvenation as measured by growth rate. Carrel, in a paper entitled "On the Permanent Life of Tissues Outside of the Organism," reported (*264*) that repeated transplantation of a tissue to new medium resulted in a stimulation of growth. Unfortunately, the cells which were usually studied were fibroblasts rather than the much more interesting parenchymal cells.

Carrel and Burrows (*263*) in a paper entitled "On the Physico-Chemical Regulation of the Growth of Tissues" showed that dilution of the culture medium actually resulted in an increase in the rate of growth. This observation suggested the presence of an inhibitor in the serum that was used, which inhibitor was the subject of much later investigation.

Carrel and Ebeling (*265*), in an extensive series of studies of the effects of varying the composition of the culture medium on the growth of fibroblasts *in vitro,* showed that their rate of multiplication drops off much more rapidly when 3-year-old blood serum is used in the medium than when serum from 3-month-old chickens is used. Further, they showed that this difference is owing to the presence of an inhibitor rather than to the absence of a stimulatory factor in the old serum because the addition of young serum to the old did not significantly reverse the inhibitory effect. Carrel and Ebeling (*266*) then showed that an inhibitory substance was produced when serum is heated to about 60° C. for one hour. Heating the serum to a higher temperature destroys this inhibitory substance.

A later study (*267*) reported the presence of two antagonistic principles in serum, a growth-stimulating one which was precipitable by bubbling CO_2 through the serum and a factor remaining in the CO_2-treated supernatant which was inhibitory. A recombination of these two factors or a dilution of the original serum followed by reconcentration gave results essentially identical with the control untreated serum (see Table XVIII.

TABLE XVIII

RELATIVE GROWTH-PROMOTING EFFECTIVENESS OF VARIOUS SERUM FRACTIONS

Fraction	Relative growth rate
Control	1.0
CO_2 precipitate	1.15
Supernate obtained from CO_2-precipitated serum	0.74
Diluted and reconcentrated serum	0.97
Recombined CO_2 precipitate and residue	0.93

A succeeding paper (*268*) showed that, although the serum from 6-year-old and 1-year-old chickens gave relative growth rates of 0.61 and 1.0, the heating of the same sera to 65°C. resulted in a greater accumulation of inhibitory substances in the young serum than in the old so that the ratio of efficacy of old to young heated sera was 0.76 to 1.0. Heated young serum was about 62% as effective as unheated serum, whereas old serum was nearly 84% as effective as unheated serum. The results obtained from a crude fractionation of sera obtained from young and old chickens (6 months and 4 to 5 years of age) are indicated in Table XIX. The cholesterol content of sera dropped from 225 mg./100 cc. to 143 mg./100 cc. between 3 months and 4 to 5 years of age.

TABLE XIX

Chemical Composition of Young and Old Chicken Serum

Protein	3.52–4.64
CO_2 precipitable material	0.60–1.24
Globulin	1.12–1.45
Albumin	1.33–1.45
Total lipid	0.876–1.059
Lecithin content:	
In 3-month-old animals	4.78 mg./100 cc.
In 6-month-old animals	5.72 mg./100 cc.
In 4- to 5-year-old animals	7.41 mg./100 cc.

In 1926, Baker and Carrel (*269*) reported that both lipid and protein components obtainable from serum were growth inhibitors. Of interest in the latter paper is a comment (p. 317) that the removal of lecithin has a salutary effect on the rate of the heart beat of explanted pieces of heart. In view of the recent findings of Wilbur, Berheim, and collaborators (*270–272*) of the strong inhibitory effects which lipid peroxides possess (a number of which are readily formed as autoxidation products of phospholipids), it may well turn out that the inhibitory factors discussed by Carrel are partial rancidification products of unsaturated lipids whose effect may be counteracted by antioxidants carried along with the protein fraction. A resolution of the many questions raised by Carrel's work would be a welcome breath in the field. It is hoped that workers conversant with modern tissue culture techniques will reexplore this important subject.

Another series of observations on the effect of substances that affect cultures of fibroblasts were reported by Simms and Stillman in 1936 and 1937 (*273–275*). They showed that adult aorta contains an inhibitor which retards the division of fibroblasts obtained from aorta. This inhibitor is precipitable with 50% alcohol plus calcium chloride. It may be prepared by treatment of minced aorta with trypsin, then with 50% alcohol in the cold and with calcium chloride. The precipitates are inhibitory. On the other hand, these workers showed that the treatment with trypsin of fibroblast cultures which had ceased to grow caused growth stimulation. Since the washing of the cultures after the trypsin treatment increased the stimulatory effect, since digested serum did not stimulate, and since plasma aged in an icebox or at higher temperatures for several days did not produce the inhibitor, they concluded that an inhibitory layer which could be removed by trypsin treatment was deposited around the margin of the culture.

Simms and Stillman also showed that serum contains a growth stimulating factor although it is not clear whether this A factor is related to or identical with the stimulatory factor of Carrel and Ebeling. Its properties are (*a*) it is dialyzable, (*b*) it may be heated to 100°C. at pH7 for 10 minutes without destroying its activity, (*c*) it is destroyed at pH2 and 12 at 100°C. in 5 minutes, (*d*) it can be stored for as long as 10 months in an icebox, (*e*) it is precipitated by copper and calcium salts, (*f*) it moves toward the anode, and (*g*) it appears to be present in urine. Whether these are all one factor or different factors was not completely clear.

In a succeeding study, serum was further fractionated into four factors—A, B, C, and D. The A factor, which was mentioned in the last paragraph, causes the growth of clear, fat-free cells, and is present in serum ultrafiltrates. The B factor was obtained from the supernatant of clotted plasma treated with 3 volumes of Tyrode's solution for 48 hours at pH 7.3 under 7% carbon dioxide. This supernatant contains 6 mg. of nonprotein nitrogen and 0.65% protein, and causes fat accumulation. A third fraction, factor C, was obtained by allowing chicken plasma to stand for 4 days in an icebox. The precipitate obtained causes cell death. Even after dialysis the euglobulin precipitate caused death of cells; similarly, the albumin precipitated with ammonium sulfate caused a degeneration of cells. Finally, a fourth fraction, factor D, a globulin obtained from ammonium sulfate fractionation of plasma, caused the adhesion of cells in culture. The B factor, it was reported in another communication, causes the deposition of fat in pieces of aorta in culture.

Neither the studies by Carrel and collaborators nor by Simms and Stillman identified the components responsible for the inhibitory and stimulatory action. Although these effects may be due to the major components of the fractions studied, they may just as well represent the activity of minor contaminants carried along with the major components. A systematic attack on optimal culture conditions and the effects of highly purified substances on the growth and other characteristics of differentiated mammalian cell types in culture is still much needed.

Shortly after these studies by Simms and Stillman, Medawar (*276*) reported that there is a logarithmic decrease with age in the capacity of chick heart explants to overcome the inhibition caused by a bacterial factor isolated by Heaton in the course of other studies. The mathematical treatment employed by Medawar and the departure of the paper from his usually lucid style make it difficult to evaluate the relation of these reported results to the problem under discussion. Margoliash *et al.* (*277*) showed that an extract of fresh adult heart will stimulate the growth of third passage fibroblasts from an 8-day chick embryo. An acetone-dried extract was also stimulatory to growth. Dialysis of either a fresh or acetonized extract resulted in their complete loss of activity whereas the dialized acetone extract possessed slight activity. Recombination of this fraction with its dialyzate resulted in almost complete restoration of stimulatory activity.

In concluding this discussion of systemic factors or environmental agents capable of influencing the growth of cells in culture or *in vivo,* attention should be called to the observations of Wolfson *et al.* (*278*) on the accumulation of lipid peroxides in regenerating rat liver, measured by the TBA (thiobarbituric acid) method. In a typical experiment, for example, in the presence of ascorbic acid, the TBA value was 0.42 optical density units. Ten hours later after hepatectomy, the TBA value was 0.62, whereas at 48 hours, when mitotic activity was vigorously proceeding, the TBA value had dropped to 0.27. It returned again to nearly normal values at 6 days after operation (0.57 TBA units). In the absence of ascorbic acid, the TBA values were 0.21, 0.21, 0.11, 0.24, respectively, for the above times. This evidence of low peroxide levels in regenerating tissue suggests that lipid peroxides may act as normal inhibitors of cell division and that their removal is a means of stimulating cell division. Other findings by the Wilbur-Bernheim (*271, 272, 279*) group are consistent with this interpretation for they have found that addition of lipid peroxides in extremely minute concentrations effectively inhibits cell division and that radiation, either with ultraviolet light or with ionizing radiation sufficient to arrest cell division, also causes an increase in the level of TBA positive material. It may be conjectured that the control of cell division is moderated by relatively modest metabolic changes (perhaps in the level of peroxide-forming and peroxide-dissipating systems—such as catalase and peroxidase) interacting with varying levels of chain-breaking substances such as the tocopherol antioxidants and sulfhydryl-containing substances.

Before concluding this discussion of factors controlling cell growth, it should also be emphasized that a steady-state population of cells within the adult organism can only be maintained by counterbalancing the rate of cell death with an equal rate of cell division and growth. We have been discussing only the systemic factors potentially controlling cell regrowth, division, etc. The nature of intracellular or systemic factors controlling cell death is another equally crucial side to the coin. The science of cell death, or thanocytology, would appear to await a more systematic exploration before answers to some obvious questions can be sensibly essayed.

B. METABOLIC TURNOVER

Evidently the classic studies on metabolic turnover by Schoenheimer and Rittenberg (*280*) in the 1930's have led to certain unwarranted generalizations. Some of these were clarified in a paper by Thompson and Ballou (*211*) in 1956 entitled "The Predominantly Non-dynamic State of Body Constituents in the Rat." This study consisted essentially of labeling rats with tritium early in life and then following the disappearance of labels from various tissues, organs, and chemically isolable fractions as a function of time. Thompson and Ballou found that they could approximate the decay curve with one long-lived component and one or two short-lived ones. Table XX, based upon data in the

TABLE XX

MAGNITUDE AND BIOLOGICAL HALF-LIFE OF TISSUE COMPOSITION OF RAT

Tissue or composition	Long-lived total tissue or fraction (%)	Half-life (days)	Short-lived half-life (days)
Carcass	4	130	22
Liver	3	140	12, 4.5
Lung	14	320	10, 3
Heart	—	—	—
Kidney	8	180	11
Stomach	20	300	20, 5
Small intestine	17	160	9
Large intestine	30	180	13, 5
Brain	54	150	16
Pelt	67	110	11
Muscle	40	100	16
Fat	69	70	17
Bone	72	240	16
Phospholipid	33	220	20
Nonsaponified lipid	30	160	20
Saturated fatty acids	60	80	15
Unsaturated fatty acids	74	80	10
Collagen	72	1000	15
Water-soluble	50	60	10
Alcohol- or ether-insoluble	36	200	25
Insoluble residue	40	300	15

Thompson and Ballou paper, shows in the first column the percentage of the total activity in a tissue or fraction which is long-lived and in the two remaining columns the half-life in days of the long and short-lived components. These results are particularly interesting in that up to 75% of the total label in certain tissues and fractions have quite long half-lives. Collagen, for example, has a half-life of 1000 days for the approximately three quarters of its label which turns over slowly. Essentially, this suggests that, at least in the rat, this constituent, when once laid down, is not turned over at all. There are significant gerontological implications in this work since nonrenewable components are subject to molecular aging. Of equal interest is the rate of turnover of various constituents, particularly mitochondria, membranes, etc., in specialized nondividing cell types. This question will be considered in greater detail in the next portion of this discussion.

C. CHANGES IN SUBCELLULAR ORGANELLES AND CONSTITUENTS

Pearl [14] did not subscribe to the view that changes at the cellular or subcellular level were the source of senescence. He held that the decline in function was a result of the interdependence of cells within the metazoan and thus a sort of "price" that an animal must pay for the advantages of cellular specialization. Nevertheless, the concept has persisted that aging of organisms is really a consequence of changes in the cells of which the animal is made rather than primarily of the failure of their functional interdependence and arrangement. In this latter view, senescence is an expression of events at the cellular level rather than at the tissue, organ system, or organism level.

While it may eventually be firmly established that this latter view is more nearly correct than the extension of Pearl's outlook, one must always bear in mind the possibility that the changes that occur in cells may be a consequence of deteriorating organization at the supracellular level rather than a cause of it. The working hypothesis that we have adopted is that both subcellular and supracellular factors are involved in the aging process but that the predominant and irreversible aspects devolve from the failure of cells.

Cells are not infinitely complicated biological systems. In searching for age changes and sources of failure, there are, structurally, only a half dozen or so possible loci to examine. These are (*a*) membranes, both cellular and nuclear; (*b*) mitochondria, which are important as devices that carry on the coupling of oxidative substrate breakdown to phosphorylative energy storage; (*c*) the endoplasmic reticulum, a third system whose components are separable and identifiable following homogenization as constituents of the microsomal fraction; (*d*) the nucleus of the cell, a fourth anatomical entity in which change may occur with age; within its confines may occur not only genetic deterioration but also an alteration in such metabolic regulation as the nucleus possesses; (*e*) the Golgi apparatus, whose very existence was subject to question until about a decade ago, when interference and electron microscopy established the presence of bodies of appropriate size, shape, and locus; regarding deterioration of its structure, little can be said; (*f*) finally, various granules, vacuoles, and inclusion bodies, such as pinocytosis vacuoles, the so-called lysosomes, and lipofuscin granules.

1. *Mitochondria*

A gross index of the change in mitochondrial activity or in the total mass of mitochondria in a tissue as a function of age is given by the respiratory rate of homogenates or slices in the presence of specific substrates and acceptors. The level of mitochondrial activity in the intact organism, of course, is a function of a number of factors among the most important of which is the availability of phosphate acceptors, as well as the appropriate substrates (*281*). Thus the multitude of reactions involving dephosphorylation of ATP (adenosine triphosphate) will affect the respiratory rate of tissue slices and homogenates.

Reiner (*282*) studied the effect of age on the carbohydrate metabolism of rat tissue homogenates and observed a decline in brain oxygen consumption only after about 2 years of age. He also observed a gradual decline in the anaerobic glycolytic rate. In these studies he used high substrate concentrations. Rafsky *et al.* (*283*), studied age differences in the respiration of guinea pig tissue homogenates. They measured oxygen consumption in the presence of glucose and buffered Ringer's solution. No significant changes were observed in the liver of guinea pigs between 8 and 100 weeks of age; kidney homogenates did show some possibly significant differences, as shown in Table XXI.

TABLE XXI

RESPIRATORY RATES OF GUINEA PIG KIDNEY HOMOGENATES VERSUS AGE

Age	N	Q_n[a]	S.D.	N	Q[b]	S.D.
Young (8 weeks)	9	18.61	8.35	9	4.06	2.71
Middle (50–52 weeks)	10	11.04	3.73	18	1.42	0.60
Old (100 weeks)	12	7.44	2.82	15	1.15	0.26

[a] Q_n: microliters O_2 consumed/mg. N/hour.
[b] Q: microliters O_2 consumed/mg. dry weight/hour.

More recently, Barrows *et al.* (*284*) have compared the rate of endogenous oxygen uptake as well as of anaerobic glycolysis in kidney and liver slices from rats 12 to 14 and 24 to 27 months of age. The rate of oxygen uptake by kidney slices was lower in old rats than in the young when it was calculated on the basis of wet weight but not on the basis of DNA. No changes were found in the rates of anaerobic glycolysis or oxygen uptake by liver slices.

The essential absence of age dependent alterations in respiratory activity was corroborated by measuring the concentration of succinoxidase in homogenates of these two tissues. A small but significant reduction in the activity of this enzyme based on DNA in both kidney and heart was found, but again no such change was observed in liver.

Barrows *et al.* (*285*) have measured the succinoxidase content of mitochondria isolated from young and old kidneys and have found no change in the activity of this enzyme per milligram of protein nitrogen. Thus, the decrease in activity of the enzyme in the crude homogenate is a consequence of decrease in the number of mitochondria rather than a change in the relative amount of the enzyme per mitochondrion.

Dempsey (*286*) in 1956 attempted to relate the age of the animal to morphological features of mitochondria. He described degenerating mitochondria in old tissues, although it is difficult to evaluate the evidence since one cannot follow the life history of a single mitochondrion. Andrew (*287*) notes that "In the cells of a young mouse one can see a good many mitochondria, some of which are filamentous in type and none of which are present as very large granules. In a cell of a senile mouse, on the other hand, we have many mitochondria which are granular in appearance. Sometimes they are in small groups or chains and very often they are single. This effect is also found in the Purkinje cells of the cerebellum so that there is some evidence that in cells such as neurons there are changes in mitochondria."

However, mitochondria are apparently extremely susceptible to changes in the environment. Some intriguing associations between mitochondria and lipid inclusions have been reported by Palade and Schidlowsky (*288*). Heat and cold produce changes in the appearance of mitochondria in intact animals. These changes were induced by short-term manipulation of the animal and are presumably reversible. The question then seems to be not whether mitochondria age but whether because of environmental factors they may have a different appearance in aged cells than in young ones.

An index of functional impairment of mitochondria under unfavorable conditions including aging might be a change in the P/O ratios. A decline in P/O ratio from about 1.3 to 0.5 was observed by Weinbach in tissue obtained from a snail, between 2 and 12 weeks of age (*289*). Weinbach, in his early study, used α-ketoglutaric acid as a substrate. He found that the ATPase activity of his old preparations increased by a factor of 2 or 3 and that this was paralleled by a diminished response to the inhibitor, pentachlorophenol. Whether these differences are a reflection of actual mitochondrial alterations during the aging process or to a differential sensitivity of the mitochondria during the isolation procedure cannot be deduced with certainty. However, in more recent publications, Weinbach (*290*) and Weinbach and Garbus (*291*) have reported some differences between mitochondria from young and old animals. They found, using β-hydroxybutyrate as a substrate for mitochondria isolated from liver, that the micromoles of phosphate taken up per milligram of nitrogen dropped from 16.8 to about 11.8 as the donor animals increased in age from 3 months to between 24 and 37 months of age. However, there was a proportional decrease in the amount of acetoacetate formed or β-hydroxybutyrate consumed so that the ratio of phosphate esterified and substrate oxidized remained constant at 2.8. Glycolytic phosphorylation, on the other hand, was relatively unaltered in liver. In brain, phosphorylation and oxygen uptake with succinate as a substrate were essentially unaffected between 3 and 30 months of age. Thus, Weinbach found that there was little difference between young and old individuals in the rate of phosphorylation and P/O ratios with α-ketoglutarate, malate, and succinate as substrates. But with β-hydroxybutyrate, the rate was down to about 60% of the original rate, even though the P/O ratio was unaffected. On the other hand, it was found that mitochondria isolated from old animals were damaged after storage for a 48- to 72-hour period at 4°C., whereas those obtained from young animals were unaffected. The P/O ratio of old mitochondria decreased as a result of this treatment.

Recently the question of the aging of mitochondria has been examined from an entirely different point of view by Fletcher and Sanadi (*292*), and personal communication). They have labeled the mitochondria of rats with radioactive acetate, iron, and sulfur and isolated mitochondrial lipid, cytochrome c, and heme protein components at various time intervals after labeling. They find that the rate of turnover of mitochondrial constituents is similar for all three types of labeling and that the half-life of the constituents is only about 12 days. Thus, except for the unlikely event that there is a small pool of cells turning over extremely rapidly, in which case the turnover rate might not be characteristic of the mass of liver mitochondria but only of a small, select fraction of them, it appears that this rapid turnover rate would preclude the type of deteriorative changes expected of unrenewable cell constituents.

2. *Nuclei*

Minot, in his paper "The Problem of Age, Growth and Death," stated as his main thesis that natural death is a consequence of cellular differentiation (*293*), of which a change in the nucleocytoplasmic ratio is an important index. He felt that factors which produce rejuvenation cause an increase in the relative size of the nucleus, whereas senescence is a result of an increase in the protoplasmic mass relative to the nucleus and of cellular differentiation. This thesis was not critically evaluated by Minot himself and only a few lines of evidence relevant to it have been obtained in the meantime. One test was reported by Smallwood and Phillips in 1916 in their study of the nuclear size of cells of bees during the life cycle. This study showed that fatigue and age do not produce significant changes in nuclear size. The application of modern radioautographic and counting techniques to histological sections should permit a more critical test of this hypothesis.

Falzone, *et al.* (*226*) have recently reported a study of the effect of age on the ploidy of rat liver nuclei as measured by their volume and mean DNA content. No significant differences were seen in this case, although Andrew had reported occasional odd karyotypes (*225*). We have already referred to the more frequent occurrence of nuclear figures suggestive of an amitotic process. Pycnosis and karyolsis could certainly be accompaniments of cell death in atrophic tissues. However, in the author's opinion, many of these observed changes in nuclear form may be an indirect consequence of the deterioration of the tissue milieu rather than a reflection of an aging process characteristic of the cells per se.

However, there are several lines of evidence suggesting a type of nuclear abnormality which is more frequent with age. The first is the fact that there is a considerable incidence of somatic aneuploidy in various tissues, particularly in the liver of dog, guinea pig, and rat, according to early studies by Hsu and Pomerat (*294*). A similar and strikingly high frequency of somatic aneuploidy was described by Yerganian (*295*) in the Chinese hamster whose 22 chromosomes, each of which can be individually identified, show incidences as high as 40 to 60% of abnormal (aneuploid) numbers. That a similar process occurs in the germ line is shown by demonstrations of Jacobs *et al.* (*296*) and others of an abnormal karyotype possessed by individuals suffering from mongolism. This genetic affliction is associated with the presence of an extra, small, acentric chromosome. Its occurrence is probably attributable to an unequal reduction division in a manner quite analogous to the somatic aneuploidy which presumably could arise from errors in chromosomal separation during the mitotic process. Although the degree of somatic aneuploidy occurring as a function of age has not been systematically studied, Curtis (personal communication) has some evidence of the occurrence of abnormal karyotypes during aging and the accentuation of the rate of occurrence of such aberrations as a result of exposure to ionizing radiation. Penrose's data (*297*) on the maternal age distribution of mongolism in England and Wales have a direct bearing on this question and are summarized in Table XXII (taken from his 1954 paper).

TABLE XXII

INCIDENCE OF MONGOLISM VERSUS MATERNAL AGE

Maternal age (years)	Average incidence of mongolism (%)
15–19	23
20–24	24
25–29	25
30–34	71
35–39	220
40–44	829
45	2080

It would be difficult to assign this 100-fold increase in mongolism strictly to the effects of time since the rate does not change for the first 15 years (15–29) examined but increases by a factor of 100 during the next 15 to 20 years. Possibly it reflects a deterioration of the milieu in which the eggs develop. Or perhaps the normal eggs are the ones released early in life, whereas abnormal ones are released only after the exhaustion of the supply of more viable ones. That it is not merely a matter of the age of the parents but possibly of the age of the egg is indicated by the fact that no similar correlation between mongolism and the age of the father has been observed.

3. *Microsomes, Endoplasmic Reticulum, and Golgi Apparatus*

Age-dependent changes in the microsomes or endoplasmic reticulum of cells are strongly suggested by the decrease in amount of Nissl substance in the nerves of older animals and humans. According to the study by Palay and Palade (*298*), Nissl bodies are granular RNA-containing concentrations of endoplasmic reticulum. The same study failed to identify definitely a unique structure in nerves as the Golgi apparatus. However, the authors suggest that the more tightly packed agranular reticulum, particularly in the region of the nuclei, is the Golgi apparatus, a description which would agree with the position of this structure according to the studies made by Gatenby (*299*) of the living sympathetic ganglion cells of the mouse as photographed by phase-contrast microscopy. In an earlier section, we reviewed the changes Andrew has observed in the Golgi apparatus of nerve cells in aging mice. The original netlike structure gives way, according to Andrew, to disconnected, disordered granules. An electron microscopic study of the Golgi apparatus in aged cells should be rewarding. Whether or not changes in the Golgi or endoplasmic reticulum are a result of changes in the milieu comparable to the mitochondrial alterations observed in older tissues, or a result of some other underlying intrinsic intracellular change cannot be answered. The presence of large numbers of apparently normal cells in "normal" old animals would support the former interpretation. Since the endoplasmic reticulum is apparently involved in synthetic activities, a decrease in it could, of course, depress cellular function, or, conversely be the result of decreased synthetic demands in older cells.

4. *Changes in Nuclear and Cellular Membranes*

Age-dependent changes either in the nuclear membrane or in the cellular membrane, as a function of age other than an accumulation of calcium in the cortex of certain cell types, as described by Lansing (*300, 301*), are relatively unknown. It is quite probable that cellular membranes, as well as nuclear membranes, are in a continual process of turnover. Time-lapse photographs of cells in tissue culture showing the mobility of membranes in phagocytotic and pinocytotic activities lend credence to the concept of their rapid physical and metabolic turnover. Critical studies of the rate of diffusion through the membranes of young and old cells, except for the studies of Kirk and Larsen (*214*) on the permeability of the human cerebellum, tentorium, and aorta of different ages, are lacking. In Kirk's studies no significant differences in diffusion resistance were found. Objective measurements of diffusion rates in various tissues of intact animals of various ages are highly desirable.

5. *Pigment Accumulation and Lysosomes*

The occurrence of pigmented inclusion bodies in such nondividing cell lines as nerve and muscle (skeletal and cardiac) has been known since the turn of the century (*302*). A basic and systematic study of the distribution of such pigments and the fluorescence which usually accompanies them was undertaken by Hamperl (*220*). He showed that a wide variety of cells possessed such fluorescent components. Bethe and Fluck (*303*), a few years later, in a study of the yellow pigment of ganglion cells showed that lipofuscin and its histological precursors are quite distinguishable from Nissl substance. They showed that the Nissl stain disappears in alkaline solution while lipofuscin retains its stability with toluidine blue under the same conditions.

Hyden and Lindstrom (*304*), in 1950, conducted a number of ingenious investigations of the biophysical properties of the yellow pigment in nerve cells. They attempted to measure the emission spectrum as well as the absorption spectrum of these pigments with a microspectrophotometer. The absorption spectrum showed an inflection at about 3700 A. The fluorescent emission was maximal in the 440 to 460 mμ and 530 to 560 mμ regions. On the basis of these spectral properties, they suggested that the material was a pteridine derivative, a conclusion which subsequent studies do not support. Gatenby (*305*) has suggested that the so-called senility pigment of the human autonomic system is, in fact, a secretory granule because it is apparently associated with the Golgi apparatus. Whether the association with the Golgi apparatus signifies a functional relationship between the two or an anatomical coincidence is not known.

Deane and Fawcett (*306*) have studied the accumulation in the ovaries of old mice of pigmented interstitial cells showing a so-called brown degeneration. Although the authors do not identify this substance with the lipofuscin of other tissues, they did note that it was insoluble in acetone, fluorescent, Schiff-negative before treatment with permanganate, but positive after permanganate oxidation. The ovaries of these animals were still apparently functional.

A different origin for the pigmented bodies in old spinal ganglia was suggested by Hess (*307*) on the basis of an electron microscopic study. He proposed that the pigment bodies arise from degenerating mitochondria. For reasons which will become apparent later, this suggested origin is not completely convincing. Sosa (*308*) suggested that the intracellular neural fibrils condensed during the aging process and are agglutinated by the pigmentary granules. Sosa (*309*) has also proposed that pigment deposition is the unifying feature in the degeneration of neurons.

Various publications by Sulkin (*310, 311*) have dealt with the histochemical characteristics of lipofuscin deposits within the nervous system of senile dogs. He noted that there is an accumulation of PAS-positive material. Since PAS (periodic acid-Schiff staining technique) positivity is usually taken to mean the presence of adjacent hydroxyl groups, this observation either means that some type of carbohydrate derivative is deposited with increasing frequency as a function of age or, more likely, as Pearse (*312*) has suggested, it may be that the intermediate products of lipid autoxidation possess adjacent hydroxyl groups which are suitable reagents for the PAS stain. Sulkin and Kuntz (*313*) also noted the presence of alkaline phosphatase activity in the pigment granules. They noted a depletion of a so-called chromidial substance in dogs as they age and "marked alterations of the Golgi." The details of the procedures used in these studies do not always permit a complete evaluation of their significance.

In 1955 Sulkin continued his reports on the accumulation of PAS-positive materials and pointed out that lipofuscin does appear to accumulate with age. More recently (*314*), he has questioned whether lipofuscin accumulation is a fundamental portion of the aging process but rather suggested that its accumulation is the result of various types of insult and injury to the animal. This view is based upon the fact that various stresses, such as, among others, the injection of cortisone, exposure to low oxygen tensions, and acetanilid feeding, are capable of causing an accumulation of lipofuscin pigment in rats at an earlier age than that at which it would normally occur.

On logical grounds, however, such observations cannot rule out an intrinsic role of age pigments in the aging process. Any process that accelerates their accumulation might well operate by a different pathway than the normally occurring one.

Jayne (*315*) has studied the occurrence of lipofuscin in cardiac muscle of human autopsy specimens of different ages and has also studied the properties of relatively insoluble particles derived from tissues containing large amounts of lipofuscin. The particles he described are insoluble in various organic and inorganic solvents including strong acids. Subsequently, Heidenreich and Siebert (*316*) isolated lipofuscin granules from heart muscle by centrifugal means and without preliminary enzymic treatment. They measured their lipid content and showed that the granules contained esterase and a protease (cathepsin?). Bondareff (*317*) in 1957 reported an electron microscopic study of lipofuscin pigment in the spinal ganglia of senile rats. He holds that the pigment is not derived from degenerating mitochondria, as Hess had suggested, but rather, as Gatenby had also suggested, that it is derived from or related to the Golgi apparatus. Bondareff's review (*318*) in the "Handbook of Aging and the Individual" will bear close reading for his current views of the function and origin of the neural pigment. Two histochemical studies, one by Gedigk and Bontke (*319*) in 1956 and a second by Essner and Novikoff (*320*) in 1960 appear to relate the lipofuscin particles of a number of tissues to an entirely different class of structures, namely, to the lysosomes that DeDuve and collaborators (*321, 322*) described in the last decade. Gedigk and Bontke showed that the pigment possesses stainability appropriate to lipofuscin and both esterase and acid phosphatase activity. The latter are also characteristics of isolated DeDuve particles from liver. They showed an essential spatial identity between pigment and acid phosphatase localization in heart and muscle; but in liver, adrenals, and testes there is not such an absolute correspondence. In liver, acid phosphatase-positive granules precede the appearance of lipofuscin. Even more recently the waxing and waning of hepatic lipofuscin in various disease states has been described. Acid phosphatase also appears in cells depositing ceroid pigment.

Essner and Novikoff studied the light and electron microscopic characteristics of human liver lysosomes and independently established an identity between the localization of the absorbing pigments and the enzymic activity. Both of these latter two elegant papers are recommended reading for those interested in the details of the subject.

In 1957, Strehler *et al.* (*7*) reported the results of quantitative measurements of the volume occupied by lipofuscin granules in the human myocardium as a function of age. They showed that there is a linear increase in the amount of pigment and that the rate of accumulation is about 0.3% of the total heart volume per decade or about 0.6% of the intracellular volume per decade. Thus, by the time that an individual reaches 90 years of age, as much as 6 or 7%

FIG. 49. *The fluorescence of aged human myocardium. The brightly fluorescing areas (yellow) are age pigment (lipofuscin) whereas the muscle fibers are much less fluorescent (blue-green) (from Strehler, ref.* 11).

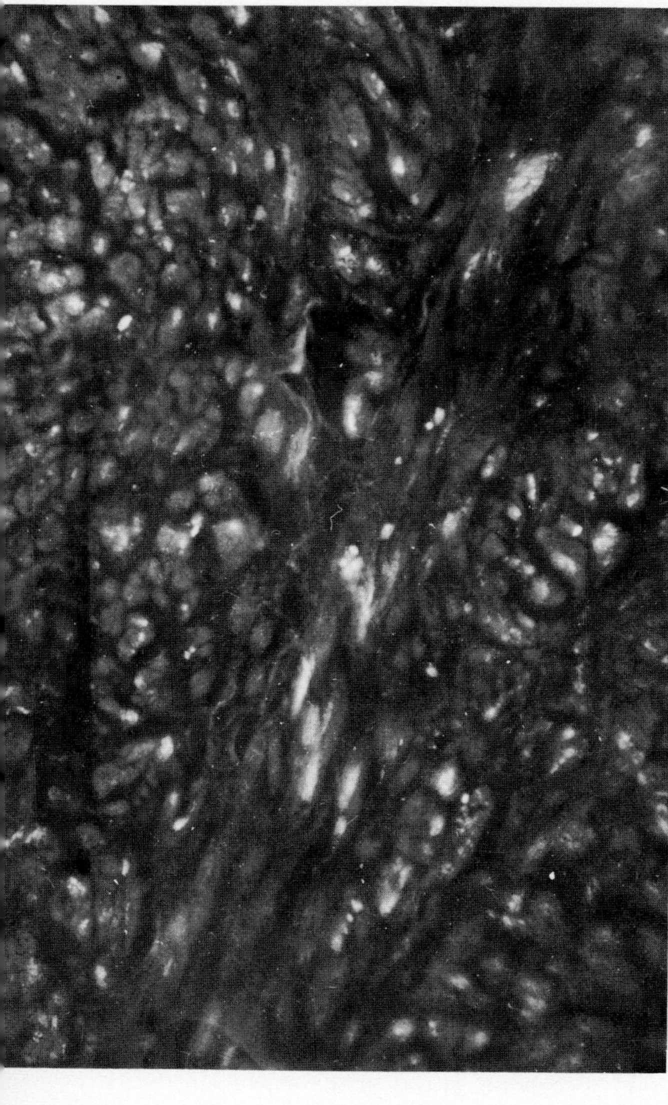

Fig. 49

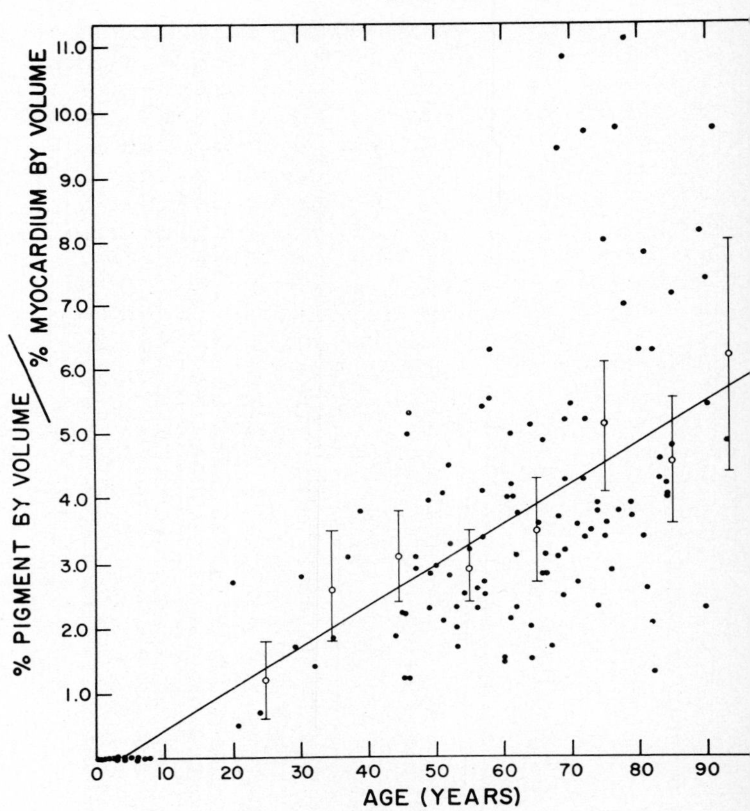

FIG. 50. *Relationship between age and pigment content of human myocardium (from Strehler* et al., *ref.* 7).

of the intracellular volume may be occupied by pigment deposit. A typical old heart section viewed by the fluorescence of the pigment deposit is shown in Fig. 49 and the agewise distribution of pigment is shown in Fig. 50.

The rate of pigment accumulation was not dependent upon the racial origin or sex of the individual. However, a more recent study on Japanese survivors of the Hiroshima bomb blast and a control sample from a similar area indicates that the rate of pigment accumulation in Japanese autopsy material is nearly twice the rate observed for Americans. No difference was noted between the two Japanese groups.

Strehler and collaborators (*323–325*) have undertaken a detailed study of the chemical constitution of lipofuscin granules isolated from the human myocardium using differential centrifugation as an isolation procedure. Both cathepsin and acid phosphatase activities were present. Contrary to expectation, it was found that a major fluorescent (*326*) component of the pigment granules was soluble in chloroform-methanol. The chromatography of this material on silicic acid columns has revealed the presence of components similar to the autoxidation products of cephalin and perhaps other unsaturated lipids. Although most of the fluorescence is removed by organic solvents, the insoluble residue still retains a considerable amount of brownish pigment, perhaps containing different chromophores. Its chemical constitution, as well as the amino acid make-up of the constituent protein, is currently under investigation.

From all of the foregoing, it appears probable that lipofuscin is a result of the accumulation and autoxidation of lipid components of lysosomes. Whether the lysosomal activity remains intact and undiminished, and whether there is a continued gradual accumulation of lysosomes in nondividing cells regardless of whether they are subsequently utilized cannot be answered at present. It seems probable that the accumulation of the pigment is an accidental by-product of its chemical constitution. The lysosome may avoid the turnover characteristic of most other cell constituents by embodying within its membranes cephalin or other phospholipids which are resistant to the lytic enzymes of the cytoplasm or of the interior of the lysosome itself. Indeed, turnover would involve the probably harmful release of the potent lytic enzymes under inappropriate conditions. Therefore, we suggest that lipofuscin accumulation (and whatever its major or minor contribution to senescence is ultimately established to be) is a result of the evolutionary difficulty of selecting an envelope for lytic enzymes (*a*) sufficiently stable to contain these catalysts, (*b*) readily broken down under appropriate conditions (e.g., when initiated by triggers for developmental resorption or removal of damaged cells), and (*c*) at the same time possessing a stability against oxygen and other reactive constituents of the intracellular environment.

CHAPTER VIII

Theories of the mechanism of cellular aging

WE HAVE OUTLINED in detail various possible sources of organismic aging and death. Although it is evident that certain changes occurring during senescence are due to the aging of extracellular structures and of cellular connective tissue elements, there appears to be little doubt that a fundamental site of age changes lies within the specialized cells making up the parenchyma or working parts of various specialized tissues. What are the chief sources of these changes in parenchmal cells?

We shall here consider three general groups of theories of cellular aging. (1) The first group has to do with the innate instability of certain cellular structures due to: (*a*) thermal accidents to functioning organelles and enzymes, (*b*) the instability of the coding and read-out machinery, and (*c*) the failure of steady state maintenance. (2) The second group of theories, so-called developmental theories of aging, have their roots in a possible failure implicit in the mechanisms of embryonic tissue and cellular development and include such topics as differentiation, size limitation, adaptation of the parenchyma to vascular supply, and cellular suicide. (*3*) The third group of theories is based on intercellular relationships and dependencies, particularly the possible immunological competition between cells, competition for substrates, intercellular toxicity, and the digestion of one cell type by another. Within this category is a subgroup which has to do with the regulatory interdependences and failures, particularly those relating to hormone effects and changes in the sensitivity of endocrine target organs.

A. DENATURATION AND THE ORIGIN OF STRUCTURAL INSTABILITY IN CELLS

A living cell, like any other portion of nature, when exposed to fluctuating energetic and chemical environment, will be subjected to various disruptive events. These disruptions may range from the subtlest accumulations of foreign substances, or alterations of submicroscopic membranes and lamellae, to the grossest alterations of whole organ systems. The only structures which will not be altered by the passage of time are those that are already in the lowest possible energy state and even these may, of course, be raised to a structurally altered, higher energy level from which they may not escape for some time.

In an effort to evaluate, in a suitable laboratory animal, the contribution which such changes as denaturation make to the aging process, we have studied the effect of exposing *Drosophila* to a short thermal shock (*98*).

Sinex (*208*) has calculated the effect of body temperature on the rate of collagen aging using the data of Wier on the shrinkage of kangaroo tail tendon. Extrapolating on the basis of a heat of activation of 141 kcal. and an entropy of activation of 349 cal./mole degree, Sinex obtained the values

TABLE XXIII

HALF-TIME FOR KANGAROO TAIL TENDON COLLAGEN SHRINKAGE VERSUS TEMPERATURE

Temperature (°C.)	Half-time
63	4.32 minutes
58	1.79 hours
53	1.82 days
48	3.58 months
43	5.77 years
38	215 years

given in Table XXIII. Sinex has pointed out that extrapolation to the lower temperatures may not be valid; certainly the shrinkage rate becomes too slow to measure in the laboratory in this range.

Cellular structures of potential importance in aging processes cannot be those which are readily destroyed by thermal accidents at "normal" temperatures, for any vital structure that is damaged by a few days' exposure to body temperature will obviously have to be replaced on a regular schedule if the organism is to exist for a period of years or decades. Similarly, structures of extreme stability, i.e., those with half-lives under intracellular conditions of several thousands of years, are similarly not of concern. *The structures which are important in aging are those whose natural lifetimes are of the order of the natural lifetime of the animal in question, for they will then not be ephemeral enough to force the evolution of a replacement mechanism and schedule, but they may on the other hand, be fragile enough to contribute to the debilities of age.*

One such factor, it has been conjectured, is the intracellular DNA, although evidence of a continuing function of all the DNA in the nucleus of the differentiated mammalian cell, particularly of the fixed postmitotics, is not conclusive. Nevertheless, according to Sinex, if one takes the stability of transforming factor DNA as an index of the stability of nuclear DNA of mammals, we should conclude that DNA is not sufficiently unstable to thermal insults to account for the normal lifespan. It may be that special, or as yet unknown, conditions within the nuclei of cells decrease the stability of genes below that observed in model systems, or that the fraction of damage required to kill a cell is minuscule.

Another intracellular locus of possible interest as a site of denaturative aging is the mitochondrion whose turnover has recently been studied by Fletcher and Sanadi (personal communication). Since they have observed a turnover time of less than 2 weeks for three different constituents of mitochondria (iron, protein sulfur, and lipid carbon), the mitochondria are not a likely locus of age changes. It is of course possible that the frequency of errors in mitochondria newly synthesized by old animals is higher than that occurring in young ones.

In addition to thermal accidents, another source of disruption that might not be so readily counterbalanced by turnover within living systems is the reaction between cell structures and labile, reactive intermediates of metabolism. Potentially important are the reactive intermediates in the reduction of molecular oxygen, such as $\cdot OH$ radicals and $HO_2\cdot$ radicals in particular. Many of the harmful effects of ionizing radiation are believed to be due to the indirect effect through the production of these highly reactive radicals (*13*). These intermediates, whether produced by radiation or metabolism, are, by virtue of their strong electron-attracting tendencies, capable of reacting with other cell constituents, particularly unsaturated fatty acids, and of extracting hydrogen from them. The organic radicals thus secondarily produced are, in turn, highly reactive to ambient molecular oxygen so that a chain reaction can be initiated. It may well be that hydrogen peroxide-destroying enzymes, such as catalase, and free radical trapping intermediates, such as vitamin E, are less significant in their short-term effects on cellular metabolism than they are as stabilizers of cellular structures against the onslaught of radicals (*327*).

B. GENETIC INSTABILITY AS A SOURCE OF AGING

Much has been written and even more has been said regarding the possibility that the instability of genetic structures is somehow responsible for the aging process. This hypothesis has one transcendent attractiveness, namely, that, if true, it could furnish a unifying view of the process which would be both aesthetically satisfying and possibly furnish a rational basis for control of the process.

The test of this theory in its most general form is not nearly as difficult as the evaluation of a number of other theories of aging. Such a test consists of determining whether conditions which result in an increased rate of mutation similarly cause an increase in the rate of aging. Thus, if gene mutations or chromosomal mutations of somatic cells are the source of aging, then the exposure of experimental animals to mutagenic agents, such as X-rays or chemical mutagens, should increase the rate of aging in direct proportion to the extent to which the natural mutation rate is accelerated. The difficulties inherent in making the appropriate measurements are that we have no direct means, at present, of measuring the rate of mutation of somatic cells, particularly of the fixed postmitatic cells, and that objective criteria of aging are neither refined nor generally accepted.

Genetic studies on dividing cell lines or of tissue culture cells in explant, such as have been recently suggested as a reasonable area for inquiry on aging processes by Puck (*328*), possess the inherent difficulty that the studied system, although subject to certain refined quantitative measurements, no longer has any obvious relationship to the sites of interest within the aging metazoan organism.

The crucial lack in evaluating such experiments is the absence of a means of measuring somatic mutation rates in nondividing cells. One is thus experimentally thrown back upon the mutation rate in dividing cell lines or even in the germ lines, since the background mutation rate in the germ line can be reasonably estimated as can the effects of environmental factors on mutation rate. In effect, the individual arising from an egg or a sperm is used as an amplifier of the initial genetic mutational event. But there is, unfortunately, no assurance either that the sensitivity of nondividing cells to radiation is similar to that of the germ line or that the "spontaneous" mutation rate frequencies in the two types of tissues are comparable.

With these qualifications firmly in mind, there are four lines of evidence bearing on this theory which will be here discussed.

As pointed out by Failla (*16*), "If radiation merely accelerates the normal aging process, we can calculate the dose required to double the normal rate of aging and this dose should also double the mutation rate. The calculated age-doubling dose is 12.8 r per day in a certain mouse colony. However, the doubling dose for germ line mutation is about 0.5 r per day. Since these two numbers should, by the present theory, be identical, we must conclude that the theory is in error and that another mechanism is here involved." In the following passage, Failla (*16*) points out

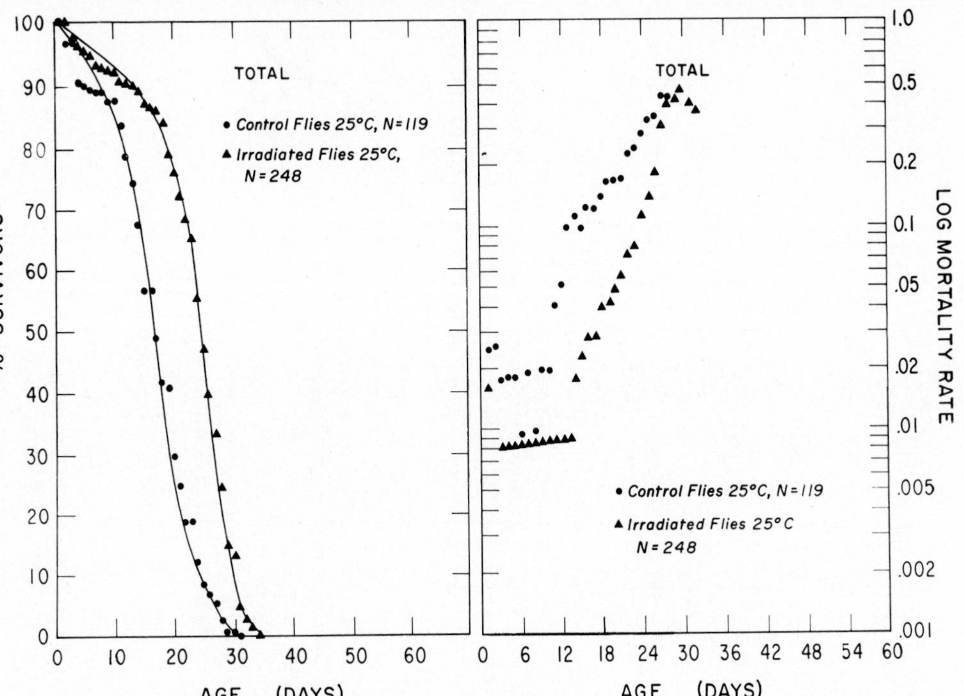

FIG. 51. *Increase of longevity in irradiated* Drosophila *over their controls (Strehler, unpublished). Dosage: 4300 röntgens.*

that the discrepancy mentioned above does not necessarily demolish his somatic mutation theory: "In Lorenz's experiments, the chronic exposure of the mice began when they were about two months old. Therefore, somatic mutations produced by radiation began to accumulate at this age, whereas spontaneous somatic mutations accumulated in all animals from conception on. It is possible that the relative positions of the Gompertz [curves for irradiated and control mice] would have been different had the chronic exposure started at conception. Results of such an experiment would provide a better basis for the calculation of the equivalent daily dose for the control curve. A different result should be expected in view of the probable higher sensitivity of the body cells during fetal life and the longer time during which the effect of radiation could exert its full influence."

The second line of evidence against a simple mutational theory of aging applicable to all animal species that age are some recent experiments conducted in our laboratory on the effects of X-radiation exposure of *Drosophila melanogaster* and of *Campanularia flexuosa* on their further life expectancy. *Drosophila,* exposed to about 4500 röntgens of ionizing radiation, actually lived longer than their controls. Sacher has also obtained similar results with *Drosophila.* This increased longevity of irradiated animals may be due to an unknown second effect of radiation that acts in opposition to the postulated detrimental effect. Sacher has suggested this explanation as a source of the decreased mortality observed in mammals exposed to low dosages of ionizing radiation. At higher dosages the detrimental life-shortening effects become apparent, but at low dosages the other factor predominates. The results obtained with *Drosophila* are shown in Fig. 51. Similar results (see Fig. 52) showing a more than 100% increase in the longevity of *Campanularia* hydranths after as much as 100,000 röntgens of X-rays are shown for comparison. The first and obvious interpretation of these experiments is that the predominant source of aging with time cannot be the accumulation of somatic mutations.

A third line of evidence is the fact that as expressed by

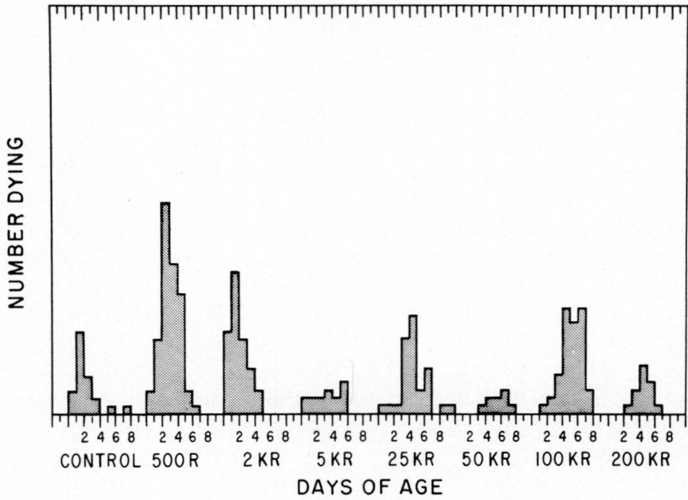

FIG. 52. *The effect of X-radiation dosage on longevity of* Campanularia *hydranths. The highest number of individuals dying per day is 25 (from Strehler, unpublished).*

longevity the females of practically all species that have been studied have greater vigor than the males. Whether the sex-determining mechanism involves a pair of identical sex chromosomes for the male or the female phenotype does not seem to affect longevity. Since, if somatic mutation were the cause of senescence, mutations within the sex chromosome would tend to lower longevity in the heterogametic sex, the absence of such a correlation is an argument against the hypothesis. Geiser (*329*) had reported in 1925 a difference in longevity of male and female Japanese turtle doves. The average longevity of the male was 42 months whereas the female's was only 19 months. However, the spread of values he reported was so extreme that it is not possible to accept these data without question. McArthur and Bailey (*330*), on the other hand, have studied a number of abraxis type species with respect to sex differences in mortality. They observed a consistently higher mortality rate in the male chicken. Similarly, by the end of the 6-month period, 70% of male pheasants had died, as compared to only 50% of the females. Also, among the Lepidoptera, the females outlived the males considerably except for one small group. Landauer and Landauer (*331*) studied chick mortality and sex ratios in the domestic fowl; their findings are shown in Table XXIV. Thus, if females actually do age

TABLE XXIV

RELATIVE MORTALITY OF MALE AND FEMALE CHICKENS

	Mortality during		
	First week	Second to fourth week	Fifth to eighth week
Crossbred chickens (percentage of males of those dying)	53.8	52.9	52.4
Leghorns (percentage of males of those dying)	52.8	51.6	54.6

more rapidly in the cases where the female is heterogametic, there must, in addition, be other factors which impart a greater vigor to the female, moreover these factors must completely compensate for the disadvantage postulated above.

Another and independent line of evidence that senescence is not caused by the accumulation of recessive mutations is furnished by the recent studies of Clark and Rubin (*79*) who has examined the natural longevity and effects of X-radiation on the length of life of a species of *Habrobracon*. This species produces both haploid and diploid males as well as diploid females. His results indicate (*a*) that unirradiated males have essentially identical lifespans whether they are haploid or diploid. On the other hand, the haploid males are much more sensitive to ionizing radiation than are the diploid males; this is shown in Fig. 53.

Clark concludes, "These data show that the life span in *Habrobracon* is not related to the number of sets of chromosomes and suggests that the aging process is not due to the occurrence and accumulation of somatic mutations. Were aging due to somatic mutation one would expect that hap-

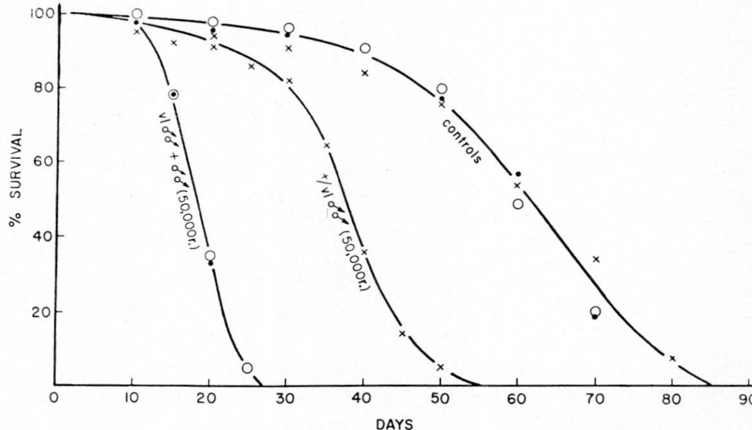

FIG. 53. *The effect of ploidy on survival of control and irradiated* Habrobracon. *X: diploid males;* ● *and* ○: *haploid males (from Clark and Rubin, ref.* 79).

loid males would have a much shorter lifespan than diploid males and that diploid males and diploid females would be similar in lifespan." And also, "The fact that the life span of diploid males is decreased less by X-rays than haploid males indicates that a genetic type injury is involved as the primary event. The equivalent decrease for diploid males and diploid females shows that the radiation sensitivity is modified more by ploidy than by sex. Thus, in the modification or radiation sensitivity, the chromosome number is more important than the sex of the organism. It seems also that the decreased life span from ionizing radiation is not comparable to the normal aging process. Thus, perhaps one should not equate radiation-induced decrease in life span with radiation-induced aging."

Clark also maintains that these results demonstrate the continued function of genes in nondividing cells. "The greater resistance of the diploids over the haploids indicates that through gene mutation or chromosome breakage the nondividing somatic cells lose some of their ability to function normally. There is no matter here of faulty chromosome allocation and subsequent loss of genic material in daughter cells but rather the dysfunction of the genic material within cells that have already become specialized. This is a further indication that the genes function in non-dividing cells and that gene action occurs in adults. It certainly seems probable that genes control biochemical synthesis not only during embryogenesis but also in the maintenance of the adult. Gene-controlled synthesis continues throughout life."

In summary, then, a number of different lines of evidence make it highly improbable that the aging process is generally a consequence of the accumulation of somatic mutations or even of chromosomal aberrations with age. That such changes do occur inevitably, because there is no means by which an absolute stability of genetic structures could be guaranteed, is obvious. However, the degree of instability is probably not a significant factor in determining the longevity of evolved species in their normal habitats. Rather, the source of cellular and organismic instability must lie in other types of disequilibria or disruptive events. Possibly the effect of a gene instability great enough to make a significant contribution to the debility of old age would also so decrease the viability of young adults that a strong selection against this kind of aging has been operative.

C. AGING AND THE PROBLEM OF STEADY-STATE MAINTENANCE

A third source of instability of cellular structure lies in factors which permit a departure from "optimum steady-state conditions." Presumably there is for each cell type of the organism an optimum concentration of its various constituent parts (enzymes, structural proteins, etc.) which results in cells, tissues, and organisms optimally adapted to the demands placed upon them by a fluctuating energetic environment.

Closely related to the above are two crucial problems that all metazoa face. These are: first, how are the various synthetic capacities represented by the genome ultimately expressed differentially in different cell types, thus leading to the maturation and development of the adult, and second, once the differentiated state has been produced, how is its stability ensured over a sufficiently long period of time for the effective propagation of the race?

The maintenance of the constancy of cellular chemical constitution can be imagined to occur through at least two quite different mechanisms. Conceptually, the simpler of the alternative schemes is a continual monitoring process in which the chemical constitution of a cell is compared with a certain fraction of the genome or of some alternative molecular representation of the genome. Implicit in this model are a number of gross complexities and subsidiary problems. First, by what mechanism is it possible to select that particular portion of the genome with which to compare the constituents of a given cell type? Second, what means are available for making the comparison, i.e., what is the nature of the postulated monitoring system? How does the corrective machinery operate when the monitor discovers a conflict between the selected pattern and the actual constitution of a cell? These are problems of design, monitoring, and control of considerable difficulty.

The alternate scheme is equally unsatisfying. It may be stated essentially as follows: Cells may occupy a number of discrete pseudo-steady-state conditions corresponding to the number of different cell types that are characteristic of a species. Thus, once developed, a muscle cell will remain a muscle cell; a nerve, a nerve, etc. Any departure from a given, stable, steady-state configuration will hypothetically set in motion a series of corrective reactions which tend to return the system to its original stable state. Of course, to outline verbally such a possibility is not to propose a mechanism but it is a necessary feature of this hypothesis that a vast series of quite automatically operating feedback systems maintaining cell constitution have been evolved.

Whichever of these two alternatives or combination thereof eventually proves to be the case, it is clear that error or gradual departure from the original steady state is an ever-present possibility. Thus, in the former case, if the pattern to which the cell contents is compared were somehow disrupted due to thermal or radiation or chemical accidents, the system would presumably deteriorate; likewise, if the read-out machinery, the monitoring machinery, or the correction machinery developed flaws, the system would no longer remain in its stable condition.

The alternative mechanism involving a series of quasi-stable steady-states is also subject to error or slow drift. Thus, even if the machinery were operating with 100% efficiency, it is possible that accidental damage or unprogrammed changes (i.e., changes beyond the genetic control) would change the conditions intracellularly in such a manner as to drive the system further and further away from its normal steady-state condition. Such disturbing influences might well be the result of rare chemical reactions within the cell resulting in the accumulation of inhibitory or toxic substances or substances which act to produce a disequilibrium or a malfunction of the monitor.

The external environment of the cell may be of central importance in producing such disturbances. Considerable effort might profitably be expended on the studies of the mechanisms controlling the stability of intracellular content. Studies on the formation of adaptive enzymes and of hormonal effects make it clear that environmental factors are of importance. We cannot, however, conclude from the presence of a few extracellular factors capable of producing such changes, that the totality or even a significant portion of intracellular homeostasis is under the control of such idealized model organismic mechanisms.

The maintenance of steady state within any system, including a cell, means that the relative proportions of the various constituents do not change beyond the limits of random fluctuation. Each steady state is thus a balance between the rates of synthesis and destruction of intracellular components. If equal rates of synthesis and of destruction of each component existed, there would be no change in the gross constitution although changes in arrangement might still supervene.

Some of the early chemical theories of aging, such as that which Loeb and Northrup based upon their own experiments on temperature and aging, consisted of the assumption that a given amount of vital substance was available to an organism at the time of fertilization of the egg and that the process of aging consisted in using up this material. The rate-of-living hypothesis of Pearl is a restatement of this theory in somewhat more biological terms but is essentially identical to the Loeb and Northrup theory. Such theories assume that the rate of synthesis of certain components is essentially zero after a certain stage of life and that as these components are utilized, the system will depart from a steady-state condition. The model certainly has validity for those insects that have no mouth parts in the adult form. Their life span is effectively limited by the stores of food material which they accumulated during their larval period. The operation of such a mechanism in higher vertebrates does not appear to be too likely.

The exact antithesis of the above hypothesis is the possibility of loss of steady state due to the accumulation of substances of an inhibitory or noxious nature. The most likely candidates for such a role are various insoluble products, both organic and inorganic, which occur in or are produced by living systems.

Among the substances which have been suggested from time to time as factors in this category is deuterium, which, because of its somewhat lower reactivity, might contribute to an altered steady state. We have attempted to evaluate this factor in the longevity of *Drosophila* by growing the animals throughout life on media containing respectively 20 and 40% heavy water. There was a significant decrease in the longevity, as shown in Fig. 8, even at 20% heavy water. However, the amount of deuterium incorporated into essential structures should so far exceed under these experimental circumstances any possible accumulation occurring under normal conditions that the decrease in viability of the animals reared on heavy water is insignificant by comparison to what should be expected. Therefore, this hypothesis of aging through the accumulation of inhibitory concentrations of heavy water in vital sites can probably be dismissed.

Much has been written concerning the accumulation during aging of calcium within cells and the connective tissue elements making up many structures. Lansing and associates (*301*) have particularly contributed to our information on this point and have shown that the calcium content of the cortex of cells does tend to increase with age, at least in certain cases. Calcium deposition in the walls of the blood vessels is a frequent concomitant of the aging process but it would be highly uncritical to assume that this is a cause of aging, or even an essential part of the process rather than a reflection of a specific pathology. The fact of the matter is that one cannot assess at present the importance or lack thereof of the accumulation of calcium salts within tissues as a function of age.

In the same category are the many theories of autointoxication as a cause of aging. Metchinkoff and his followers maintained that the accumulation of toxic substances as a result of intestinal putrefactive processes were the real cause of aging and recommended various exotic surgical or dietary excursions to remedy the difficulty. DeRopp's recent book (*2*) ironically summarizes Metchnikoff's opinion: "Civilization has made the colon superfluous. Worse than superfluous, said Metchnikoff. Positively dangerous. This great sac of gut is aswarm with bacteria, an absolute heaven for microorganisms, warm, wet and full of the by-products of digestion. What a stinking brew it contains, especially in man! And how can one expect the nerve cells, with their delicate constitutions, to remain in good shape while such a foul mess of poison is being cooked by the putrefactive organisms in the large intestine, absorbed by the blood, and distributed to every corner of the body?

"A shocking state of affairs! But what is the remedy? One remedy would be to remove the offending gut. Metchnikoff was quite prepared to advocate this heroic measure. He dug up several surgical cases in which the large intestine had been removed for one reason or another, and waxed lyrical on how well these patients managed without the wretched thing."

Finally, among the inhibitory substances are the postulated remains of molecular accidents such as denatured proteins or the insoluble residues of intracellular tanning processes. Ruszicka and Bjorksten (*332, 333*) have suggested the importance of intracellular cross-linking between proteins as a source of aging. Even more suggestive is the fact that unsaturated fats are particularly liable to cross-reaction and linkage, a fact that makes them extremely useful in the paint and varnish industry but which may be highly detrimental to biological systems over the long run. The accumulation of substances containing groups that are too large or too polar to dissolve readily in the lipid phase and too hydrophobic to dissolve in the aqueous phase may pose a real problem for the cellular mechanisms maintaining cell constancy. The gradual accumulation of a layer of varnish over various intracellular structures is an unpleasant prospect. The observation that the rate of accumulation of cardiac lipofuscin is higher in the Japanese, who incidentally consume a diet richer in unsaturated fats, is suggestive.

D. FAILURE OF CELLS DUE TO CONSEQUENCES OF EMBRYONIC DEVELOPMENT

The inevitability of senescence is one of the possibilities that has fascinated both philosophers and scientists in the field of aging. This concept has been stated and restated many times in such clichés as "We begin to age from the time that the egg is fertilized," or "Senescence is the price we pay for our multicellular organization," or "Aging is an inevitable consequence of development." These statements generally have a theological quality in that they assume a kind of bargaining process in which the privilege of being a higher form of life must be paid for by a corresponding defect in some other phase of life. Its origin may be in the religious mythology of the West, particularly in the story of the fall of Adam and Eve in the garden of Eden. Death and pain were the price paid for disobedience of "Nature's law" in their case; the concept is readily transferred into the thinking of scientists in our culture even though such generalizations are clearly of the most nonscientific nature.

It is, of course, not only possible that development sets the stage for an eventual decline but that there is something in the developmental process that obligates an organism to senesce. Minot (*293*) gave an early expression to this point of view which is interesting not only because of its vivid anthropomorphism but also because his concepts have dominated so many of the clichés relating embryology and senescence. "Death is not a universal accompaniment of life. In the lower organisms, death does not occur as a natural and necessary result of life. Death with them is purely the result of an accident, some external cause. Natural death is a thing which has been acquired in the process of evolution. Why should it have been acquired? You will, I think, readily answer this question by saying that it is due to differentiation, that when the cells acquire the additional faculties of passing beyond the simple stage to the more complicated organization, they lose something of their vitality, something of their power of growth, something of their possibilities of perpetuation; and as the organization in the process of evolution becomes higher and higher, this necessity for change becomes more and more imperative. But it involves the end. Differentiation leads up as its inevitable conclusion to death. Death is the price we are obliged to pay for our organization, for the differentiation which exists in us. Is it too high a price? To that organization we are indebted for the great array of faculties with which we are endowed. To it we are indebted for the means of appreciating the sort of world, the kind of universe, in which we are placed. To it we are indebted for all the conveniences of existence, by which we are able to carry on our physiological processes in a far better and more comfortable manner than can the lower forms of life. To it, we are indebted for the possibilities of those human relations which are among the most precious parts of our experience. And we are indebted to it also for the possibility of the higher spiritual emotions. All this is what we have bought at the price of death, but it does not seem to me too much for us to pay." Somewhat later Minot observes that "This is the scientific view of death. It leaves death with all its mystery, with all its sacredness; we are not in the least able at the present time to say what life is, still less perhaps to say what death is. You say of certain things they are alive, of certain other things they are dead; but what the differences may be, what is the essential to those two states scientists are utterly unable to tell us at the present time. It is a phenomenon with which we are so familiar that perhaps we do not think enough about it."

Minot's more objective views were recapitulated by him in the following manner: "We may say that we have established, if my arguments before you be correct, the following four laws of age. First, rejuvenation depends on the increase of the nuclei. Second, senescence depends upon the increase of the protoplasm, and on the differentiation of the cells. Third, the rate of growth depends on the degree of senescence. Fourth, senescence is at its maximum in the very young stages, and the rate of senescence diminishes with age. As the corollary from these, we have this: Natural death is the consequence of cellular differentiation."

The experimental evidence upon which this point of view was based was primarily that senescence was associated with a decreased growth rate. Minot studied the growth rate of various forms of organisms as they developed and discovered that their growth rate decreased as they matured. This decrease, he concluded, must be due to a senescence phenomenon. Minot also based his hypothesis on the Hertwigs' reports that there is a change in the nucleocytoplasmic ratio with age.

Pearl expressed a similar point of view. Although his writings never approached Minot's in their lack of objective detachment, he nevertheless also felt that senescence was a result of differentiation and consequently of the interdependence of different cell types.

Ebert has recently said *(334)*, "I do not believe there is significant evidence to support the generalization that aging is an extension of differentiation. There is a tendency to equate differentiation with aging, because, when viewed broadly, certain of the characteristics of the two processes are similar.

"For example, in many instances differentiation involves cell death: The development of a number of organs is, in part, effected through localized cell death or through the loss of synthetic capacity. But the fact that these major processes are similar, at least in bold outline, does not prove that the intrinsic processes are the same. I question whether we have found evidence leading us to equate these two phenomena."

And more recently, Konigsberg (*335*) has masterfully reviewed the evidence bearing on the problem of the relationship between development and aging in the following terms, "The categorical acceptance of an ontogenetic basis for senescence is so widely held that one is astonished by the scant evidence upon which this premise is constructed. Such statements as 'aging begins at conception' and 'aging is most rapid during embryogenesis' are such tantalizing paradoxes that even the very critically minded seem unable to reject them." Konigsberg observes, "This view can be traced to the speculations of a number of embryologists during the early years of this century and to the influence particularly of Charles Minot. Little of the specific substance of Minot's arguments can withstand a critical examination from the vantage point of the current status of experimental embryology. Nor would Minot's treatment of senescence primarily as a progressive diminution in growth potential be generally accepted by today's gerontologists. While it may be true that the rate of proliferation decelerates most rapidly during the earliest phases of development, other physiological parameters are initially at low levels, pass through maxima at different times during life, and subsequently decline. The evidence needed to evaluate Minot's suggestion is lacking not, to be sure, because it has eluded research but because it has not been searched for. Even the head and tail of a snake might appear to be different species if we could not see what was in between them. Certainly no definitive evidence of a causal relationship between differentiation and senescence is offered. However, these investigations were not pursued to test this relationship."

Konigsberg then raises three crucial questions that must obviously be answered before a sensible and objective judgment of the question can be made. These are: (*a*) Are the characteristics of senescent change compatible with developmental change? (*b*) What types of processes, other than developmental, could be operating to produce senescence? (*c*) What types of developmental events could preclude potential immortality? With respect to the first, Ebert recently has come to the conclusion that superficially, at least, senescence and development resemble each other in their temporal characteristics, the only distinction between them being the deleterious nature of senescence. Citing the differential cell death which participates in certain morphogenetic processes as an example, Ebert observed that the same process may at different times have both adaptive and deadaptive value. Konigsberg then points out that "The criterion of deleteriousness is useful in distinguishing between strictly developmental and the developmental-senescent changes (that may exist). It does not preclude a contribution by developmental processes to senescence."

With regard to the second question, Konigsberg points out that there are processes occurring in organisms that are not built into the genetic design of the system except by the wildest possible stretch of the imagination. "Somatic mutation, if indeed it does contribute significantly to senescence, could not be considered a developmental manifestation. It is not a consequence nor is it an extension of cellular differentiation, in view of the strong arguments against any role of gene mutation, in the classical sense in embryogenesis." Konigsberg also viewed the molecular aging of collagen as a nondevelopmental process if it can be reproduced as readily in pure solutions of the molecular species. These are consequences of the architecture of molecules and not a reflection of changes in the synthetic processes producing them.

Konigsberg then observes that all of the events which Strehler has classified as microaccidents are essentially nondevelopmental in nature. But he reserves his most telling comment for the third of these questions. "It is frequently suggested that differentiation entails restriction of potential cellular function, which it unquestionably does, and that this restriction is eventually responsible for senescence and death. A concrete example proposed by numerous theoreticians from Minot to the present is that differentiation curtails the proliferative capacity of the cell, senescence being a consequence of the post-mitotic condition.

"It is generally true that little, if any, mitotic activity is observed in differentiated tissues. Under tissue culture conditions and in regeneration, however, luxuriant proliferation is frequently obtained. The ambiguities of cell morphology in these experimental situations make it difficult to state in every case, that differentiated cells are participating in this renewed growth. From the well-documented evidence which is available, however, the generality of an irreversible loss of proliferative capacity of differentiated cells is open to question. As it relates to senescence, the problem may be rather why cell replacement does not repair the lesion in the senescent tissue.

"The restriction of proliferative activity may not itself be or produce primary senescent change. Instead, continued proliferation may permit the cell to escape from the deleterious effects of such a primary change. The conclusion has been drawn that senescence does not occur in proliferating cells and that rejuvenation is effected by the resumption of proliferation in wound healing and regeneration. Various interpretations of this conclusion are indeed possible. The most parsimonious would seem to be that cell proliferation dilutes out aged cytoplasm at a rate faster than aging occurs. That senescence occurs at all may indicate that a true steady-state cannot be maintained, that breakdown of cell constituents is never balanced quantitatively or qualitatively by resynthesis except when synthesis greatly exceeds breakdown.

"Although the relationship between differentiation and the loss of proliferative activity is problematical, the restrictive character of differentiation on the synthetic capacity of the cell is firmly grounded. One excellent example is the progressive restriction of immunologically detectable cardiac myosin to the actual heart-forming area during early embryogenesis. The interpretation most compatible with the experimental data is that the ability to synthesize myosin, although initially present, is lost in the non-heart-forming areas. If a similar process of differential loss is true also of proteins more crucial to cell maintenance, a more gradual and protracted loss could produce those alterations of morphology and function which we recognize as senescence.

"The converse of this possibility has also been formulated.

As a result of a continued increase in the acquisition of a specialized component, its concentration may pass through an optimum level to levels which may actually impair function. Minot used the example of continued ossification of the vertebral column. A plausible kinetic model of overdifferentiation has been discussed by Strehler. Unfortunately, the data needed to test this model are not available."

Finally, Konigsberg observes, "One may conclude that the characteristics of senescent change are in no way incompatible with developmental phenomena. Further, the extension of our knowledge of development which has occurred since Minot's day permits more detailed speculation. However, we must not lose sight of the fact that these are only speculations.

"In testing these speculations, it would be well to recognize the probability that several quite different processes may contribute to senescence. When the mechanisms of these several processes are better understood, it will become evident which features are common to all and which features are unique to each. At the present time, it would seem that there was more to be gained by treating each parameter of senescence individually rather than groping blindly several levels of complexity lower than the phenomena for a universal aging process."

In summary, then, recent opinion maintains that there is no demonstrable causal relationship between development and senescence except for the obvious fact that the development of an ordered structure is a necessary prerequisite to its disintegration. The progressive decrease in growth rate during the maturation of animals of finite body size may or may not be a cause of the aging process. It is certainly feasible for a great many, if not all, subcellular structures to be replaced on a regular schedule without interfering seriously with the function of the cells.

On the other hand, differentiation, depending on the mechanism of its achievement and upon the factors which stabilize a differentiated cell, may indeed give rise to cells which go through an optimum with respect to their chemical constituents. The model of differentiation alluded to by Konigsberg was recently presented in a discussion of various dynamic theories of aging (*11*). The essence of the theory is that the steady-state condition in a fully differentiated cell may be beyond the viable limit. Thus, a cell may differentiate rapidly (in terms of the total life span of the organism) toward a value which is near the optimum and then ultimately approach a much less viable condition as differentiation slowly continues. This possibility is illustrated in Fig. 54 and the derivation of the equation is given in reference *11*.

One of the objections to such theories of aging is the extremely long time required for the results of such processes to express themselves. A mammalian cell is, after all, a rather small object and it is difficult to imagine that a period of 70 to 90 years should elapse before steady state is achieved within such a small compartment. The alternative would, of course, be an approach to a stable-limiting condition based on some supracellular control system such as hormonal control of growth, vascular supply, etc. *It is this very slowness of the senescence process in long-lived mammals that casts serious doubt, in my opinion, on any theory of senescence which uses the intrinsic-determinant properties of cells as a direct cause of senescent change.*

It may well be, as Konigsberg has pointed out, that the continuation of growth permits a dilution of senescent changes. The thesis that growth cessation per se causes senescence is not nearly so defensible. If there is a causal relationship between the two phenomena one of the means by which the limitation of an organism's size might lead to eventual senescence is the adaptation of the numbers of functioning parenchymal cells to the vascular supply. A simple hypothesis is that during maturation the parenchymal cells continue to grow and fill in the space supplied by the capillary bed until the rate of diffusion of some one or more limiting nutrients or the rate of removal of inhibitory products prevents further growth. If, as a result of aging, injury, or failure of replacement mechanisms, the impermeability or inadequacy of the capillary network became more pronounced and if there were not a compensatory stimulus to promote its proliferation so as to meet a change in demand, the parenchymal cells might well deteriorate to

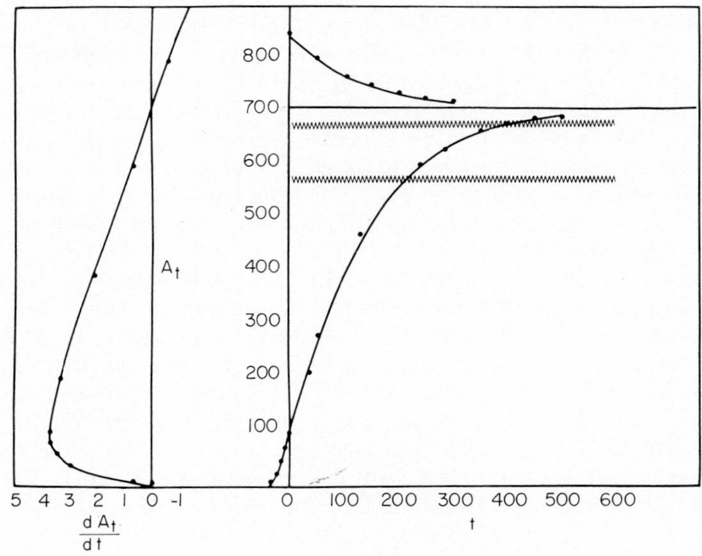

FIG. 54

a lower level of functional capacity. Ultimately, in order to evaluate this specific proposition we need to understand the mechanism by which capillary proliferation is controlled and the factors which regulate proliferation of parenchymal cells and their adaptation to the locus they inhabit.

Another source of cellular instability lies in the presence of lytic enzymes such as are contained in the lysosomes. Such enzymes, capable of destroying intracellular components, would have a survival value for an organism possessing them in at least two circumstances. The first of these is the eventuality that a cell or tissue is damaged. As a preliminary to an effective repair process, a means of disposing of the damaged or dead cells is an obvious necessity. An alternative possibility is phagocytosis by other cell types evolutionally selected for such emergency function. But the rapid and effective removal of dead cells can perhaps best be achieved by an intrinsic self-digesting system located in each cell.

A second function in which autolytic enzymes might be

of advantage to an organism whose cells possess them is as part of a continuous replacement regimen at the subcellular level. The importance of destructive reactions in any steady-state system is only apparent after cursory inspection. No steady state is feasible in a cell carrying on any synthetic activities whatsoever unless the rate of destruction or loss of the specialized products exactly balances their rates of synthesis. Thus we reach the odd paradox that organisms made up of nonreplenishing cells will probably ultimately senesce; likewise, cells incapable of replacing and replenishing all of their constituent parts can certainly not last indefinitely. It may well be the very capacity of cells to repair themselves

---

FIG. 54. *Balance of synthesis of component* A *in a specialized cell versus time, assuming Michaelis-Menton synthetic rates, first-order destructive reactions, and second-order autocatalytic synthetic reactions. On the left is illustrated the net rate of synthesis of* A *as the total concentration of* A(A_t) *varies. On the right is illustrated* A_t *versus time as obtained by graphical integration of* A_t *synthesis. The jagged lines enclose the hypothetical "viable" range of concentration of* A_t *in the differentiating system. The asymptote approached by* A_t *is the solid horizontal line, whereas the upper descending curve shows the hypothetical approach to steady state of a highly overdifferentiated system. The lowering of the asymptote to a lower value commensurate with continued function (a value between jagged lines) would postpone the attainment of the optimally differentiated state. Therefore, one would expect a correlation between duration of the prereproductive period and total life span. By increasing the rate of synthesis and destruction it would be possible to design a system capable of continued existence and maturing early, but such a system would be wasteful of raw materials and possibly possess other undesirable features that might mitigate against its evolutionary persistence. The equation describing the rate of change of* A_t *with time is:*

$$\frac{d[A_t]}{dt} = \frac{k_s([C_t]-[A_t])\left[[A_t]+\frac{K}{2}-K\left(\frac{[A_t]}{K}+\frac{1}{4}\right)^{\frac{1}{2}}\right]}{K_s+\left[[A_t]+\frac{K}{2}-K\left(\frac{[A_t]}{K}+\frac{1}{4}\right)^{\frac{1}{2}}\right]} - k_d[A_t]$$

where C_t *is total concentration of all components,* A_t *is total concentration of* A, E_t *is the concentration of synthetic system,* K_s *is the dissociation constant of the* Aa *synthesizing reaction,* R_s *is rate of synthesis of* A *by* E, R_d *is rate constant for destruction of* A_t *and* C_t, K *is dissociation constant of the synthetic template* Aa (K = [A][a]/[Aa]) *and* R_s *is a rate constant for synthesis of all components of system by* E *(see reference* 11 *for derivation of equation* $E_t = C_t - A_t$).

that has permitted their persistence over long periods of time. Ironically this persistence may ultimately lead to the senescence of the organism as a whole unless all cellular components are replaced regularly. Organisms may die because they possess nonreplenishing cell types. Long-lived nonreplenishing cell types are themselves made possible by virtue of their efficient mechanisms for self-repair and subcellular replenishment. However paradoxically, since there may be no means of repairing parts of the repair machinery, organismic death may well be an indirect result of the evolution of imperfect, but generally adequate, repair processes at the cellular level.

E. INTERCELLULAR RELATIONSHIPS AND DEPENDENCIES

The evolution of metazoa necessitates the subjugation of the individual cell to the organism. Only through the collaborative venture which the multicellular organisms represent was it possible for these genetic lines to achieve the dominance they presently enjoy. Such evolutionary pathways as metazoa represent carry with them a concurrent danger of loss of coordinated cellular function. Two main types of failure are readily visualized. These are the decreasing adequacy or outright failure of either neuronal or hormonal regulatory systems or the responsivity of the target organs. Certain hormonal dysfunctions may well be due to a depletion of the capacity of the endocrine system (e.g., pituitary) to supply sufficient levels of hormone to maintain a dependent tissue or endocrine system. Failure may also be due to a decrease in the capacity of the receptor system to respond to the ordinary level of hormone. This appears to be the case in several of the pituitary-steroid axes where the monitoring system of the pituitary detects the output of steroid hormones and responds by an increased or decreased output of the appropriate pituitary trophic hormones. For a while, as the responsivity of the steroid-producing system decreases, the compensatory change in the pituitary is apparently sufficient to counterbalance the decreased sensitivity of the target organ. But ultimately the system fails. The reader is referred to the monograph by Engel and Pincus on hormones in the aging process for the detailed treatment which the subject deserves (*336*).

The multicellular state may be unstable not only because of the failure of the communication systems to transmit adequate signals to provide for coordination but because the ancestors of organisms are single cells whose own evolutionary history reflects among other things the competition for space, energy, and substance. Relics of this competitive ancestry might well become dominant as the coordinative forces, whatever they may be, gradually lose control.

In addition to processes applicable to all cells of a given type, there may be individual changes in cellular function and adaptation to a given milieu which can express themselves as disruptive effects. One such example of competition between cells may well be the development of tumors that occur with increasing frequency during aging (see Fig. 23). Tumors are either normal cells which have somehow escaped the growth restraints of the tissue environment as a result of some presently undefined change in the tissue, or they are abnormal cells which are unresponsive to those factors that normally adjust the rate of cell division to the steady-state replacement level. In order to ascertain which of these two alternatives is the dominant feature in a given type of tumor, it would be necessary to know what factors normally restrain growth and division of individual cell types.

Possibly related to the question of growth limitation is the concept of a nutritional competition among cells for the ambient substrate supply. It is attractive to visualize the control of growth and size as a result of the depletion of one or more diffusible nutrients to a level where a steady-state balance between growth and nutrition or simply maintenance and growth is reached. If a substance, X, necessary both for cell division and cell maintenance, is supplied to a given compartment containing cells capable of division at a rate, a, then presumably the cells within this compartment will continue to increase in number until their rate of utilization of the limiting nutrient equals its rate of supply. Such a situation could be expected to yield a reasonably steady condition if the maintenance function had a high priority on substrate utilization, particularly under limiting conditions. One of the unfortunate features of a system such as that outlined above is that the cells within the compartment would clearly be adversely affected if the supply of nutrients were for any reason to drop below the maintenance-demand level. In such an instance the only alternative left to the cells making up the tissue is either a decrease in intracellular volume until supply once again matches demand or a loss of cells until the same end is reached.

A completely unstable situation might arise if an aberrant cell arose in a tissue locus whose demand for the limiting nutrient was lower than that of the normal tissue. Such a cell might arise because through mutation it had developed a capacity to produce the nutrient at some level and was thus independent of the external substrate supply. It could also produce an unstable situation if it utilized the ambient level of substrate more efficiently for growth or if its maintenance and repair functions were less demanding, perhaps because of a lower rate of breakdown of cell constituents. Such a cell type would gradually take over the supply of nutrients from the parenchymal cells in its vicinity and crowd them out. Fibroblasts, which appear to be more resistant to unfavorable environmental conditions than many other cell types, since they persist in tissue culture under conditions where nearly all highly differentiated cell types fail, may be an appropriate example. And such a proliferation of fibroblasts and the deposition of their products may be one of the specific mechanisms underlying the collagen accumulation that takes place during aging. A second, more striking example is the tumor cell with its frequent catastrophic effects not only on the tissue locus that it primarily invades but upon the life of the organism as a whole.

Competition between cells may involve much more than competition for substrates. It may even involve such bizarre processes as cellular cannibalism. In such cases one cell type may actually engulf or digest another cell type. The phagocytosis of one cell type by another has been observed in biological systems, although the impression is usually given that only cells which have been somehow damaged by infection, malnutrition, or atrophy are the victims of such cellular cannibalism or phagocytosis. Andrew has described cases in which neurons are attacked by phagocytic satellite cells in the brains of old animals. Whether these digestive processes are a cause of or prelude to cell death or whether they are responses to the prior occurrence of cell death or injury is not clear although the latter possibility seems the more probable.

The final type of intercellular competition to be discussed here is that devolving from the mechanisms of immunological reactions. There is, as yet, no unambiguous evidence even of the occurrence of such intercellular warfare as a part of the aging process. However, there is a growing consensus that certain diseases such as lupus and a number of other poorly understood degenerative diseases may have as a common factor cross-reactions between antibodies produced by one cell and antigens present in another differentiated cell type.

The potentiality for such a cross-reaction is apparent from the now classical studies of the phenomenon of immune tolerance. In particular, the studies by Medawar and his associates (*337, 338*) have shown that an organism may develop immune tolerance for a given foreign cell or substance if it is exposed to this foreign material prior to a certain critical period in its development; this phenomenon is called immune tolerance. If, during the life of an animal, the immunochemical memory should develop inaccuracies, the animal might well develop immunological sensitivities to certain of his own proteins or other constituents. The development of sensitivity to one's own tissues might, in this case, be considered a sensitivity of the first type, i.e., one in which the memory mechanism, whatever it is, is inaccurate.

A second type is also possible in which certain transformations taking place over a long period of time in major constituents of a number of different cell types might give rise to antigens for which the animal had not developed a tolerance and which therefore would serve as autoimmune inducers. A third type might involve mutant cell lines containing novel antigens. Whether or not mechanisms of this type contribute to aging could better be judged if we possessed a knowledge of the mechanism underlying immune tolerance. One specific test of the theory would consist of the assay of an animal's tissues for immunologically active substances which were absent in the same animal's tissues when it was young.

These comments on the intercellular reactions potentially leading to the decline and fall of metazoa furnish one framework for future systematic and intensive investigations, although, in almost every instance, we lack those critical facts upon which a realistic evaluation of the premises of the specific postulates could be based.

CHAPTER IX

The evolution of cellular aging

THROUGHOUT THIS DISCUSSION we have related individual facts and hypotheses to the general framework of metazoan evolution and the peculiar problems faced by multicellular organisms. Ultimately, the processes of aging must be understood in the case of each individual species as an evolutionary manifestation either in a positive sense or in a negative sense.

Three contrasting possibilities regarding the evolution of senescence will be considered; The first is that the decline of individual organisms is a process which has a definite and positive survival value for the species; the second states that senescence is merely a by-product of the evolution of other characteristics which better adapt organisms to their normal environments; the third possibility is that senescence is neither a positively selected characteristic nor a by-product of some advantageous evolutionary adaptation but rather that the selection pressure against senescence is so weak by comparison with the other pressures operating to mold the outlines of evolution that it (senescence) has, in effect, been ignored.

These three points of view have been elegantly expressed by others and we shall therefore simply quote here the relevant points of view.

Weismann in his "Essays Upon Heredity and Kindred Biological Problems," in 1891, presented the argument for a positive selective advantage of a finite life span (*20*). "From this follows, on one hand, the necessity of reproduction and, on the other, the utility of death. Worn-out individuals are not only valueless to the species, but they are even harmful, for they take the place of those which are sound. Hence by the operation of natural selection, the life of our hypothetically immortal individual would be shortened by the amount which he was useless to the species. It would be reduced to a length which would afford the most favorable conditions for the existence of as large a number as possible of vigorous individuals at the same time.

"If by these considerations death is shown to be a beneficial occurrence, it by no means follows that it is to be solely accounted for on grounds of utility. Death might also depend upon causes which lie in the nature of life itself. The floating of ice upon water seems to us to be a useful arrangement, although the fact that it does float depends upon its molecular structure and not upon the fact that its doing so is of any advantage to us. In like manner, the necessity of death has been hitherto explained as due to causes which are inherent in organic nature, and not to the fact that it may be advantageous.

"I do not, however, believe in the validity of this explanation; I consider that death is not a primary necessity, but that it has been secondarily acquired as an adaptation. I believe that life is endowed with a fixed duration, not because it is contrary to its nature to be unlimited but because the unlimited existence of individuals would be a luxury without any corresponding advantage. The above-mentioned hypothesis upon the origin and necessity of death leads me to believe that the organism did not finally cease to renew the worn-out cell material because the nature of the cells did not permit them to multiply indefinitely, but because the power of multiplying indefinitely was lost when it ceased to be of use. I consider that this view, if not exactly proved, can at any rate be rendered extremely probable."

Comfort *(5)*, with more than usual acidity, criticizes Weismann's argument "both because it assumes what it sets out to explain, that the survival value of an individual decreases with increasing age, and denies its own premise, by suggesting that worn-out individuals threaten the existence of the young." It does not appear to the present writer that the Weismann argument is strictly circular for it might well be, and probably is, true that individual organisms which do not have a means of replenishing all of their parts will undergo a senescence with time; insofar as such individuals compete with their offspring for food, space, and energy they may indeed decrease the reproductive probability of their descendants. Under certain very special circumstances, therefore, it does not seem impossible that Weismann's view may be operating. To the extent that senescence acts to limit populations to sizes which are more commensurate with food supply, particularly during adverse periods, it could again have a positively adaptive value, as we have proposed may be the case in *Campanularia*. Comfort's comments are particularly germane. "The theoretical difficulties of devising circumstances in which short life is selected as a character of fitness are considerable though not insuperable. In any circumstances where a high number of generations per unit time has an adaptive value, the Weismannian argument against individual longevity might hold. The most conspicuous adaptive modifications of life span in phylogeny seem, however, to be chiefly in the other direction. The development of social insects probably depended on the evolution of long-lived sexual forms, and it is very likely that a similar process may have operated in human phylogeny, in connection with the development of social behavior and the family unit. Not only was the evolution of neurones having a long potential life, a condition for the development of elaborate learned behavior and long parental dependence, but with the development of rational power and social organization, the advantage of possessing the experience of a few long-lived members was probably very high in an early humanoid community. The social animals, especially man, provide one of the best examples where longevity depending on factors outside the reproductive period can theoretically be subject to positive selection in terms of fitness.

"The chief objection to Weismann's idea of senescence as an adaptive effect is the rarity of its demonstrable occurrence in nature. In all but a few forms discussed, senescence is a potentiality, not a benefit or a handicap; it is realized only when we interfere artificially with the animal or its environment, and it is arguable whether evolution can select for such potentialities. Bidder [see (*339*)], it will be recalled, considered that senescence in mammals was an evolutionarily unimportant 'by-product' of an important positive adaptation, the limitation of size. It would indeed be possible to attribute senile change to the accumulation of such by-products outside the reproductive period.

"More recently, it has been suggested that senescence is to be regarded not as the positively beneficial character which Weismann believed it to be, but as a potentiality lying outside the part of the life cycle which is relevant to evolution. It has certainly been evolved, in that the living system which senesces has evolved, but it has not evolved as a physiological mechanism. The line of argument which appears most plausible is that suggested by Medawar. Death from senescence is itself in many species so rare an event in the wild state that failure to senesce early, or at all, has little value from the point of view of survival. In many forms the cessation or reduction of breeding capacity precedes senescence proper. With certain exceptions in social animals, events occurring in the post-reproductive period are theoretically outside the reach of selection, and irrevelant to it. A consequence more important than the mere failure of evolutionary processes to operate in favor of the postponement of senescence follows from the same fact. In view of the constant reproductive preponderance of young individuals, the postponement of the action of a harmful genetic effect until late in the reproductive life is almost equivalent, in selective value, to its complete elimination; the longer the postponement, the longer the equivalent."

The third view, which considers senescence to be a by-product of evolutionarily advantageous features of organisms, was stated by Bidder in an explicit form relating to the mechanism of body-size limitation. A more general statement of the hypothesis was recently given by Williams (*9*): "Senescence might be regarded as a group of adaptively unfavorable morphogenetic changes that were brought in as side-effects of otherwise favorable genes, and which have only been partly expurgated by further selection. There are, therefore, two opposing selective forces with respect to the evolution of senescence. One is an indirect selective force that acts to increase the rate of senescence by favoring vigor in youth at the price of vigor later on. The other is the direct selection which acts to reduce or postpone the 'price' and thereby decrease the rate of senescence. The rate of senescence shown by any species would depend on the balance between these opposing forces."

Among the consequences of his explicit mathematical statements regarding the selective effects of senescent-producing genes which Williams foresees are the following: "Senescence should always be a generalized deterioration, and never due largely to changes in a single system. The earlier an adverse genic effect, the greater will be the associated 'p' value and the intensity of adverse selection. So if the adverse genic effects appeared earlier in one system than any other, they would be removed by selection from that system more readily than from any other. In other words, natural selection would always be in greatest opposition to the decline of the most senescent prone system.

"Successful selection for increased longevity should result in decreased vigor in youth. If senescence results from genes that increase youthful vigor at the price of vigor later on, the loss of some of these genes through selection should result in decreased youthful vigor. It does not follow that puny youths are necessarily long-lived nor that very old individuals were necessarily below average in youthful vigor. Most of the genes or gene combinations that favor vigor early in life probably also favor longevity. Only a small proportion of the genes need be of the sort that produce opposite effects on fitness at different ages and of these only a certain proportion would have available alleles that could reduce the rate of senescence. It does follow that an individual could not be exceptionally gifted with both youthful vigor and long life. I would predict that no human being who is over 100 years old was unusually vigorous as a young adult." Birren's recent counterpart theory of aging (*340*) bears considerable resemblance to William's theory.

In summary, then, the evolution of senescence can be viewed as consequences of (*a*) the inclusion, within the genome of existing species, of genes which are inadequate to compensate for some of the effects of time (inadequacy of design); (*b*) errors of design in the sense that the successful means for avoiding senescence available to the ancestors of a given line may have been lost in the rough and tumble of evolutionary processes, (*c*) the fact that contradictory aspects of the function of genes or gene products either as regards the time of gene action or as regards pleiotropy of gene action may at the same time impose a built-in source of senescence; or finally (*d*) that the evolutionary process has simply not been operating on the question of aging or deathlessness but rather on issues of more immediate concern to the reproductive efficacy of a species.

I believe it is obvious that any living system will be subject to some adverse change with time unless it has a means for replacing all of its constituent parts. To the extent that such a replacement regimen imposes structural or functional handicaps on an organism when in competition with other systems not so endowed, it might be expected that this replacement capacity will manifest itself only in certain restricted evolutionary diverticula, such as perhaps among the Anthozoa. In the absence of specific genes fostering the continual replacement of organismic structures, there might be a secondary advantage to removing decrepit individuals from the population à la Weismann, particularly if either evolutionary plasticity via short generation time or keen competition for space and food were determinative of the survival of a line of animals or plants.

It is also probable that certain of the well-established features of cell senescence are a result of an uncompensated deleterious property of some gene action which also has an opposing developmentally advantageous or simultaneously beneficial effect on the survival of the line. However, I tend generally to concur with Comfort that senescence is not an evolved characteristic in the ordinary sense but that it is essentially a result of the lack of sufficient selection pressure to foster the development of immortal races of metazoa. *It appears to me that there is no inherent contradiction, no inherent property of cells or of metazoa which precludes their organization into perpetually functioning and self-*

replenishing individuals. On the other hand, the evolutionary dereliction is probably so manifold and so deeply ingrained in the physiology and biochemistry of existing forms, including man, that the abolition of the process is a practical impossibility.

CHAPTER X

Some unexplored avenues of cellular aging—current and future research

IN THESE CONCLUDING pages are presented some areas of potential specific research on cellular aging. It appears from the foregoing discussion that data in these areas would be useful in unraveling the puzzle.

1. *Temperature Effects in Mammals*

It would be of extreme interest to determine whether the rate of senescence in homeotherms is subject to modification by altering the body temperature, as is the case in poikilotherms. Methods of inducing hypothermia and hyperthermia over the lifetimes of sufficient numbers of individual animals to determine actuarial constants would be of interest. One possible investigation that might be of use is the study of relationships between mean body temperature of long-lived human families and short-lived ones. The mechanism controlling the temperature regulating thermostat of homeotherms would be of interest both from a theoretical standpoint and from the point of view of controlling or resetting such a thermostat. The possibility that the thermostat operates on a change in phase of some lipid whose melting point is at the normal body temperature of the animal in question should be subject to experimental tests, as are the effects of such factors as the degree of lipid unsaturation in the diet on the performance of the thermostat.

2. *Regenerative Capacity*

Despite the fact that certain species possess considerable capacity to regenerate various lost organs or limbs, we still do not have an accurate index of the extent to which this is possible among mammals and particularly in humans. Neither do we understand the stimuli that are necessary to call forth regenerative capacity and whether latent within human beings lie regenerative capacities, capacities for cell replacement and organ regrowth, which could be called forth by appropriate chemical manipulation. Whether regeneration, when it occurs in mammals, depends on the presence of reserve undifferentiated cells or whether it involves the process of dedifferentiation, regrowth, and redifferentiation are fundamental questions for current inquiry.

3. *Control of Lysosome Synthesis and Breakdown*

Both because lysosomes appear to be related to the age pigment inclusions which may have a bearing on gradual parenchymal cell dysfunction and because the process of cell death, resorption, and atrophy may involve the malfunction of systems controlling lysosomal activity, it is extremely important to conduct basic studies on the factors, both systemic (such as hormones) and intracellular, which control the synthesis and breakdown of lysosomes.

4. *Control of Synthesis and Degradation of Cellular Components*

In a more general sense, the control of the synthesis of all cellular components including subcellular organelles, such as lysosomes, mitochondria, microsomes, etc., is a fertile area for intensive inquiry.

5. *The Biochemistry of Cellular Death*

Little is known regarding the exact sequence of events transpiring when a cell dies. Certain tissues in which systematic cell death is a necessity, such as in the skin where cell death precedes keratinization, might furnish models appropriate to the general question. The death of cells in tissue culture under adverse conditions of pH, anoxia, etc., should also be examined to see whether there is some common denominator triggering the dissolution of the cell interior. For certain cell types, this may simply be anaerobicity, even of short duration. For others, it may be an entirely different type of factor, but the morphological sequences, as well as the biochemical events transpiring, are certainly appropriate to intensive study.

6. *Longevity of Subcellular Structures*

The utilization of appropriate labeling techniques coupled with the isolation of specific subcellular components at various time intervals after labeling should furnish the basic information about the rate of turnover of cellular structures that is necessary for the proper evaluation of a number of theories of cellular aging and death. These studies should not be limited to homogenates and tissue breis, but should rather be oriented toward an appraisal of longevity of subcellular components in specific cell types. This would probably be most feasible through the use of tritium or N^{15}-labeled substrates and radioautography.

7. *Factors Controlling Cell Growth*

A general study of the factors normally limiting cell division in metazoa is of obvious importance since the control of regeneration, size, and a multitude of other side factors related to senescence may be clarified by such an understanding.

8. *Changes in Immunological Properties*

Further studies of the changes in immunological properties of animals as they grow older, particularly the possibility that an autoimmune reaction occurs with age, should be undertaken. The feasibility of developing immune tolerance in adult organisms should also be undertaken, although this would seem to await a prior understanding of the normal mechanism whereby immune tolerance is achieved. Methods of transplanting tissues or organs between adult animals, as well as the possibility of culturing replacement organs and tissues *in vitro* for ultimate substitution in senescent animals, should be explored. Finally, the stability of various chemical species over very long periods of time under conditions approximating those occurring intercellularly should be continued, particularly for those components, which on the basis of tracer techniques or radioautographic studies appear to be particularly low in their turnover rates.

It is not to be expected that all of these questions can be answered in the next few years but it does seem apparent, unless a considerably more systematic attack on those fundamental areas directly related to the phenomenon of cellular aging is undertaken, that it will be another score of years before we can even evaluate the feasibility of therapeutic measures directed toward slowing down this or that senescence process.

In prosecuting the rapid exploration of this frontier in biology, there are at least three prerequisites. The first of these is a sufficient awareness on the part of the biologists, biochemists, and biophysicists who will eventually unravel this problem, with all its challenges, pitfalls, and uncertainties. With such awareness, the needed influx of highly capable and imaginative workers will be assured.

The second prerequisite is the sponsorship—moral, financial, and administrative—of a long-term program of research in this area. For too long has this area been regarded as a sort of step-child of other more legitimate areas. This has resulted in a near void where administrative leadership could have been exercised. The difficulties stem from the acute complexity of the problem, the reluctance of individual scientists to commit themselves to long-term research ventures without some guarantee of continued support in the event of temporary failure, the conservatism of some scientific administrators and advisory and granting committees to whom aging research may appear as an imponderable and ill-defined quantity.

The establishment of a central governmental agency such as a National Institute of Gerontology to channel funds, facilities, and capable personnel into this field would do much to solve these problems. Such an institute was unanimously recommended by the research panels of the recent White House Conference on Aging. The membership on these panels represented many areas of basic science other than gerontology and included many distinguished biologists.

A final need and one toward which this book is directed is the formulation and setting forth of a reasonably comprehensive, factual, and theoretical framework of the problem of aging. Because of the diffuseness of the problem, the manifold sources of possibly relevant information, the multidisciplinary approach required for a really comprehensive understanding, and the difficulty of evaluating the relevance of much of the published literature to the essence of the problem, this present effort leaves many questions unanswered that others in the scientific community may well have answered. We tender them our humble apologies with the request that we be informed of our clear omissions and errors. Where directly relevant factual evidence was lacking, we have attempted to sketch in, in greater or lesser detail, some of the more plausible theoretical formulations that seemed to us appropriate. Many of them are undoubtedly in error, but, as Weismann observed, "Theories are by no means useless. They are the first and often the indispensable steps which we must take on our way to the understanding of complex phenomena. They form the foundation upon which real theories can gradually be raised. Above all, they supply the impulse to reexamine again and again the phenomena they attempt to explain."

References

1. Smith, H., "From Fish to Philosopher," 1st ed., 264 pp. Little, Brown, Boston, 1953.
2. de Ropp, R. S., "Man against Aging," 310 pp. St. Martin's Press, New York, 1960.
3. Birren, J. E. (ed.), "Handbook of Aging and the Individual," 939 pp. Univ. of Chicago Press, Chicago, 1959.
4. Schroedinger, E., "What is Life?" Macmillan, New York, 1946.
5. Comfort, A., "The Biology of Senescence," 257 pp. Rinehart, New York 1956.
6. Medawar, P. B., "An Unsolved Problem of Biology." Lewis, London, 1951. (An inaugural lecture delivered at University College, London.)
7. Strehler, B. L., Mark, D., Mildvan, A. S., and Gee, M., Rate and magnitude of age pigment accumulation in the human myocardium. *J. Geront* **14**: (4), 430–439 (1959).
8. Eden, M., An analogy between probabilistic automata and living organisms. *In* "The Biology of Aging" (B. L. Strehler *et al.*, eds.), pp. 167–169. Publ. No. 6, Am. Inst. Biol. Sci., Washington, 1960.
9 Williams, G C., Pleiotropy, natural selection and the evolution of senescence. *Evolution* **11**: 398–411 (1957).
10. Strehler, B. L., Origin and comparison of the effects of time and high-energy radiations on living systems. *Quart. Rev. Biol.* **34**: (2), 117–142 (1959).
11. Strehler, B. L., Dynamic theories of aging. *In* "Aging: Some Social and Biological Aspects" (N. W. Shock, ed.), pp. 273–303. Publ. No. 65, Am. Assoc. Advancement Sci., Washington, 1960.
12. Franck, J., and Platzman, R., Physical principles underlying photochemical, radiation-chemical and radiobiological reactions. *In* "Radiation Biology" (A. Hollaender, ed.), Vol. I, Pt. I, pp. 191–254. McGraw-Hill, New York, 1954.
13. Hollaender, A. (ed.), "Radiation Biology," Vol. I, pp. 1–626; Vol. II, pp. 627–1265. McGraw-Hill, New York, 1954.
14. Pearl, R., The biology of death. VII. Natural death, public health, and the population problem. *Sci. Monthly* March–Sept., pp. 193–212 (1921).
15. Bidder, G. P., The mortality of plaice. *Nature* **115**: 495 (1925).

16. Failla, G., The aging process and somatic mutations. *In* "The Biology of Aging" (B. L. Strehler *et al.*, eds.), pp. 170–175. Publ. No. 6, Am. Inst Biol. Sci., Washington, 1960.

17. Szilard, L., On the nature of the aging process. *Proc. Natl. Acad. Sci. U.S.* **45**: 30–45 (1959).

18. Strehler, B. L., and Mildvan, A. S., General theory of mortality and aging. *Science* **132**: (3418), 14–21 (1960).

19. Yockey, H. P., The use of information theory in aging and radiation damage. *In* "The Biology of Aging" (B. L. Strehler *et al.*, eds.), pp. 338–347. Publ. No. 6, Am. Inst. Biol. Sci., Washington, 1960.

20. Weismann, A., "Essays Upon Heredity and Kindred Biological Problems." Oxford Univ. Press (Clarendon), London and New York, 1891.

21. Maupas, E., Recherches experimentales sur la multiplication des infusoires ciliés. *Arch zool. exptl. gén.* **6**: (2), 165–277 (1888).

22. Ashworth, J. H., and Annandale, N., Observations on some aged specimens of *Sagartia troglodytes* and on the duration of life in coelenterates. *Proc. Roy. Soc. Edinburgh* **25**: 295 (1904).

23. Stephenson, R. A., "British Sea Anemones." The Royal Society, London, 1935.

24. Oliver, J. A., "Young Billy Johnson's Old Box Turtle." *Animal Kingdom* **56**: 51 (1935).

25. Flower, S. S., Contributions to the knowledge of the duration of life in vertebrate animals. V. Mammals. *Proc Zool. Soc., London,* **145**: 145–234 (1931).

26. Mast, S. O., Effect of salts, hydrogen ion concentration and pure water on length of life in *Amoeba proteus. Physiol. Zoöl.* **4**: 58–71 (1931); *Biol. Abstr.* **6**: No. 250 (1932).

27. Jennings, H. S., Senescence and death in protozoa and invertebrates. *In* "Problems of Ageing" (E. V. Cowdry, ed.), Chapter 2. Williams & Wilkins, Baltimore, 1939, 1st ed., pp. 32–52; 1942, 2nd ed., pp. 29–48.

28. Calkins, G. N., *Uroleptus mobilis Engelm.* II. Renewal of vitality through conjugation. *J. Exptl. Zool.* **29**: 121–156 (1919).

29. Calkins. G. N., Factors controlling longevity in protozoan protoplasm. *Biol. Bull. Woods Hole* **67**: 410–431 (1934); *Biol. Abstr.* **9**: No. 10289 (1935).

30. Woodruff, L. L., *Paramecium aurelia* in pedigree culture for 25 years. *Trans. Am. Microscop. Soc.* **51**: (3), 196–198 (1932).

31. Woodruff, L. L., Eleven thousand generations of paramecium. *Quart. Rev. Biol.* **1**: 436–438 (1926).

32. Sonneborn, T. M., and Rofolko, M., Aging in the *P. aurelia*-multimicronucleatum complex. *J. Protozool.* **4**: 21 (1957).

33. Beers, C. D., On the possibility of indefinite reproduction in the ciliate *Didinium* without conjugation or endomixis. *Am. Naturalist,* **63**: 125 (1929).

34. Austin, M. L., Studies on *Uroleptus mobilis.* I. An attempt to prolong the life cycle. II. The conditions necessary for conjugation. *J. Exptl. Zool.* **49**: 149–216 (1927); *Biol. Abstr.* **2**: No. 7515 (1928).

35. Strehler, B. L. (ed.), "The Biology of Aging," 364 pp. Publ. No. 6, Am. Inst. Biol. Sci., Washington, 1960.

36. Sonneborn, T. M., Enormous differences in length of life of closely related ciliates and their significance. *In* "The Biology of Aging" (B. L. Strehler *et al.,* eds.), p. 289. Publ. No. 6, Am. Inst. Biol. Sci., Washington, 1960.

37. Sonneborn, T. M., and Dippell, R., Cellular changes with age in Paramecium. *In* "The Biology of Aging" (B. L. Strehler *et al.,* eds.), p. 285. Publ. No. 6, Am. Inst. Biol. Sci., Washington, 1960.

38. Sonneborn, T. M., and Schneller, M., Age-induced mutations in Paramecium. *In* "The Biology of Aging" pp. 286–287. Publ. No. 6, Am. Inst. Biol. Sci., Washington, 1960

39. Gelber, J., The effect of shorter than normal interendomictie intervals on mortality after endomixis in *Paramecium aurelia. Biol. Bull. Woods Hole* **74**: 244–246 (1938).

40. Rudzinska, M. A., The influence of amount of food on the reproduction rate and longevity of a suctarian (*Tokophyra infusionum*). *Science* **113**: 10–11 (1951).

41. Boecker, E., Depression und Missbildungen bei Hydra. *Zool. Anz.* **44**: 75 (1914).

42. Berninger, J., Über Einwirkung des Hungers auf Hydra. *Zool. Anz.* **36**: 271 (1910).

43. Hertwig, R., Über Knospung und Geschlechtentwicklung von Hydra fusca. *Biol. Zentr.* **26**: 498 (1906).

44. Goetsch, W., Lebensdauer und geschlechtige Fortpflanzung bei Hydra. *Biol. Zentr.* **42**: 231 (1922).

45. Pearl, R., and Miner, J. R., Experimental studies in the duration of life. XIV. The comparative mortality of certain lower organisms. *Quart. Rev. Biol.* **10**: 60 (1935).

46. Hase, A., Über die deutschen Süsswasser-polypen Hydra fusca. *Arch. Rossen-u. Gesellschaftsbiologie* **6**: 721 (1909).

47. David, K., Zur Frage der potentiellen Unsterblichkeit der Metazoen. *Zool. Anz.* **64**: 126 (1925).

48. Schlottke, E., Zellstudien an Hydra. I. Altern und Abbau von Zellen und Kernen. *Z. mikroskop anat. Forsch.* **22**: 493 (1930).

49. Brien, P., La Pérennité Somatique. *Biol Revs.* **28**: 308 (1953).

50. Brock, M., and Strehler, B., Unpublished results.

51. Huxley, J. B., and De Beer, G. R., Studies in dedifferentiation. IV. Resorption and differential inhibition in *Obelia* and *Campanularia. Quart. J. Microscop.* Sci. **67**: 473 (1923).

52. Hammett, F. S., The role of amino acids and nucleic acid components in developmental growth. I. The growth of an *Obelia* hydranth. *Growth* **7**: 331 (1943).

53. Crowell, S., The regression-replacement cycle of hydranths of *Obelia* and *Campanularia*. *Physiol. Zoöl.* **26**: 319 (1953).

54. Crowell, S., Differential responses of growth zones to nutritive level, age and temperature in the colonial hydroid, *Campanularia*. *J. Exptl. Zool.* **134**: 63 (1957).

55. Crowell, S., and Wyttenbach, C., Factors affecting terminal growth in the hydroid, *Campanularia*. *Biol. Bull. Woods Hole* **113**: 233 (1957).

56. Strehler, B. L., and Crowell, S., Studies on comparative physiology of aging. I. Function vs. *age of Campanularia flexuosa Gerontologia* (in press) (1961).

57. Miner, R. W., "Field Book of Seashore Life," 888 pp. Putnam, New York, 1950.

58. Child, C. M., The asexual cycle of *Planaria velata* in relation to senescence and rejuvenescence. *Biol. Bull. Woods Hole* **25**: (3), 181–203 (1913).

59. Child, C. M., A study of senescence and rejuvenescence based on experiments with *Planaria dorotocephala*. *Arch. Entwicklungsmech. Organ.* **31**: 537–616 (1911).

60. Child, C. M., Starvation, rejuvenescence and acclimation in *Planaria doretocephala*. *Arch. Entwicklungsmech. Organ.* **38**: 418–446 (1914).

61. Child, C. M., "Senescence and Rejuvenescence." Univ. of Chicago Press, Chicago, 1915.

62. Sonneborn, T. M., Genetic studies on *Stenostomum Incaudatum*. *J. Expertl. Zool.* **57**: (1), 57–107 (1930).

63. Finesinger, J. E., Effect of certain chemical and physical agents on fecundity and length of life, and on their inheritance in a rotifer, *Lecane (Distyla) inermis (Bryce)*. *J. Exptl. Zool.* **44**: 63–94 (1926); *Biol. Abstr.* **1**: No. 4410 (1926–27).

64. Lynch, R. S., and Smith, H. B., A study of the effects of modifications of the culture medium upon length of life and fecundity in a rotifer, *Proales sordida*, with special relation to their heritability. *Biol. Bull. Woods Hole* **60**: 30–59 (1931); *Biol. Abstr.* **8**: No. 2736 (1934).

65. Lansing, A. I., A transmissible, cumulative, and reversible factor in aging. *J. Gerontol* **2**: (3), 228–239 (1947).

66. Crozier, W. J., Growth and duration of life in *Chiton tuberculatus*. *Proc. Natl. Acad. Sci. U.S.* **4**: 322–325 (1918).

67. Szabó, I., and Szabó, M., Todesursachen und pathologische Erscheinungen bei Pulmonaten. III. *Arch. Molluskenk.* **65**: (1), 11–15 (1933).

68. Terao, A., and Tanska, T., Duration of life of the water-flea, *Moina macrocopa Strauss*, in relation to temperature. *J. Imp. Fisheries Inst.* (Japan) **25**: 67 (1930).

69. Ingle, L., Wood, T. R., and Banta, A. M., A study of longevity, growth, reproduction, and heart rate in *Daphnia longispina* as

influenced by limitations in quantity of food. *J. Exptl. Zool.* **76**: 325–352 (1937).

70. McCay, C. M., Maynard, L. A., Sperling, G., and Barnes, L. L., Retarded growth, life span, ultimate body size and age changes in the albino rat after feeding diets restricted in calories. *J. Nutrition* **18**: 1–13 (1939).

71. Banta, A. M., and Wood, T. R., The accumulation of recessive physiological mutations during long-continued parthenogenesis. *Genetics* **22**: 183 (1937).

72. Schechter, V., Effect of heparin and of vitamin K on the life span of *Daphnia magna*. *Proc. Soc. Exptl. Biol. Med.* **74**: 747–748 (1950); *Biol. Abstr.* **25**: No. 7529 (1951).

73. Needham, A. E., Growth and regeneration in *Asellus aquaticus* (Linn.) in relation to age, sex, and season. *J. Exptl. Zool.* **112**: 49–78 (1949).

74. Liebmann, E., The correlation between sexual reproduction and regeneration in a series of oligochaeta. *J. Exptl. Zool.* **91**: 373–389 (1942).

75. Ewer, D. W., and Ewer, R. F., The biology and behaviour of *Pinus Tectus* Boie (*Coleptera Ptinidae*), a pest of stored products. III. The effect of temperature and humidity on oviposition, feeding and duration of life cycle. *J. Exptl. Biol.* **18**: 290–305 (1942); *Dissertation Abstr.* **16**: No. 3032 (1942).

76. Bodenstein, D., Le Role des hormones dans la régeneration des organes des insectes. *Scientia* **53**: 1–6 (1959).

77. Bodenstein, D., Hormones and tissue competence in the development of *Drosophila*. *Biol. Bull. Woods Hole* **84**: 35–148 (1943).

78. Griffiths, J. T., and Tauber, O. E., Fecundity, longevity, and parthenogenesis of the American roach, *Periplaneta americana*. *Physiol. Zoöl.* **15**: 196 (1942).

79. Clark, A. M., and Rubin, M. A., The modification by X-rays of the life span of haploids and diploids of the wasp, *Habrobracon* species. *Radiation Research* (in press).

80. Hodge, C. F., Changes in human ganglion cells from birth to senile death. Observations on man and honeybee. *J. Physiol.* (*London*) **17**: 129 (1894–1895).

81. Rockstein, M., The relation of cholinesterase activity to change in cell number with age in the brain of the adult worker honeybee. *J. Cellular Comp. Physiol.* **35**: 11023 (1950); *Biol. Abstr.* **24**: No. 29194 (1950).

82. Loeb, J., and Northrop, J. H., Is there a temperature coefficient for the duration of life? *Proc. Natl. Acad. Sci. U.S.* **2**: 456 (1916).

83. Loeb, J., and Northrop, J. H., On the influence of food and temperature upon the duration of life. *J. Biol. Chem.* **32**: (1), 103–121 (1917).

84. Alpatov, W. W., and Pearl, R., Experimental studies on the duration of life. XII. Influence of temperature during the larval

period and adult life on the duration of life of the imago of *Drosophila melanogaster*. *Am. Naturalist* **63**: 37–67 (1929); *Biol. Abstr.* **4**: No. 21461 (1930).

85. Pearl, R., Miner, J. R., and Parker, S. L., Experimental studies on the duration of life. XI. Density of population and life duration in Drosophila. *Am. Naturalist* **61**: 289–318 (1927).

86. Pearl, R., and Parker, S. L., On the influence of density of population upon the rate of reproduction in *Drosophila*. *Proc. Natl. Acad. Sci. U.S.* **8**: (7), 212–219 (1922).

87. Pearl, R., and Parker, S. L., Experimental studies on the duration of life. X. The duration of life of *Drosophila melanogaster* in the complete absence of food. *Am. Naturalist* **58**: 193–218 (1924).

88. Pearl, R., and Parker, S. L., Experimental studies on the duration of life. III. The effect of successive etherizations on the duration of life of *Drosophila*. *Am. Naturalist* **56**: 273–280 (1922).

89. Pearl, R., White, F. B., and Miner, J. R., Age changes in alcohol tolerance in *Drosophila melanogaster*. *Proc. Natl. Acad. Sci. U.S.* **15**: (5), 425–429 (1929).

90. Pearl, R., Parker, S. L., and Gonzalez, B. M., Experimental studies on the duration of life. VII. The mendelian inheritance of duration of life in crosses of wild type and quintuple stocks of *Drosophila melanogaster*. *Am. Naturalist* **57**: 153–192 (1923).

91. Northrop, J., The effect of prolongation of the period of growth on the total duration of life. *J. Biol. Chem.* **32**: 123 (1917).

92. Crozier, W. J., and Enzmann, E. V., Concerning critical periods in the life of adult *Drosophila*. *J. Gen. Physiol.* **20**: 595–602 (1937); *Psychol. Abstr.* **11**: No. 2686 (1937).

93. Gardner, T. S., The use of *Drosophila melanogaster* as a screening agent for longevity factors. I. Pantothenic acid as a longevity factor in royal jelly. *J. Gerontol.* **3**: 1–8 (1948).

94. Gardner, T. S., The use of *Drosophila melanogaster* as a screening agent for longevity factors. II. The effects of biotin, pyridioxine, sodium yeast nucleate and pantothenic acid on the life span of the fruit fly. *J. Gerontol.* **3**: 9–13 (1948).

95. Strehler, B. L., (unpublished).

96. Sacher, G. A., Relation of lifespan to brain weight and body weight in mammals. *In* "Ciba Foundation Colloquia on Aging" (G. E. W. Wolstenholme *et al.*, eds.), Vol 5: The Lifespan of Animals, pp. 115–132. Little, Brown, Boston, 1959.

97. Maynard-Smith, J., Prolongation of the life of *D. subobscura* by a brief exposure of adults to a high temperature. *Nature* **181**: 496–497 (1958).

98. Strehler, B. L., Studies on the comparative physiology of aging. II. On the mechanism of temperature life shortening in *Drosophila melanogaster*. *J. Gerontol.* **16**: (1), 2–12 (1961).

99. Clarke, J. M., and Maynard-Smith, J., The genetics and cytology of *Drosophila subobscura.* XI. Hybrid vigor and longevity. *J. Genet.* **53**: 172 (1955).

100. Maynard-Smith, J., The rate of ageing in *Drosophila subobscura. In* "Ciba Foundation Colloquia on Aging" (G. E. W. Wolstenholme and M. O'Connor, eds.), Vol. 5: The Lifespan of Animals, pp. 269–280. Little, Brown, Boston, 1959.

101. Gonzàlez, B. M., Experimental studies on the duration of life. VIII. The influence upon duration of life of certain mutant genes of *Drosophila melanogaster. Am. Naturalist* **57**: 289–25 (1923).

102. Gowen, J. W., On chromosome balance as a factor in duration of life. *J. Gen. Physiol.* **14**: 447–461 (1931); *Biol. Abstr.* **6**: No. 15259 (1932).

103. Gowen, J. W., Metabolism as related to chromosome structure and the duration of life. *J. Gen. Physiol.* **14**: 463–472 (1931); *Biol. Abstr.* **6**: No. 24383 (1942).

104. Rubner, N., Probleme des Wachstums und der Lebensdauer. *Mitt. Geschichte inn. Med., Wien* **7**: (Suppl. 9), 58–81 (1908).

105. Stern, C., An effect of temperature and age on crossing-over in the first chromosome of *Drosophila melanogaster. Proc. Natl. Acad. Sci., U.S.* **12**: 530–532 (1926); *Biol. Abstr.* **2**: No. 15756 (1928).

106. Bridges, C. B., The relation of the age of the female to crossing-over in the third chromosome of *Drosophila melanogaster. J. Gen. Physiol.* **8**: 689–700 (1927); *Biol. Abstr.* **2**: No. 15707 (1928).

107. Hannah, A., The effect of aging of the maternal parent upon the sex ratio in *Drosophila melanogaster. Z. induktive Abstammungs-u. Vererbungs lehre,* **86**: 574–599 (1955).

108. Comfort, A., Absence of a Lansing effect in *Drosophila subobscura. Nature* **172**: 83 (1953).

109. Glass, B., The influence of immediate vs. delayed mating on the life span of *Drosophila. In* "The Biology of Aging" (B. L. Strehler *et al.,* eds.), pp. 185–187. Publ. No. 6, Am. Inst. Biol. Sci., Washington, 1960.

110. Gompertz, B., On the nature of the function expressive of the law of human mortality and on a new mode of determining life contingencies. *Phil. Trans. Roy. Soc. (London),* **Ser. A. 115**: 513–585 (1825).

111. Benjamin, B., Actuarial aspects of human life spans. *In* "Ciba Foundation Colloquia on Aging" (G. E. W. Wolstenholme and M. O'Connor, eds.), Vol. 5: The Lifespan of Animals, pp. 2–15. Little Brown, Boston, 1959.

112. Beeton, M., and Pearson, K., Data for the problem of evolution in man. A first study of the inheritance of longevity, and the selective death rate in man. *J. Inst. Actuaries* **35**: 112–129 (1900).

113. Pütter, A., Lebensdauer und Alternsfaktor. *Z. allgem. Physiol.,* **19**: 9–36, (1921).

114. Glass, B., Genetics of aging. *In* "Aging: Some Social and Biological Aspects" (N. W. Shock, ed.), pp. 67–100. Publ. No. 65, Am. Assoc. Advancement Sci., Washington, 1960.

115. Maynard-Smith, J. M., A theory of ageing. *Nature* **184**: 956–958 (1959).

116. Szilard, L., A theory of ageing. *Nature* **184**: 956–958 (1959).

117. Brody, S., The kinetics of senescence. *J. Gen. Physiol.* **6**: 245–257 (1923).

118. Failla, G., The aging process and cancerogenesis. *Proc. N. Y. Acad. Sci.* **71**: 1124–1140 (1958).

119. Failla, G., The aging process and somatic mutations. *In* "The Biology of Aging" (B. L. Strehler *et al.*, eds.), pp. 170–175. Publ. No. 6, Am. Inst. Biol. Sci., Washington, 1960.

120. Simms, H. S., Logarithmic increase in mortality as a manifestation of aging. *J. Gerontol* **1**: (1), 13–26 (1946).

121. Jones, H. B., A special consideration of the aging process, disease and life expectancy. *Advances in Biol. and Med. Phys.* **4**: 281–337 (1956).

122. Simms, H. S., The use of a measurable cause of death (hemorrhage) for the evaluation of aging. *J. Gen. Physiol.*, **26**: (2), 169–178, (1942).

123. Sacher, G., On the statistical nature of mortality with especial reference to chronic radiation. *Radiology* **67**: 250–257 (1956).

124. Strehler, B. L., Fluctuating energy demands as determinants of the death process (a parsimonious theory of the Gompertz function). *In* "The Biology of Aging" (B. L. Strehler *et al.*, eds.), pp. 309–314. Publ. No. 6, Am. Inst. Biol. Sci., Washington, 1960.

125. Lenhoff, H. M., Migration of C^{14} labeled cnidoblasts *Exptl. Cell Research* **17**: 570–573 (1959).

126. Mildvan, A. S., and Strehler, B. L., A critique of theories of mortality. *In* "The Biology of Aging" (B. L. Strehler *et al.*, eds.), pp. 216–235. Publ. No. 6, Am. Inst. Biol. Sci., Washington, 1960.

127. Henderson, R., "Mortality Laws and Statistics," 1st ed. Wiley, New York, 1915.

128. Pearl, R., On the embryological basis of human mortality. *Proc. Natl. Acad. Sci. U.S.* **5**: (12), 593–598 (1919).

129. Spiegelman, M., Factors in human mortality. *In* "The Biology of Aging" (B. L. Strehler *et al.*, eds.), pp. 292–308. Publ. No. 6. Am. Inst. Biol. Sci., Washington, 1960.

130. Landowne, M., Brandfonbrener, M., and Shock, N. W., The relation of age to certain measures of performance of the heart and circulation. *Circulation* **12**: (4), 567–576 (1955).

131. Davies, D. F., and Shock, N. W., Age changes in glomerular filtration rate, effective renal plasma flow, and tubular excretory capacity in adult males. *J. Clin. Invest.* **29**: 496–507 (1950).

132. Silver, H. M., and Landowne, M., The relation of age to certain electrocardiographic responses of normal adults to a standardized exercise. *Circulation* **8**: 510–520 (1953).

133. Miller, J. H., and Shock, N. W., Age differences in the renal tubular response to antidiuretic hormone. *J. Gerontol.* **8**: 446–450 (1953).

134. Brandfonbrener, M., Landowne, M., and Shock, N. W., Changes in cardiac output with age. *Circulation* **12**: (4), 557–566 (1955).

135. Shock, N. W., and Yiengst, M. J., Age changes in basal respiratory measurements and metabolism in males. *J. Gerontol* **10**: 31–40 (1955).

136. Falzone, J. A., Jr., and Shock, N. W., Physiological limitations and age. *Public Health Repts* (*U.S.*) **71**: (12), 1185–1193 (1956).

137. Shock, N. W., Some physiological aspects of aging in man. *Bull. N.Y. Acad. Med.* **32**: (4), 268–283 (1956).

138. Norris, A. H., Shock, N. W., and Yiengst, M. J., Age differences in ventilatory and gas exchange responses to graded exercise in males. *J. Gerontol.* **10**: 145–155 (1955).

139. Botwinick, J., and Shock, N. W., Age differences in performance decrement with continuous work. *J. Gerontol.* **7**: 41–46 (1952).

140. Norris, A. H., Shock, N. W., Landowne, M., and Falzone, J. A., Jr., Pulmonary function studies; age differences in lung volumes and bellows function. *J. Gerontol.* **11**: (4), 379–387 (1956).

141. Williams, C. H., Barnes, L. A., and Sawyer, W. H., The utilization of glycogen by flies during flight and some aspects of the physiological ageing of *Drosophila. Boil. Bull. Woods Hole* **84**: 263–272 (1943).

142. Hügin, F., and Verzár, F., Untersuchugen über die Arbeitshypertrophie des Herzens bei jungen und alten Ratten. *Pflüger's Arch. ges. Physiol.* **262**: 181 (1956).

143. Hügin, F., and Verzár, F., Versagen der Wärmeregulation bei Kälte als Alterserscheinung. *In* "Experimentelle Alternsforschung" (F. Verzár, ed.), pp. 96–99. Birkhäuser, Basel, 1956.

144. Flückiger, E., Der O_2-Verbrauch der Ratte bei vermindertem O_2-Partialdruck. *Helv. Physiol. Acta.* **14**: 501 (1956).

145. Verzár, F., and Flückiger, E., Lack of adaptation to low oxygen pressure in aged animals. *J. Gerontol.* **10**: 306 (1956).

146. Verzár, F., Compensatory hypertrophy of kidney and adrenal in the lifespan of rats. *In* "Old Age in the Modern World" (Proc. 3rd Congr. Intern. Assoc. Gerontol., London, 1954), pp. 139–150. Livingstone, London, 1955.

147. Verzár, F., and McDougall, E. J., Learning and memory tests in young and old rats. *Schweiz. med. Wochschr.* **84**: 1321 (1954).

148. Verzár, F., and Freydberg, V., Changes of thyroid activity in the rat in old age. *J. Gerontol.* **11**: 53 (1956).

149. Lindop, P. J., and Rotblat, J., Shortening of life span of mice as a function of age at irradiation. *Gerontologia* **3**: 122–127 (1959).

150. Curtis, H. J., and Gebhard, K. L., Aging effect of toxic and radiation stresses. *In* "The Biology of Aging" (B. L. Strehler *et al.*, eds.), pp. 162–166. Publ. No. 6, Am. Inst. Biol. Sci., Washington, 1960.

151. Shock, N. W., Age changes in physiological functions in the total animal: The role of tissue loss. *In* "The Biology of Aging" (B. L. Strehler *et al.*, eds.), pp. 258–264. Publ. No. 6, Am. Inst. Biol. Sci., Washington, 1960.

152. Shock, N. W., Some of the facts of aging. *In* "Aging: Some Social and Biological Aspects" (N. W. Shock, ed.), pp. 241–260. Publ. No. 65, Am. Assoc. Advancement Sci., Washington, 1960.

153. Bortz, E., Background paper. Medical Research on Aging, White House Conference on Aging, Washington, 1961.

154. Olansky, S., Background paper. Medical Research on Aging, White House Conference on Aging, Washington, 1961.

155. Polland, W. S., Histamine test meals, an analysis of 988 consecutive tests. *Arch. Internal Med.* **51**: 903–919 (1933).

156. Bloomfield, A. L., and Polland, W. S., "Gastric Anacidity: Its Relation to Disease," 188 pp. Macmillan, New York, 1933.

157. Boyd, E., Normal variability in weight of the adult human liver and spleen. *Arch. Pathol.* **16**: 350–372 (1933).

158. Kocour, E. J., Diverticulosis of the colon. *Am. J. Surgery* **37**: 433–436 (1937).

159. Ivy, A. C., Digestive system. *In* "Problems of Ageing" (E. V. Cowdry, ed.), 2nd ed., pp. 254–301. Williams & Wilkins, Baltimore, 1942.

160. Landowne, M., Characteristics of impact and pulse wave propagation in brachial and radial arteries. *J. Appl. Physiol.* **12**: (1), 91–97 (1958).

161. Landowne, M., and Stanley, J., Aging of the cardiovascular system. *In* "Aging: Some Social and Biological Aspects" (N. W. Shock, ed.), pp. 159–188. Publ. No. 65, Am. Assoc. Advancement Sci., Washington, 1960.

162. Woerner, C. A., Vasa vasorum of arteries, their demonstration and distribution. *In* "The Arterial Wall-Aging, Structure, and Chemistry" (A. T. Lansing, ed.), pp. 1–14. Williams & Wilkins, Baltimore, 1959.

163. Zweifach, B. W., Structure and behavior of vascular endothelium. *In* "The Arterial Wall-Aging, Structure, and Chemistry" (A. T. Lansing, ed.), pp. 15–45. Williams & Wilkins, Baltimore, 1959.

164. Norris, A. H., Shock, N. W., and Wagman, I. H., Age changes in the maximum conduction velocity of motor fibers of human ulnar nerve. *J. Appl. Physiol.* **5**: 589–593 (1953).

165. Beasley, W. C., The general problem of deafness in the population. *Laryngoscope* **50**: 856–905 (1940).

166. Weiss, A. D., Sensory Functions. *In* "Handbook of Aging and the Individual" (J. E. Birren, ed.), pp. 503–542. Univ. of Chicago Press, Chicago, 1959.

167. Friedenwald, J. S., The eye. *In* "Problems of Ageing" (E. V. Cowdry, ed.), pp. 535–555. Williams & Wilkins, Baltimore, 1942.

168. Duane, A., Accommodation. *Arch. Ophthalmol.* **5**: 1–14 (1931).

169. Bernstein, F., and Bernstein, M., Law of physiologic aging as derived from long range data of refraction of the human eye. *Arch. Ophthalmol.* **34:** 378–388 (1945).

170. Jerome, E. A., Age and learning—experimental studies. *In* "Handbook of Aging and the Individual" (J. E. Birren, ed.), pp. 655–699. Univ. of Chicago Press, Chicago, 1959.

171. Willoughby, R. S., Incidental learning. *J. Educ. Psychol.* **20:** 671–682 (1929).

172. Shock, N. W., Yiengst, M. J., and Watkin, D. M., Age change in body water and its relationship to basal oxygen consumption in males. *J. Gerontol.* **8**: 388 (1953).

173. Shock, N. W., and Yiengst, M. J., Age changes in basal respiratory measurements and metabolism in males. *J. Gerontol.* **10**: 31–40 (1955).

174. Kochakian, C. D., and Tillotson, C., Hormonal regulation of muscle development. *In* "Hormones and the Aging Process" (E. T. Engle and G. Pincus, eds.), pp. 63–74. Academic Press, New York, 1956.

175. Ufland, J. M., Einfluss des Lebensalters, Geschlechts, der Konstitution und des Berufs ouf die Kraft verschiedener Muskelgruppen. I. Mitteilungen über den Einfluss des Lebensalters auf die Muskel Kraft. *Arbeitsphysiologie* **6**: 653–663 (1933).

176. Norris, A. H., Shock, N. W., and Yiengst, M. J., Age changes in heart rate and blood pressure responses to tilting and standardized exercise. *Circulation* **8**: 521–526 (1953).

177. Norris, A. H., and Shock, N. W., Age changes in ventilatory and metabolic responses to submaximal exercise. *In* Proc. 4th Congr. of the International Association of Gerontology, Merano, Italy, July 14–19, 1957. Tito Mattioli, Fidenza, 1957, Vol. II, pp. 512–522.

178. Gaffney, G. W., Gregerman, R. I., Yiengst, M. J., and Shock, N. W., Serum protein-bound iodine concentration in blood of euthyroid men aged 18–94 years. *J. Gerontol.* **15**: 234–241 (1960).

179. Baker, S. P., Gaffney, G. W., Shock, N. W., and Landowne, M., Physiological responses of five middle-aged and elderly men to repeated administration of thyroid stimulating hormone (thyrotropin; TSH). *J. Gerontol.* **14**: (1), 37–47 (1959).

180. Pincus, G., Aging and urinary steroid excretion. *In* "Hormones and the Aging Process" (E. T. Engle and G. Pincus, eds.), pp. 1–19. Academic Press, New York, 1956.

181. Samuels, L. T., Effect of aging on the steroid metabolism as reflected in plasma levels. *In* "Hormones and the Aging Process" (E. T. Engle and G. Pincus, eds.), pp. 21–32. Academic Press, New York, 1956.

182. Albert A., Randall, R. V., Smith, R. A., and Johnson, C. E., Urinary excretion of gonadotropin as a function of age. *In* "Hormones and the Aging Process" (E. T. Engle and G. Pincus, eds.), pp. 49–57. Academic Press, New York, 1956.

183. Parfentjev, I. A., Immunological reactions and age. *In* "The Biology of Aging" (B. L. Strehler *et al.,* eds.), pp. 236–240. Publ. No. 6, Am. Inst. Biol. Sci., Washington, 1960.

184. Verzár, F., Adaptation to environmental changes at different ages. *In* "The Biology of Aging" (B. L. Strehler *et al.,* eds.), pp. 324–327. Publ. No. 6, Am. Inst. Biol. Sci., Washington, 1960.

185. Gregerman, R. I., Adaptive enzyme responses in the senescent rat: tryptophan peroxidase and tyrosine transaminase. *Am. J. Physiol.* **197**: (1), 63–64 (1959).

186. Gross, J., and Schmitt, F. O. The structure of human skin collagen as studied with the electron microscope. *J. Exptl. Med.* **88**: 555 (1948).

187. Gross, J., A study of certain connective tissue constituents with the electron microscope. *Ann. N. Y. Acad. Sci.* **52**: (7), 964–970, (1950).

188. Gross, J., Aging of connective tissue. *J. Gerontol.* **7**: 584–588 (1952).

189. Gross, J., Studies on the formation of collagen. I. Properties and fractionation of neutral salt extracts of normal guinea pig connective tissue. *J. Exptl. Med.* **107**: 267 (1958).

190. Lansing, A. I., Aging of elastic tissue and the systemic effects of elastase. *In* "Ciba Foundation Colloquia on Aging" (G. E. W. Wolstenholme and M. P. Cameron, ed.), Vol. 1: General Aspects, pp. 88–102. Little, Brown, Boston, 1955.

191. Lansing, A. I., Rosenthal, T. B., Alex, M., and Dempsey, E. W., The structure and chemical characterization of elastic fibers as revealed by elastase and by electron microscopy. *Anat. Record* **114**: (4), 555–575 (1952).

192. Hass, G. M., Elastic tissue. III. Relations between the structure of the aging aorta and the properties of the isolated aortic elastic tissue. *Arch Pathol.* **35**: 29 (1943).

193. Lansing, A. I., Changes with age in amino acid composition of arterial elastin. *Proc. Soc. Exptl. Biol. Med.* **76**: 714 (1951).

194. Ham, A. W., "Histology," 3rd ed. Lippincott, Philadelphia, 1957.

195. Leblond, C. P., Distribution of periodic acid reactive carbohydrates in the adult rat. *Am. J. Anat.* **86**: 1 (1950).

196. Gersh, I., and Catchpole, H. R., Ground substance and basement membrane. *Am. J. Anat.* **85**: 457–517 (1949).

197. Meyer, K., Chemistry and biology of mucopolysaccharides and glycoprotein. *Cold Spring Harbor Symposia Quant. Biol.* **6**: 91 (1938).

198. Meyer, K., Mucoids and glycoproteins. *Advances in Protein Chem.* **2**: 249 (1945).

199. Gross, J., Studies on the formation of collagen. II. Influence of growth rate on neutral salt extracts of guinea pig dermis. *J. Exptl. Med.* **107**: 265 (1958).

200. Kirk, E., and Kvorning, S. A., Quantitative measurement of the elastic properties of the skin and subcutaneous tissue in young and old individuals. *J. Gerontol.* **4**: 273 (1949).

201. Evans, R. Cowdry, E. V., and Nielson, P. E., Ageing of human skin. *Anat. Record* **86**: 545 (1943).

202. Kohn, R. R., and Rollerson, E., Studies on the mechanism of the age-related change in swelling ability of human myocardium. *Circulation Research* **7**: 740 (1959).

203. Kohn, R. R., Age and swelling in acid of perivascular connective tissue in human lung. *J. Gerontol.* **14**: 16–18 (1959).

204. Verzár, F., Veränderungen der thermoelastischen Kontraktion von Sehnenfasern beim Altern. *Experientia,* **11**: 230 (1955).

205. Verzár, F., and Thoenen, H., Die Wirkung von Elektrolyten auf die thermische Kontraktion von Collagenfäden. *Gerontologia* **4**: 112–119, (1960).

206. Verzár, F., and Huber, K., Thermic contraction of single tendon fibers from animals of different ages after treatment with formaldehyde, urethane, glycerol, acetic acid and other substances. *Gerontologia* **2**: 81–103 (1958).

207. Chvapil, M., and Hruza, Z., The influence of aging and undernutrition on chemical contractility and relaxation of collagen fibres in rats. *Gerontologia* **3**: 241–252 (1959).

208. Sinex, F. M., Aging and lability of irreplaceable molecules. *In* "The Biology of Aging" (B. L. Strehler *et al.,* eds.), pp. 268–273. Publ. No. 6, Am. Inst. Biol. Sci., Washington, 1960.

209. Sobel, H., Studies on the measurement of aging. *In* "The Biology of Aging" (B. L. Strehler *et al.,* eds.), pp. 274–278. Publ. No. 6, Am. Inst. Biol. Sci., Washington, 1960.

210. Sobel, H., and Marmorston, J., The possible role of the gel-fiber ratio of connective tissue in the aging process. *J. Gerontol.* **11**: 2–7 (1956).

211. Thompson, R. C., and Ballou, J. E., Studies of metabolic turnover with tritium as a tracer. V. The predominantly non-dynamic state of body constituents in the rat. *J. Biol. Chem.* **223**: 795–809 (1956).

212. Jackson, D. S., Connective tissue growth stimulated by Carrageenin. I. The formation and removal of collagen. *Biochem.* J. **65**: 277 (1957).

213. Gross, J., Comments. *In* "The Biology of Aging" (B. L. Strehler *et al.,* eds.), pp. 32–34. Publ. No. 6, Am. Inst. Biol. Sci., Washington, 1960.

214. Kirk, J. E., and Laursen, T. J. S., Changes with age in diffusion coefficients of solutes for human tissue membranes. *In* "Ciba Foundation Colloquia on Aging" (G. E. W. Wolstenholme and M. P. Cameron, eds.), Vol. 1: General Aspects. pp. 69–75. Little, Brown, Boston, 1955.

215. Dribben, I. S., and Wolfe, J. M., Structural changes in the connective tissue of the adrenal glands of female rats associated with advancing age. *Anat. Record* **98:** 557 (1947).

216. Smith, C., Study of argyrophil fibers during ageing in mice. *Anat. Record* **81**: (Suppl.) 116–117 (1941).

217. Kirk, J. E., and Dyrbye, M., Hexosamine and acid-hydrolyzable sulfate concentrations of the aorta and pulmonary artery in individuals of various ages. J. Gerontol. **11**: 273–281 (1956).

218. Rasquin, P., and Hafter, E., Age changes in the testis of the teleost, *Astyanax americanus*. *J. Morphol.* **89**: 397 (1951).

219. Tatchi, H., On the fundamental morphology of the senile changes. *Nagoya J. Med. Sci.* **22**: 1–36 (1960).

220. Hamperl, H., Die Fluorescenzmikoskopie menschlicher Gewebe. *Virchows Arch. pathol. Anat. u. Physiol.* **292**: 1–51 (1934).

221. Andrew, W., Age changes in the skin of Wistar Institute rats with particular reference to the epidermis. *Am. J. Anat.* **89**: (2), 283–320 (1951).

222. Andrew, W., Age changes in the vascular architecture and cell content in the spleen of 100 Wistar Institute rats including comparisons with human material. *Am. J. Anat.* **79**: 1–73 (1946).

223. Andrew, W., and Andrew, N. V., Age changes in the deep cervical lymph nodes of 100 Wistar Institute rats. *Am. J. Anat.* **82**: 105–165 (1948).

224. Andrew, W., and Pruett, D., Senile changes in the kidney of Wistar Institute rats. *Am. J. Anat.* **100**: (1), 51–80 (1957).

225. Andrew, W., Senile changes in the liver of mouse and man, with special reference to the similarity of the nuclear alterations. *Am. J. Anat.* **72**: (2), 199–221 (1943).

226. Falzone, J. A., Jr., Barrows, C. H. Jr., and Shock, N. W., Age and polyploidy of rat liver nuclei as measured by volume and DNA content. *J. Gerontol.* **14**: (1), 2–8 (1959).

227. Andrew, W., Senile changes in the pancreas of Wistar Institute rats and of man with special regard to the similarity of locule and cavity formation. *Am. J. Anat.* **74**: 97–127 (1944); *Biol. Abstr.* **18**: No. 264 (1945).

228. Payne, F., The cellular picture in the anterior pituitary of normal fowls from embryo to old age. *Anat. Record,* **96**: (1), 77–92 (1946).

229. Payne, F., Cytological changes in the cells of the pituitary, thyroids, adrenals and sex glands of ageing fowl. *In* "Cowdry's Problems of Ageing" (A. I. Lansing, ed.), 3rd ed., pp. 381–402. Williams & Wilkins, Baltimore, 1952.

230. Hunt, T. E., Mitotic activity in the anterior hypophysis of mature female rats of different age groups and at different periods of the day. *Endocrinology* **32**: 334 (1943).

231. Blumenthal, H. T., Studies on aging processes in the endocrine glands of the guinea pig. II. The effect of estrogen and luteum hormone on mitotic activity in the thyroid, parathyroid, and adrenal glands of guinea pigs of various ages. *J. Gerontol.* **5**: 387 (1950). **(Abstr.)**

232. Andrew, W., The Golgi apparatus in the nerve cells of the mouse from you to senility. *Am. J. Anat.* **64**: 351–376 (1939).

233. Andrew, W., The Purkinje cell in man from birth to senility. *Z. Zellforsch u. mikroskop, Anat.* **27**: 534–554 (1938).

234. Andrew, W., and Andrew N. V., Comparison of the changes caused by fatigue and by aging in the cerebral cortex of mice. *J. Comp. Neurol.* **72**: (3), 525–533 (1940).

235. Andrew, W., Amitotic division in senile tissues as a probable means of self-preservation of cells. *J. Gerontol.* **10**: 1–12 (1955).

236. Andrew, W., Structural alterations with aging in the nervous system. *In* "The Neurologic and Psychiatric Aspects of the Disorders of Aging" (J. E. Moore, H. H. Merritt, and R. J. Masselink, eds.), Chapter 11, Vol. 35, pp. 129–170. Williams & Wilkins, Baltimore, 1956.

237. Andrew, W., "Cellular Changes with Age," 74 pp. Charles C. Thomas, Springfield, 1952.

238. Vogt, C., and Vogt, O., Age changes in neurones. *Nature* **158**: 304 (1946).

239. Gardner, E., Decrease in human neurones with age. *Anat. Record* **77**: 529–536 (1940).

240. Corbin, K. B., and Gardner, E., Decrease in number of myelinated fibers in human spinal roots with age. *Anat. Record* **68**: 63–74 (1937).

241. Ellis, R. S., Norms for some structural changes in the human cerebellum from birth to old age. *J. Comp. Neurol.* **32**: 1–34 (1920).

242. Brody, H., Organization of the cerebral cortex. III. A study of aging in the human cerebral cortex. *J. Comp. Neurol.* **102**: 511–556 (1955).

243. Birren, J. E., and Wall, P. D., Age changes in conduction velocity, refractory period, number of fibres, connective tissue space and blood vessels in sciatic nerve of rats. *J. Comp. Neurol,* **104**: 1–16 (1956).

244. Furth, J. Upton, A. C., Christenberry, K. W., Benedict, W. H., and Moshman, J., Some late effects in mice of ionizing radiation from an experimental nuclear detonation. *Radiology* **63**: 562–569 (1954).

245. Upton, A. C., Ionizing radiation and aging. *Gerontologia* **4**: 162–176 (1960).

246. Berlin, N. I., Waldmann, A., and Weissman, S. M., Life span of red blood cell. *Physiol, Revs.* **37**: (3), 577–616 (1959).

247. Bernstein, R. E., Alterations in metabolic energetics and cation transport during aging of red cells. *J. Clin. Invest.* **38**: (9), 1572–1568 (1959).

248. Marks, P. A., and Johnson, A. B., Relationship between the age of human erythrocytes and their osmotic resistance. A basis for separating young and old erythrocytes. *J. Clin. Invest.* **37**: 1542–1547 (1958).

249. Brock, M. A., Production and life span of erythrocytes during hibernation in the golden hamster. *Am. J. Physiol.* **198**: (6), 1181–1186 (1960).

250. Huennekens, F. M., *In Vitro* aging of erythrocytes. *In* "The Biology of Aging" (B. L. Strehler *et al.,* eds.), pp. 200–203. Publ. No. 6, Am. Inst. Biol. Sci., Washington, 1960.

251. Gabrio, B. W., Stevens, A. R., and Finch, C. A., Erythrocyte preservation. II. A study of extra-erythrocyte factors in the storage of blood in acid-citrate-dextrose. *J. Clin. Invest.* **33**: 247 (1954).

252. Gabrio, B. W., and Huennekens, F. M., The role of nucleoside phosphorylase in erythrocyte preservation. *Biochim. et Biophys. Acta* **18**: 585 (1955).

253. Glinos, A. D., The mechanism of liver growth and regeneration. *In* "The Chemical Basis of Development" (W. D. McElroy and B. Glass, eds.), pp. 813–842. Johns Hopkins Press, Baltimore, 1958.

254. Norris, J. L., Blanchard, J., and Polovny, C., Regeneration of rat liver at different ages. *Arch. Pathol.* **34**: 208–217 (1942).

255. Bucher, N. L. R., and Glinos, A. D., The effect of age on regeneration of rat liver. *Cancer Research* **10**: 324 (1950).

256. Bucher, N. L. R., Scott, J. F., and Aub, J. C., Regeneration of liver in parabiotic rats. *Cancer Research* **10**: 207 (1950).

257. Glinos, A. D., and Bartlett, E. G., The effect of regeneration on the growth potentialities *in vitro* of rat liver at different ages. *Cancer Research* **11**: 164–168 (1951); *Biol. Abstr.* **25**: No. 19912 (1951).

258. Swartz, G. E., Heteroplastic transplantation of variously aged intact and macerated kidney tissue of the rat to the chorioallantoic membrane of the chick. *J. Exptl. Zool.* **103:** 335–363 (1946).

259. LeGros Clark, W. E., and Wajda, H. S., The growth and maturation of regenerating striated muscle fibers. *J. Anat.* **81**: 56–63 (1947).

260. Konigsberg, I. R., The development potency of the outgrowth of adult skeletal muscle tissue *in vitro.* (Abstract). *In* Final Program. International Association of Gerontology, 5th Congress, San Francisco, California, August, 1960, pp. 67–68.

261. DuNouy, P. L., Cicatrization of wounds. *J. Exptl. Med.* **24**: 461–470 (1916).

262. Howes, E. L., and Harvey, S. C., Age factor in velocity of growth of fibroblasts in the healing wound. *J. Exptl. Med.* **55**: 577 (1932).

263. Carrel, A., and Burrows, M. T., On the physicochemical regulation of the growth of tissues. *J. Expertl. Med.* **13**: (4), 562–574 (1911).

264. Carrel, A., On the permanent life of tissues outside of the organism. *J. Exptl. Med.* **15**: 516–528 (1912).

265. Carrel, A., and Ebeling, A. H., Age and multiplication of fibroblasts. *J. Exptl. Med.* **35**: 599–623 (1921).

266. Carrel, A., and Ebeling, A. H., Heat and growth inhibiting action of serum. *J. Exptl. Med.* **35**: 647–656 (1922).

267. Carrel, A., and Ebeling, A. H., Antagonistic growth-activating and growth-inhibiting principles in serum. *J. Expertl. Med.* **37**: (5), 653–658 (1923).

268. Carrel, A., and Ebeling, A. H., Antagonistic growth principles of serum and their relation to old age. *J. Expertl. Med.* **38**: (4), 419–425 (1923).

269. Baker, L. E., and Carrel, A., Au sujet du pouvoir inhibiteur du serum pendant la veillesse. (*Compt rend. soc. biol.* **95**: 958 (1926).

270. Wolfson, N., Wilbur, K. M., and Bernheim, F., Lipid peroxide formation. *Exptl. Cell Research* **10**: (2), 556–558 (1956).

271. Barber, A., and Wilbur, K., The effect of X-irradiation on the antioxidant activity of mammalian tissues. *Radiation Research* **10**: (2), 167–175 (1959).

272. Wilbur, K. M., Wolfson, N., Kenaston, C., Ottolenghi, A., Gaulden, M. E., and Bernheim, F., Inhibition of cell division by ultraviolet irradiated unsaturated fatty acid. *Exptl. Cell Research* **13**: (3), 503–509 (1957).

273. Simms, H. S., and Stillman, N. P., Substances affecting adult tissue *in vitro*. II. A growth inhibitor in adult tissue. *J. Gen. Physiol.* **20**: 621–629 (1936).

274. Simms, H. S., and Stillman, N. P., Substances affecting adult tissues *in vitro*. III. A stimulant (the 'A' factor) in serum ultra-filtrate involved in overcoming adult tissue dormancy. *J. Gen. Physiol.* **20**: 649 (1937).

275. Simms, H. S., and Stillman, N. P., Production of fat granules and of degeneration in cultures of adult tissue by agents from blood plasma. *Arch. Pathol.* **23**: 316–331 (1937).

276. Medawar, P. B., The growth, growth-energy and ageing of the chicken's heart. *Proc. Roy. Soc.* **B129**: 332 (1940).

277. Margoliash, E., Tenenbaum, E., and Doljanski, L., Studies on the growth-promoting factor of adult tissue extract. V. The effects of dialysis. *Growth* **12**: 1–13 (1948).

278. Norris, A. H., and N. Shock, Exercise in the adult years with special references to advanced years. *In* "Science and Medicine of Exercise and Sports" (W. L. Johnson, ed.), p. 466f. .Harper, New York, 1960.

279. Stillwell, E. F., Maroney, S., and Wilbur, K., Effect of irradiated fatty acids on the growth of *Escherichia coli*. *J. Bacteriol.* **77**: (4), 510–511 (1959).

280. Schoenheimer, R., and Rittenberg, D., *Physiol. Revs.* **20**: 218 (1940).

281. Chance, B., and Hess, B., On the control of metabolism in ascites tumor cell suspensions. *Ann. N. Y. Acad. Sci.* **63**: (5), 1008–1016 (1956).

282. Reiner, J. M., The effect of age on the carbohydrate metabolism of tissue homogenates. *J. Gerontol.* **2**: 315 (1947).

283. Rafsky, H. A., Newman, B., and Horonick, A., Age differences in respiration of guinea pig tissues. *J. Gerontol.* **7**: 38–40 (1952).

284. Barrows, C. H., Yiengst, M. J., and Shock, N. W., Senescence and the metabolism of various tissues of rats. *J. Gerontol.* **13**: (4), 351–355 (1958).

285. Barrows, C. H., Jr., Falzone, J. A., and Shock, N. W., Age differences in the succinoxidase activity of homogenates and mitochondria from the livers and kidneys of rats. *J. Gerontol.* **15**: (2), 130–133 (1960).

286. Dempsey, E. W., Mitochondrial changes in different physiological states. *In* "Ciba Foundation Colloquia on Ageing" (G. E. W. Wolstenholme and E. C. P. Millar, eds.), Vol. 2: Ageing in Transient Tissues, pp. 100–102. Little, Brown, Boston, 1956.

287. Andrew W., Comments. *In* "The Biology of Aging" (B. L. Strehler *et al.,* eds.), p. 37. Publ. No. 6, Am. Inst. Biol. Sci., Washington, 1960.

288. Palade, G., and Schidlowsky, G., Functional association of mitochondria and lipide inclusions. *Anat. Record* **130**: 352–353 (1958).

289. Weinbach, E. C., The influence of pentachlorophenol on oxidative and glycolytic phosphorylation in snail tissue. *Arch. Biochem. Biophys.* **64**: 129–143 (1956).

290. Weinbach, E. C., Oxidative phosphorylation in mitochondria from aged rats. *J. Biol. Chem.* **234**: 412–417 (1959).

291. Weinbach, E. C., and Garbus, J., Age and oxidative phosphorylation in rat liver and brain. *Nature* **178**: 1225–1226 (1956).

292. Fletcher, M. J., and Sanadi, D. R., Turnover of rat liver mitochondria. *Biochim. et Biophys. Acta* **51**: 356–360. (1961).

293. Minot, C. S., The problem of age, growth and death. *Popular Sci. Monthly* **71**: June pp. 481–496, Aug. pp. 97–120, Dec. p. 509–523 (1907).

294. Hsu, T. C., and Pomerat, C. M., Mammalian chromosomes *in vitro.* III. On somatic aneuploidy. *J. Morphol.* **93**: 301 (1953).

295. Yerganian, G., and Gagnon, H., Chromosomes of an adenocarcinoma in the Chinese hamster. *Proc. Am. Assoc. Cancer Research,* **2**: 358–359 (1958).

296. Jacobs, P. A., Baikie, A. G., Court Brown, W. M., and Strong, J. A., The somatic chromosomes in Mongolism. *Lancet* **1**: 710 (1959).

297. Penrose, L. S., Mongolian idiocy (mongolism) and maternal age. *Ann. N. Y. Acad. Sci.* **57**: 494–502 (1954).

298. Palay, S. L., and Palade, G. E., The fine structure of neurons. *J. Biophys. Biochem. Cytol.* **1**: 69–88 (1955).

299. Gatenby, J. B., The Golgi apparatus of the living sympathetic ganglion cells of the mouse, photographed by phase contrast microscopy. *J. Roy. Microscop. Soc.* **73**: 61–68 (1953).

300. Lansing, A. I., Increase of cortical calcium with age in the cells of a rotifer, euchlanis dilatata, a planarian, phagocata sp., and a toad, bufo fowleri, as shown by the microincineration technique. *Biol. Bull. Woods Hole* **82**: (3), 392–400 (1942).

301. Lansing, A. I., Alex, M., and Rosenthal, T. B., Calcium and elastin in human arteriosclerosis. *J. Gerontol.* **5**: (2), 112–119 (1950).

302. Stübel, H., Die Floureszenz tienscher Gewebe in ultraviolettem Licht. *Pflüger's Arch. ges. Physiol.* **142**: 1–14 (1911).

303. Bethe, A., and Fluck, M., Über das gelbe Pigment der Ganglienzellen, seine kolloidchemischen und topographischen Beziehungen zu andern Zells-trukturen und eine elekive Methode zu seiner Darstellung. *Z. Zellforsch.* **27**: 211–221 (1937).

304. Hyden, H., and Lindstrom, B., Micro spectrographic studies on the yellow pigment in nerve cells. *Discussions Faraday Soc.* **No. 9**: 436–441 (1950).

305. Gatenby, J. B., The neurone of the human autonomic system and the so-called senility pigment. *J. Physiol.* **114**: 252–254 (1951).

306. Deane, H. W., and Fawcett, D. W., Pigmented interstitial cells showing brown degeneration in the ovaries of old mice. *Anat. Record* **113**: (2), 247–252 (1952).

307. Hess, A., The fine structure of young and old spinal ganglia. *Anat. Record* **123**: 399–423 (1955).

308. Sosa, J. M., Aging of neurofibrils. *J. Gerontol.* **7**: 191–195 (1952).

309. Sosa, J. M., Discussion of the senility. *In* Proc. First Intern. Congr. Neuropathol., Rome, September, 1952.

310. Sulkin, N. M., The occurrence, distribution and nature of PAS-positive substances in the nervous system of the senile dog. *In* "Old Age in the Modern World" (Proc. 3rd Congr. Intern. Assoc. Gerontol, London, 1954), pp. 156–157. Livingstone, London, 1955. Also in: *J. Gerontol.* **10**: 135–144 (1955).

311. Sulkin, N. M., Histochemical studies on mucoproteins in nerve cells of the dog. *Cytologia* **1**: 459–468 (1955).

312. Pearse, A. G. E., "Histochemistry, Theoretical and Applied," 2nd ed. Little, Brown, Boston, 1960.

313. Sulkin, N. M., and Kuntz, A., Histochemical alterations in autonomic ganglion cells associated with aging. *J. Gerontol.* **7**: 533–543 (1952).

314. Sulkin, N. M., and Srivanij, P., The experimental production of senile pigments in the nerve cells of young rats. *J. Gerontol.* **15**: 2–9 (1960).

315. Jayne, E. P., Cytology of the adrenal gland of the rat at different ages. *Anat. Record* **115**: 459–483 (1953).

316. Heidenreich, O., and Siebert, G., Untersuchungen an isoleirtem, unverändertem Lipofuscin aus Herzmuskulatur. *Virchows Arch. pathol. Anat. u. physiol.* **327**: 112–126 (1955).

317. Bondareff, W., Genesis of intracellular pigment on the spinal ganglia of senile rats. An electron miscroscope study. *J. Gerontol.* **12**: 364–369 (1957).

318. Bondareff, W., Morphology of the aging nervous system. *In* "Handbook of Aging and the Individual" (J. E. Birren, ed.), pp. 136–172. Univ. Chicago Press, Chicago, 1959.

319. Gedigk, P., and Bontke, E., Über den Nachweis von hydrolytischen Enzymen in Lipopigmenten. *Z. Zellforsch.* **44**: 495–518 (1956).

320. Essner, E., and Novikoff, A., Human hepatocellular pigments and lysosomes. *J. Ultrastructure Research* **3**: 374–391 (1960).

321. DeDuve, C., The enzymatic heterogeneity of cell fractions isolated by differential centrifugation. *Symposia Soc. Exptl. Biol.* **No. 10**: 50–61 (1957).

322. Novikoff, A. B., Beaufay, H., and DeDuve, C., Electron microscopy of lysosome-rich fractions from rat liver. *J. Biophys. Biochem. Cytol.* **179**: Suppl. 2, 84 (1956).

323. Mildvan, A. S., and Strehler, B. L., Fluorescent lipids from heart age pigment. (Abstract.) *Federation Proc.* **19**: (1), 231 (1960).

324. Hendley, D. D., Strehler, B. L., Reporter, M. C., and Gee, M. V., Further studies on human cardiac age pigment. (Abstract). *Federation Proc.* **20**: (1), 298 (1961).

325. Strehler, B. L., and Mildvan, A. S., Studies on the Chemical properties of lipofuscin age pigment. *In* Proc. 5th Intern. Gerontol. Congr. (to be published).

326. Lang, K., and Siebert, G., Isolierung Des Alternspigmente. *In* "Thurfelders Handbuch der physiologisch and pathologisch-chemischen Analyse" (K. Lang and E. Lehnartz, eds.), Vol. 2, p. 10. Springer, Berlin, 1955.

327. Tappel, A., Brown, W. D., Zalkin, H., and Maier, Z. P., Unsaturated lipid peroxidation catalyzed by hematin compounds and its inhibition by vitamin E. *J. Am. Oil Chemists' Soc.* **38**: 5 (1961).

328. Puck, T. T., *In vitro* studies on the radiation biology of mammalian cells. *Progr. in Biophys. and Biophys. Chem.* **10**: 237–258 (1960).

329. Geiser, S. W., Evidences of a differential death rate of the sexes among animals. *Am. Midland Naturalist* **8**: (7), 153–163 (1923).

330. MacArthur, J. W., and Baillie, W. H. T., Sex differences in mortality in Abraxas-type species. *Quart. Rev. Biol.* **7**: (3), 313–325 (1932).

331. Landauer, W., and Landauer, A. B., Chick mortality and sex ratios in the domestic fowl. *Am. Naturalist* **65**: 492 (1931).

332. Růžička, V., Beiträge zum Stadium der Protoplasmahysteresis und der hysterelischen Vorgänge (zur Kausalität des Alterns). I. Die Protoplasmahysteresis als Entropieerscheinung. *Arch. Mikr. Anat.* **101**: 459–482 (1924).

333. Bjorksten, J., The limitation of creative years. *Sci. Monthly* **62**: 94 (1946).

334. Ebert, J., Comments. *In* "The Biology of Aging" (B. L. Strehler *et al.*, eds.), p. 63. Publ. No. 6, Am. Inst. Biol. Sci., Washington, 1960.

335. Konigsberg, I. R., On the relationship between development and aging. *Newsletter* (*Gerontol. Soc.*) **7**: (3), 33–34 (1960).

336. Engle, E. T., and Pincus, G. (eds.), "Hormones and the Aging Process." Academic Press, New York, 1956.

337. Billingham, R. E., Brent, L., and Medawar, P. B., Actively acquired tolerance of foreign cells. *Nature* **172**: 603 (1953).

338. Billingham, R. E., Actively acquired tolerance and its role in development. *In* "The Chemical Basis of Development" (W. D. McElroy and B. Glass, eds.), pp. 575–592. Johns Hopkins Press, Baltimore, Maryland, 1958.

339. Bidder, G. P., Senescence. *Brit. Med. J.* **2**: 5831 (1932).

340. Birren, J. E., Behavioral theories of aging. *In* "Aging: Some Social and Biological Aspects" (N. W. Shock, ed.), pp. 305–332. Publ. No. 65, Am. Assoc. Advancement Sci., Washington, 1960.

341. Clark, A. M., and Rubin, M. A., The modification by X-rays of the life span of haploids and diploids of the wasp, *Habrobracon* sp. *Radiation Research* (in press).

Author Index

NUMBERS IN ITALIC INDICATE THE PAGE ON WHICH THE REFERENCE IS LISTED.

Subject Index